HUMAN UNIVERSE

Professor Brian Cox
& Andrew Cohen

WILLIAM
COLLINS

WHAT A PIECE OF WORK IS A MAN, HOW NOBLE IN REASON, HOW INFINITE IN FACULTIES, IN FORM AND MOVING HOW EXPRESS AND ADMIRABLE, IN ACTION HOW LIKE AN ANGEL, IN APPREHENSION HOW LIKE A GOD! THE BEAUTY OF THE WORLD, THE PARAGON OF ANIMALS — AND YET, TO ME, WHAT IS THIS QUINTESSENCE OF DUST? MAN DELIGHTS NOT ME — NOR WOMAN NEITHER, THOUGH BY YOUR SMILING YOU SEEM TO SAY SO,

What is a human being? Objectively, nothing of consequence. Particles of dust in an infinite arena, present for an instant in eternity. Clumps of atoms in a universe with more galaxies than people. And yet a human being is necessary for the question itself to exist, and the presence of a question in the universe – any question – is the most wonderful thing. Questions require minds, and minds bring meaning. What is meaning? I don't know, except that the universe and every pointless speck inside it means something to me. I am astonished by the existence of a single atom, and find my civilisation to be an outrageous imprint on reality. I don't understand it. Nobody does, but it makes me smile.

This book asks questions about our origins, our destiny, and our place in the universe. We have no right to expect answers; we have no right to even ask. But ask and wonder we do. *Human Universe* is first and foremost a love letter to humanity; a celebration of our outrageous fortune in existing at all. I have chosen to write my letter in the language of science, because there is no better demonstration of our magnificent ascent from dust to paragon of animals than the exponentiation of knowledge generated by science. Two million years ago we were apemen. Now we are spacemen. That has happened, as far as we know, nowhere else. That is worth celebrating.

WHERE ARE WE?

We shall not cease from exploration,
And the end of all our exploring
Will be to arrive where we started
And know the place for the first time.

T.S. Eliot

OAKBANK AVENUE, CHADDERTON, OLDHAM, GREATER MANCHESTER, ENGLAND, UNITED KINGDOM, EUROPE, EARTH, MILKY WAY, OBSERVABLE UNIVERSE ... ?

For me, it was an early 1960s brick-built bungalow on Oakbank Avenue. If the wind was blowing from the east you could smell vinegar coming from Sarson's Brewery – although these were rare days in Oldham, a town usually subjected to Westerlies dumping Atlantic moisture onto the textile mills, dampening their red brick in a permanent sheen against the sodden sky. On a good day, though, you'd take the vinegar in return for sunlight on the moors. Oldham looks like Joy Division sounds – and I like Joy Division. There was a newsagent on the corner of Kenilworth Avenue and Middleton Road and on Fridays my granddad would take me there and we'd buy a toy – usually a little car or truck. I've still got most of them. When I was older, I'd play tennis on the red cinder courts in Chadderton Hall Park and drink Woodpecker cider on the bench in the grounds of St Matthew's Church. One autumn evening just after the start of the school year, and after a few sips, I had my first kiss there – all cold nose and sniffles. I suppose that sort of behaviour is frowned upon these days; the bloke in the off-licence would have been prosecuted by Oldham Council's underage cider tsar and I'd be on a list. But I survived, and, eventually, I left Oldham for the University of Manchester.

Everyone has an Oakbank Avenue; a place in space at the beginning of our time, central to an expanding personal universe. For our distant ancestors in the East African Rift, their expansion was one of physical experience alone, but for a human fortunate to be born in the latter half of the twentieth century in a country like mine, education powers the mind beyond direct experience – onwards and outwards and, in the case of this little boy, towards the stars.

As England stomped its way through the 1970s, I learned my place amongst the continents and oceans of our blue planet. I could tell you about polar bears on Arctic ice flows or gazelle grazing on central plains long before I physically left our shores. I discovered that our Earth is one planet amongst nine (now redefined as eight) tracing out an elliptical orbit around an average star, with Mercury and Venus on the inside and Mars, Jupiter, Saturn, Uranus and Neptune beyond. The Sun is one star amongst 400 billion in the Milky Way Galaxy, itself just one galaxy amongst 350 billion in the observable universe. Later, at university, I discovered that physical reality extends way beyond the 90-billion-light-year visible sphere into – if I had to guess based on my 46-year immersion in the combined knowledge of human civilisation – infinity.

This is my ascent into insignificance; a road travelled by many and yet one that remains intensely personal to each individual who takes it. The routes we follow through the ever-growing landscape of human knowledge are chaotic; the delayed turn of a page in a stumbled-upon book can lead to a lifetime of exploration. But there are common themes amongst our disparate intellectual journeys, and the relentless relegation from centre stage that inevitably followed the development of modern astronomy has had a powerful effect on our shared experience. I am certain that the voyage from the centre of creation to an infinitesimally tiny speck should be termed an ascent, the most glorious intellectual climb. Of course, I also recognise that there are many who have struggled – and continue to struggle – with such a dizzying physical relegation.

John Updike once wrote that 'Astronomy is what we have now instead of theology. The terrors are less, but the comforts are nil'. For me, the choice between fear and elation is a matter of perspective, and it is a central aim of this book to make the case for elation. This may appear

FROM THE EARTH TO THE SUN

1 astronomical unit (AU)

FROM EARTH TO NEAREST STAR
265,000 AU

FROM EARTH TO CENTRE OF MILKY WAY
1,580,000,000 AU

FROM EARTH TO ANDROMEDA
1,580,000,000,000 AU

FROM EARTH TO FARTHEST GALAXY
8,532,000,000,000,000 AU

THE ROLE OF THE CREATOR
In Rome I visited the Vatican Observatory (established in 1787), one of the oldest astronomical research institutions in the world.

at first sight to be a difficult challenge – the very title *Human Universe* appears to demonstrate an unjustifiable solipsism. How can a possibly infinite reality be viewed through the prism of a bunch of biological machines temporarily inhabiting a mote of dust? My answer to that is that *Human Universe* is a love letter to humanity, because our mote of dust is the only place where love certainly exists.

This sounds like a return to the anthropocentric vision we held for so long, and which science has done so much to destroy in a million humble cuts. Perhaps. But let me offer an alternative view. There is only one corner of the universe where we know for sure that the laws of nature have conspired to produce a species capable of transcending the physical bounds of a single life and developing a library of knowledge beyond the capacity of a million individual brains which contains a precise description of our location in space and time. We know our place, and that makes us valuable and, at least in our local cosmic neighbourhood, unique. We don't know how far we would have to travel to find another such island of understanding, but it is surely a long long way. This makes the human race worth celebrating, our library worth nurturing, and our existence worth protecting.

Building on these ideas, my view is that we humans represent an isolated island of meaning in a meaningless universe, and I should immediately clarify what I mean by meaningless. I see no reason for the existence of the universe in a teleological sense; there is surely no final cause or purpose. Rather, I think that meaning is an emergent property; it appeared on Earth when the brains of our ancestors became large enough to allow for primitive culture – probably between 3 and 4 million years ago with the emergence of Australopithecus in the Rift Valley. There are surely other intelligent beings in the billions of galaxies beyond the Milky Way, and if the modern theory of eternal inflation is correct, then there is an infinite number of inhabited worlds in the multiverse beyond the horizon. I am much less certain that there are large numbers of civilisations sharing our galaxy, however, which is why I use the term 'isolated'. If we are currently alone in the Milky Way, then the vast distances between the galaxies probably mean that we will never get to discuss our situation with anyone else.

We will encounter all these ideas and arguments later in this book, and I will carefully separate my opinion from that of science – or rather what we know with a level of certainty. But it is worth noting that the modern picture of a vast and possibly infinite cosmos, populated with uncountable worlds, has a long and violent history, and the often-visceral reaction to the physical demotion of humanity lays bare deeply held prejudices and comfortable assumptions that sit, perhaps, at the core of our being. It seems appropriate, therefore, to begin this tour of the human universe with a controversial figure whose life and death resonates with many of these intellectual and emotional challenges.

Giordano Bruno is as famous for his death as for his life and work. On 17 February 1600, his tongue pinioned to prevent him from repeating his heresy (which recalls the stoning scene in Monty Python's *Life of Brian* when the admonishment 'you're only making it worse for yourself' is correctly observed to be an empty threat), Bruno was burned at the stake in the Campo de' Fiori in Rome and his ashes thrown into the Tiber. His crimes were numerous and included heretical ideas such as denying the divinity of Jesus. It is also the opinion of many historians that Bruno was irritating, argumentative and, not to put too fine a point on it, an all-round pain in the arse, so many powerful people were simply glad to see the back of him. But it is also true that Bruno embraced and promoted a

wonderful idea that raises important and challenging questions. Bruno believed that the universe is infinite and filled with an infinite number of habitable worlds. He also believed that although each world exists for a brief moment when compared to the life of the universe, space itself is neither created nor destroyed; the universe is eternal.

Although the precise reasons for Bruno's death sentence are still debated amongst historians, the idea of an infinite and eternal universe seems to have been central to his fate, because it clearly raises questions about the role of a creator. Bruno knew this, of course, which is why his return to Italy in 1591 after a safe, successful existence in the more tolerant atmosphere of northern Europe remains a mystery. During the 1580s Bruno enjoyed the patronage of both King Henry III of France and Queen Elizabeth I of England, loudly promoting the Copernican ideal of a Sun-centred solar system. Whilst it's often assumed that the very idea of removing the Earth from the centre of the solar system was enough to elicit a violent response from the Church, Copernicanism itself was not considered heretical in 1600, and the infamous tussles with Galileo lay thirty years in the future. Rather, it was Bruno's philosophical idea of an eternal universe, requiring no point of creation, which unsettled the Church authorities, and perhaps paved the way for their later battles with astronomy and science. As we shall see, the idea of a universe that existed before the Big Bang is now central to modern cosmology and falls very much within the realm of observational and theoretical science. In my view this presents as great a challenge to modern-day theologians as it did in Bruno's time, so it's perhaps no wonder that he was dispensed with.

Bruno, then, was a complex figure, and his contributions to science are questionable. He was more belligerent free-thinker than proto-scientist, and whilst there is no shame in that, the intellectual origins of our ascent into insignificance lie elsewhere. Bruno was a brash, if portentous, messenger who would likely not have reached his heretical conclusions about an infinite and eternal universe without the work of Nicolaus Copernicus, grounded in what can now clearly be recognised as one of the earliest examples of modern science, and published over half a century before Bruno's cinematic demise.

BRUNO'S HERETICAL SCIENCE
This bas-relief shows Giordano Bruno (1548–1600) being burned at the stake for his heretical and revolutionary ideas, among which was his belief that the universe is infinite and contained numerous habitable worlds.

VATICAN OBSERVATORY
The Vatican Observatory is based in Castel Gandolfo, the pope's summer residence outside Rome.

OFF CENTRE

Nicolaus Copernicus was born in the Polish city of Torun in 1473 and benefited from a superb education after being enrolled at the University of Cracow at 18 by his influential uncle, the Bishop of Warmia. In 1496, intending to follow in the footsteps of his uncle, Copernicus moved to Bologna to study canon law, where he lodged with an astronomy professor, Domenica Maria de Novara, who had a reputation for questioning the classical works of the ancient Greeks and in particular their widely accepted cosmology.

The classical view of the universe was based on Aristotle's not unreasonable assertion that the Earth is at the centre of all things, and that everything moves around it. This feels right because we don't perceive ourselves to be in motion and the Sun, Moon, planets and stars appear to sweep across the sky around us. However, a little careful observation reveals that the situation is in fact more complicated than this. In particular, the planets perform little loops in the sky at certain times of year, reversing their track across the background stars before continuing along their paths through the constellations of the zodiac. This observational fact, which is known as retrograde motion, occurs because we are viewing the planets from a moving vantage point – the Earth – in orbit around the Sun.

This is by far the simplest explanation for the evidence, although it is possible to construct a system capable of predicting the position of the planets months or years ahead and maintain Earth's unique stationary position at the centre of all things. Such an Earth-centred model was developed by Ptolemy in the second century and published in his most famous work, *Almagest*. The details are extremely complicated, and aren't worth describing in detail here because the central idea is totally wrong and we won't learn anything. The sheer contrived complexity of an Earth-centred description of planetary motions can be seen in the illustration opposite, which shows the apparent motions of the planets against the stars as viewed from Earth. This tangled Ptolemaic system of Earth-centred circular motions, replete with the arcane terminology of epicycles, deferents and equant, was used successfully by astrologers for thousands of years to predict where the planets would be against the constellations of the zodiac – presumably allowing them to write their horoscopes and mislead the gullible citizens of the ancient world. And if all you care about are the predictions themselves, and your philosophical prejudice and common-sense feeling of stillness require the Earth to be at the centre, then everything is fine. And so it remained until Copernicus became sufficiently offended by the sheer ugliness of the Ptolemaic model to do something about it.

Copernicus's precise objections to Ptolemy are not known, but sometime around 1510 he wrote an unpublished manuscript called the *Commentariolus* in which he expressed his dissatisfaction with the model. 'I often considered whether there could perhaps be found a more reasonable arrangement of circles, from which every apparent irregularity would be derived while everything in itself would move uniformly, as is required by the rule of perfect motion.'

The *Commentariolus* contained a list of radical and mostly correct assertions. Copernicus wrote that the Moon revolves around the Earth, the planets rotate around the Sun, and the distance from the Earth to the Sun is an insignificant fraction of the distance to the stars. He was the first to suggest that the Earth rotates on its axis, and that this rotation is responsible for the daily motion of the Sun and stars across the sky. He also understood that the retrograde motion of the planets is due to the motion of the Earth and not the planets themselves. Copernicus

always intended *Commentariolus* to be the introduction to a much larger work, and included little if any detail about how he had come upon such a radical departure from classical ideas. The full justification for and description of his new cosmology took him a further 20 years, but by 1539 he had finished most of his six-volume *De revolutionibus*, although the completed books were not published until 1543. They contained the mathematical elaborations of his heliocentric model, an analysis of the precession of the equinoxes, the orbit of the Moon, and a catalogue of the stars, and are rightly regarded as foundational works in the development of modern science. They were widely read in universities across Europe and admired for the accuracy of the astronomical predictions contained within. It is interesting to note, however, that the intellectual turmoil caused by our relegation from the centre of all things still coloured the view of many of the great scientific names of the age. Tycho Brahe, the greatest astronomical observer before the invention of the telescope, referred to Copernicus as a second Ptolemy (which was meant as a compliment), but didn't accept the Sun-centred solar system model in

PTOLEMY'S MODEL
This diagram shows the apparent motions of the Sun and planets across the sky as seen from the perspective of the Earth.

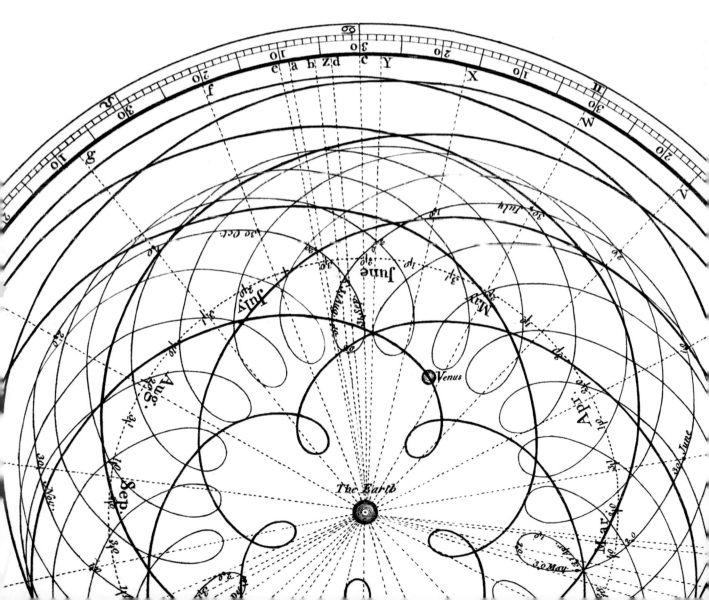

its entirety, partly because he perceived it to be in contradiction with the
Bible, but partly because it does seem obvious that the Earth is at rest.
This is not a trivial objection to a Copernican solar system, and a truly
modern understanding of precisely what 'at rest' and 'moving' mean
requires Einstein's theories of relativity – which we will get to later! Even
Copernicus himself was clear that the Sun still rested at the centre of the
universe. But as the seventeenth century wore on, precision observations
greatly improved due to the invention of the telescope and an increasingly
mature application of mathematics to describe the data, and led a host of
astronomers and mathematicians – including Johannes Kepler, Galileo
and ultimately Isaac Newton – towards an understanding of the workings
of the solar system. This theory is good enough even today to send space
probes to the outer planets with absolute precision.

At first sight it is difficult to understand why Ptolemy's contrived
mess lasted so long, but there is a modern bias to this statement that is
revealing. Today, a scientifically literate person assumes that there is a
real, predictable universe beyond Earth that operates according to laws of

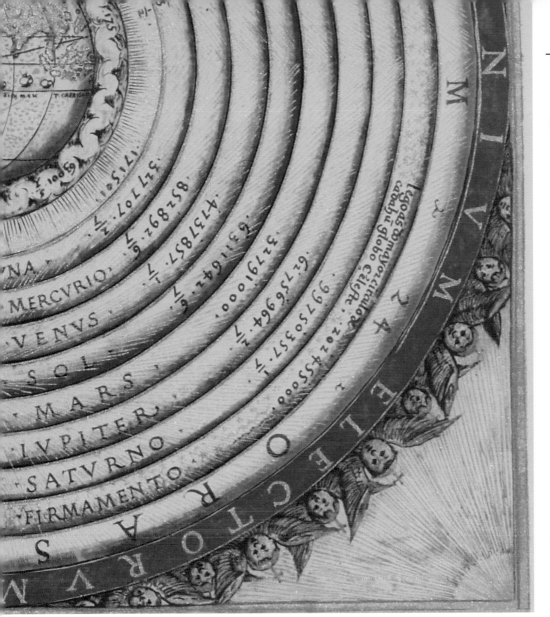

nature – the same laws that objects obey here on Earth. This idea, which is correct, only emerged fully formed with the work of Isaac Newton in the 1680s, over a century after Copernicus. Ancient astronomers were interested primarily in predictions, and although the nature of physical reality was debated, the central scientific idea of universal laws of physics had simply not been discovered. Ptolemy created a model that makes predictions that agree with observation to a reasonable level of accuracy, and that was good enough for most people. There had been notable dissenting voices, of course – the history of ideas is never linear. Epicurus, writing around 300 BCE, proposed an eternal cosmos populated by an infinity of worlds, and around the same time Aristarchus proposed a Sun-centred universe about which the Earth and planets orbit. There was also a strong tradition of classic orthodoxy in the Islamic world in the tenth and eleventh centuries. The astronomer and mathematician Ibn al-Haytham pointed out that, whilst Ptolemy's model had predictive power, the motions of the planets as shown in the figure on page 19 represent 'an arrangement that is impossible to exist'.

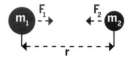

$$F_1 = F_2 = G\,\frac{m_1 \times m_2}{r^2}$$

The end of the revolution started by Copernicus around 1510, and the beginning of modern mathematical physics can be dated to 5 July 1687, when Isaac Newton published the *Principia*. He demonstrated that the Earth-centred Ptolemaic jumble can be replaced by a Sun-centred solar system and a law of universal gravitation, which applies to all objects in the universe and can be expressed in a single mathematical equation:

$$F = G\,\frac{m_1 m_2}{r^2}$$

The equation says that the gravitational force between two objects – a planet and a star, say – of masses m_1 and m_2 can be calculated by multiplying the masses together, dividing by the square of the distance r between them, and multiplying by G, which encodes the strength of the gravitational force itself. G, which is known as Newton's Constant, is, as far as we know, a fundamental property of our universe – it is a single number which is the same everywhere and has remained so for all time. Henry Cavendish first measured G in a famous experiment in 1798, in which he managed (indirectly) to measure the gravitational force between lead balls of known mass using a torsion balance. This is yet another example of the central idea of modern physics – lead balls obey the same laws of nature as stars and planets. For the record, the current best measurement of $G = 6.67 \times 10^{-11}$ N m²/kg², which tells you that the gravitational force between two balls of mass 1kg each, 1 metre apart, is just less than ten thousand millionths of a Newton. Gravity is a very weak force indeed, and this is why its strength was not measured until 71 years after Newton's death.

This is a quite brilliant simplification, and perhaps more importantly, the pivotal discovery of the deep relationship between mathematics and nature which underpins the success of science, described so eloquently by the philosopher and mathematician Bertrand Russell: 'Mathematics, rightly viewed, possesses not only truth, but supreme beauty – a beauty cold and austere, like that of sculpture, without appeal to any part of our weaker nature, without the gorgeous trappings of painting or music, yet sublimely pure, and capable of a stern perfection such as only the greatest art can show. The true spirit of delight, the exaltation, the sense of being more than Man, which is the touchstone of the highest excellence, is to be found in mathematics as surely as in poetry.'

Nowhere is this sentiment made more clearly manifest than in Newton's Law of Gravitation. Given the position and velocity of the planets at a single moment, the geometry of the solar system at any time millions of years into the future can be calculated. Compare that economy – you could write all the necessary information on the back of an envelope – with Ptolemy's whirling offset epicycles. Physicists greatly prize such economy; if a large array of complex phenomena can be described by a simple law or equation, this usually implies that we are on the right track.

The quest for elegance and economy in the description of nature guides theoretical physicists to this day, and will form a central part of our story as we trace the development of modern cosmology. Seen in this light, Copernicus assumes even greater historical importance. Not only did he catalyse the destruction of the Earth-centred cosmos, but he inspired Brahe, Kepler, Galileo, Newton and many others towards the development of modern mathematical physics – which is not only remarkably successful in its description of the universe, but was also necessary for the emergence of our modern technological civilisation. Take note, politicians, economists and science policy advisors of the twenty-first century; a prerequisite for the creation of the intellectual edifice upon which your spreadsheets, air-conditioned offices and mobile phones rest was the curiosity-driven quest to understand the motions of the planets and the Earth's place amongst the stars.

AT THE CENTRE OF THE SOLAR SYSTEM

Matching the observations of the wandering stars – the planets – of the night sky with the idea that the Earth was at the centre of the solar system required extremely complex models. In the case of Venus, combining the Earth at the centre with the observations meant that Venus had a circular orbit around a point midway between the Earth and the Sun, so-called epicycles, with all the other planets having similar complicated orbits around various points scattered around the solar system. Placing the Sun at the centre of the solar system, with the planets arranged in their familiar order, with the Moon orbiting the Earth, gave a much simpler system.

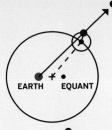

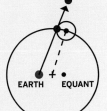

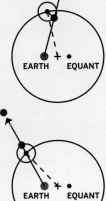

PTOLEMY'S SYSTEM

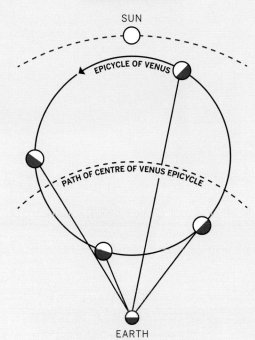

SUN

EPICYCLE OF VENUS

PATH OF CENTRE OF VENUS EPICYCLE

EARTH

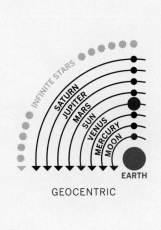

INFINITE STARS

SATURN
JUPITER
MARS
SUN
VENUS
MERCURY
MOON
EARTH

GEOCENTRIC

COPERNICUS'S SYSTEM

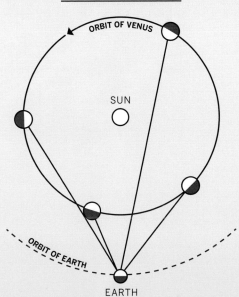

ORBIT OF VENUS

SUN

ORBIT OF EARTH

EARTH

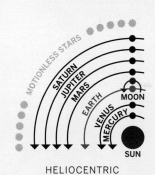

MOTIONLESS STARS

SATURN
JUPITER
MARS
EARTH
MOON
VENUS
MERCURY
SUN

HELIOCENTRIC

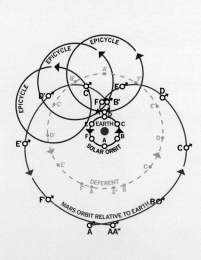

CHANGING PERSPECTIVE

Borman: Oh my God! Look at that picture over there.
Here's the Earth coming up. Wow, is that pretty.
Anders: Hey, don't take that, it's not scheduled.
Borman: (laughing) You got a color film, Jim?
Anders: Hand me that roll of color quick, will you...?
Lovell: Oh, man, that's great!

1968 was a difficult year on planet Earth. The Vietnam War, the bloodiest of Cold War proxy tussles, was at its height, ultimately claiming over three million lives. Martin Luther King Jr. was assassinated in Memphis, prompting presidential hopeful Bobby Kennedy to ask the people of the United States 'to tame the savageness of man and make gentle the life of this world.' Kennedy himself was assassinated before the year was out. Elsewhere, Russian tanks rolled into Prague, and France teetered on the edge of revolution. As I approached my first Christmas, my parents could have been forgiven for wondering what kind of world their son would inhabit in 1969. And then, as Christmas Eve drifted into Christmas morning, an unexpected snowfall decorated Oakbank Avenue and Borman, Lovell and Anders, 400,000 kilometres away, saved 1968.

Apollo 8 was, in the eyes of many, the Moon mission that had the most profound historical impact. It was a terrific, noble risk; a magnificent roll of the dice; a distillation of all that is great about exploration; a tribute to the sheer balls of the astronauts and engineers who decided that, come what may, they would honour President Kennedy's pledge to send 'a giant rocket more than 300 feet tall, the length of this football field, made of new metal alloys, some of which have not yet been invented, capable of standing heat and stresses several times more than have ever been experienced, fitted together with a precision better than the finest watch, carrying all the equipment needed for propulsion, guidance, control, communications, food and survival, on an untried mission, to an unknown celestial body, and then return it safely to Earth, re-entering the atmosphere at speeds of over 40,000 kilometres per hour, causing heat about half that of the temperature of the Sun – almost as hot as it is here today – and do all this, and do it right, and do it first before this decade is out'. If I heard that from a leader today I'd be first on the rocket. Instead I have to listen to vacuous diatribes about 'fairness', 'hard working families', and how 'we're all in it together'. Sod that, I want to go to Mars.

To set Apollo 8 in context, Apollo 7, the first manned test flight of the Apollo programme, was flown by Schirra, Eisele and Cunningham in October 1968. Apollo 8 was supposed to be a December test flight for the Lunar Lander, conducted in the familiar surroundings of Earth orbit, but delivery delays meant that it was not ready for flight and the aim of meeting Kennedy's deadline looked to be dead. But this wasn't the twenty-first century, it was the 1960s and NASA was run by engineers. The programme manager was George Low, an army veteran and aeronautical engineer who knew the spacecraft inside out and had the strength of character to make decisions. Why not send Apollo 8 directly to the Moon without the Lunar Lander, proposed Low, allowing Apollo 9 to test-fly the LEM (Lunar Excursion Module) in Earth orbit in early 1969 when it became available and pave the way for a landing before the decade was out? Virtually every engineer at NASA is said to have agreed, and so it was that only the second manned flight of the Apollo spacecraft lifted off from Kennedy on 21 December, ten short weeks after Apollo 7, bound for the Moon. The crew later said that they estimated their chance of succeeding to be fifty-fifty.

Precisely 69 hours, 8 minutes and 16 seconds after launch, the Command Module's engine fired to slow the spacecraft down and allow

EARTHRISE, APOLLO 8
This famous image was taken by US astronauts on board the Apollo 8 spacecraft on 24 December 1968 as they orbited the Moon. This photograph has become iconic for its depiction of the beauty and fragility of the Earth.

it to be captured by the Moon's gravity, putting the three astronauts into lunar orbit. Newton's almost three-hundred-year-old equations were used to calculate the trajectory. This was a spectacular, practically unbelievable engineering triumph. Less than a decade after Yuri Gagarin became the first human to orbit the Earth, three astronauts travelled all the way to the Moon. But the mission's powerful and enduring cultural legacy rests largely on two very human actions by the crew. One was the famous and moving Christmas broadcast, the most-watched television event in history at that time, when distant explorers read the first lines from the Book of Genesis; 'We are now approaching lunar sunrise, and for all the people back on Earth, the crew of Apollo 8 has a message that we would like to send to you,' began Anders. 'In the beginning God created the heaven and the Earth. And the Earth was without form, and void; and darkness was upon the face of the deep.' Borman concluded with a sentence clearly spoken by a lonely man 400,000 kilometres from home. 'And from the crew of Apollo 8, we close with goodnight, good luck, a Merry Christmas – and God bless all of you, all of you on the good Earth.'

The mission's most potent legacy, however, is NASA image AS8-14-2383, snapped by Bill Anders on a Hasselblad 500 EL at f/11 and a shutter speed of 1/250th of a second on Kodak Ektachrome film. It was, in other words, a very bright photograph. The image is better known as Earthrise. When viewed with the lunar surface at the bottom, Earth is tilted on its side with the South Pole to the left, and the Equator running top to bottom. Little landmass can be seen through the swirling clouds, but the bright sands of the Namib and Saharan deserts stand out salmon pink against the blackness beyond. Just 368 years and ten months after a man was burned at the stake for dreaming of worlds without end, here is Earth, a fragile crescent suspended over an alien landscape, the negative of a waxing Moon in the friendly skies of Earth. This is an unfamiliar, planetary Earth, no longer central; just another world. When Kennedy spoke of Apollo as a journey to an unknown celestial body, he meant the Moon. But we discovered Earth and, in the words of T.S. Eliot, came to know the place for the first time.

OUTWARDS TO THE MILKY WAY

Newton's laws are the keys to understanding our place in our local neighbourhood. Coupled with precision observations of the motion of the planets and moons, they allow the scale and geometry of the solar system to be deduced, and their positions to be calculated at any point in the future. The nature and location of the stars, however, requires an entirely different approach because at first sight they appear to be point-like and fixed. The observation that the stars don't appear to move is important if you know something about parallax, as the ancients did. Parallax is the name given to a familiar effect. Hold your finger up in front of your face and alternately close each of your eyes, keeping your finger still. Your finger appears to move relative to the more distant background, and the closer your finger is to your face, the more it appears to move. This is not an optical illusion; it's a consequence of viewing a nearby object from two different spatial positions; in this case the two slightly different positions of your eyes. We don't normally perceive this parallax effect because the brain combines the inputs from the eyes to create a single image, although the information is exploited to create our sense of depth. Aristotle used the lack of stellar parallax to argue that the Earth must be stationary at the centre of the universe, because if the Earth moved then the nearby stars would be observed to move against the background of the more distant ones. Thousands of years later,

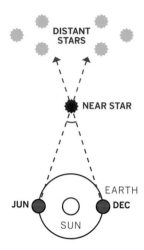

STELLAR PARALLAX

Nearby stars appear to move with respect to more distant stars due to the motion of the Earth around the Sun.

The line of sight to the star in December is different than that in June, when the Earth is on the other side of its orbit. Seen from Earth, the nearby star appears to sweep through the angle shown.

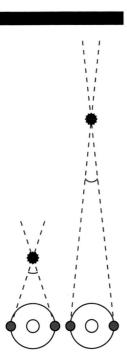

As the distance to a star increases, its parallax decreases. In the left figure, the star is about 2.5 times nearer than the star in the right figure, and has a parallax angle 2.5 times larger.

Tycho Brahe used a similar argument to refute the conclusions reached by Copernicus. Their logic was completely sound, but the conclusion is wrong because the nearby stars *do* move relative to the more distant background stars as the Earth orbits the Sun, and indeed as the Sun orbits the galaxy itself. You just have to look extremely carefully to see the effect.

Amongst the thousands of stars visible to the naked eye, 61 Cygni is one of the faintest. It's not without interest, being a binary star system of two orange K-type dwarf stars, slightly smaller and cooler than the Sun, orbiting each other at the lethargic rate of around 700 years. Despite the pair's relative visual anonymity, however, 61 Cygni has great historical significance. The reason for this quiet fame is that this faint star system was the first to have its distance from Earth measured by parallax.

Friedrich Bessel is best known to a physicist or mathematician for his work on the mathematical functions that bear his name. Pretty much any engineering or physical problem that involves a cylindrical or spherical geometry ends up with the use of Bessel functions, and, in blissful ignorance, you will probably encounter some piece of technology that has relied on them in the design process at some point today. But Bessel was first and foremost an astronomer, being appointed director of the Königsberg Observatory at the age of only 25. In 1838, Bessel observed that 61 Cygni shifted its position in the sky by approximately two-thirds of an arcsecond over a period of a year as viewed from Earth. That's not very much – an arcsecond is one 3600th of a degree. It is enough, however, to do a bit of trigonometry and calculate that 61 Cygni is 10.3 light years away from our solar system. This compares very favourably with the modern measurement of the distance, 11.41 ± 0.02 light years. Parallax is so important in astronomy that there is a measurement system completely based on it, which allows you to do these sums in your head. Astronomers use a distance measurement known as a parsec – which stands for 'per arcsecond'. This is the distance of a star from the Sun that has a parallax of 1 arcsecond. 1 parsec is 3.26 light years. Bessel's measurement of the parallax of 61 Cygni was 0.314 arcseconds, and this immediately implies that it's around 10 light years away.

Even today, stellar parallax remains the most accurate way of determining the distance to nearby stars, because it is a direct measurement which uses only trigonometry and requires no assumptions or physical models. On 19 December 2013 the Gaia space telescope was launched on a Soyuz rocket from French Guiana. The mission will measure, by parallax, the positions and motions of a billion stars in our galaxy over five years. This data will provide an accurate and dynamic 3D map of the galaxy, which in turn will allow for an exploration of the history of the Milky Way, because Newton's laws, which govern the motions of all these stars under the gravitational pull of each other, can be run backwards as well as forwards in time. Given precise measurements of the positions and velocities of 1 per cent of the stars in the Milky Way, it is possible to ask what the configuration of the stars looked like millions or even billions of years ago. This enables astronomers to build simulations of the evolution of our galaxy, revealing its history of collisions and mergers with other galaxies over thirteen billion years, stretching back to the beginning of the universe. Newton and Bessel would have loved it.

Stellar parallax, when deployed using a twenty-first-century orbiting observatory, is a powerful technique for mapping our galaxy out to distances of many thousands of light years. Beyond our galaxy, however, the distances are far too great to employ this direct method of distance measurement. In the mid-nineteenth century, this might have appeared an insurmountable problem, but science doesn't proceed by measurement alone. As Newton so powerfully demonstrated, scientific progress often proceeds through the interaction between theory and observation. Newton's Law of Gravitation is a theory; in physics this usually means a mathematical model that can be applied to explain or predict the behaviour of some part of the natural world. How might we measure the mass of a planet? We can't 'weigh' it directly, but given Newton's laws we can determine the planet's mass very accurately if it has a moon. The logic is quite simple – the moon's orbit clearly has something to do with the planet's gravity, which in turn has something to do with its mass. These relationships are encoded in Newton's law, and careful observation of the moon's orbit around the planet therefore allows for the planet's mass to be determined. For the more mathematical reader, the equation is:

$$M_{planet} + M_{moon} = 4\pi^2 a^3/GP^2$$

where a is the (time-averaged) distance between the planet and the moon, G is Newton's gravitational constant and P is the period of the orbit. (This equation is in fact Kepler's third law, discovered empirically by Kepler in 1619. Kepler's laws can be derived from Newton's law of gravitation.) Under the assumption that the mass of the planet is far larger than the mass of the Moon, this equation allows for the mass of the planet to be measured. This is how theoretical physics can be used to extract measurements from observation, given a mathematical model of the system. To measure the distance to objects that are too far away to use parallax, therefore, we need to find a theory or mathematical relationship that allows for a measurement of something – anything – to be related to distance. The first relationship of this type, which opened the door to all other methods of distance measurement out to the edge of the observable universe, was discovered at the end of the nineteenth century by an American astronomer named Henrietta Leavitt.

HENRIETTA LEAVITT
It was the studies of US astronomer Henrietta Leavitt (1868–1921) on the photographic magnitudes of stars that led her to discover the Cepheid variables in the Magellanic Clouds. She noticed that there was a regular variation in their brightness, and that the brighter stars had longer periods. By 1912, she had established a method which became the foundation of the one we use today to measure cosmic distances.

THE ARC IN THE SKY
Hipparcos (High Precision Parallax Collecting Satellite) was launched on 8 August 1989, but was stranded in geostationary transfer orbit by a booster failure. Despite this, the satellite has managed to measure the parallax, proper motion and position of over 120,000 stars to an accuracy of 0.002 arcseconds, about 20 times better than Earth-bound observations.

SEARCHING FOR PATTERNS IN STARLIGHT

The history of astronomy is a history of receding horizons.
Edwin Hubble

DARK SIDE OF THE MOON
This spectacular image, taken from on board the Apollo 8 spacecraft during its December 1968 mission, shows the craters that pepper the surface of the Moon. The image is taken looking towards the Southern Sea, as viewed from Earth.

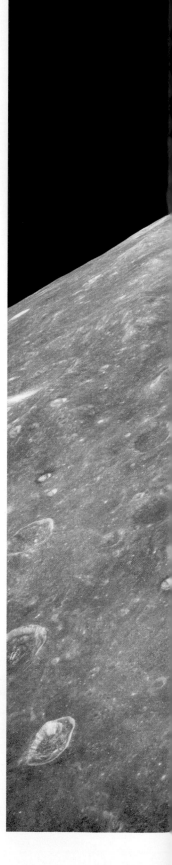

The Earth is replete with features named after rogues, because history is the province of the rich and powerful and the deserving rarely become either. To find more worthy geographical nomenclature it is necessary to look further afield, to a place that escaped the attention of the vain. The dark side of the Moon is such a place, because nobody had seen it until the Soviet spacecraft Luna 3 photographed it in 1959. It isn't dark, by the way; it permanently faces away from Earth due to an effect called tidal locking, and receives the same amount of sunlight as the familiar Earth-facing side. The first humans to see it were the crew of Apollo 8, when Bill Anders memorably described it as looking like 'a sand pile my kids have played in for some time. It's all beat up, no definition, just a lot of bumps and holes.' Lacking the smooth lunar maria, the dark side is an expanse of craters, and many of these have been named entirely appropriately after deserving scientists. Giordano Bruno is there, of course, alongside Pasteur, Hertz, Millikan, D'Alembert, Planck, Pauli, Van der Waals, Poincaré, Leibnitz, Van der Graaf and Landau. Arthur Schuster, the father of the physics department at the University of Manchester, is honoured. And tucked away in the southern hemisphere, next to a plain named Apollo, is a 65-kilometre-wide partly eroded crater called Leavitt.

Henrietta Swan Leavitt was one of the 'Harvard Computers', a group of women employed to work at the Harvard College Observatory by Professor Edward Charles Pickering. By the late nineteenth century Harvard had collected a large amount of data in the form of photographic plates, but the professional astronomers had neither the time nor resources to process the reams of material. Pickering's answer was to hire women as skilled, and cheap, analysts. Scottish astronomer Williamina Fleming was his first recruit, whom he employed after proclaiming that 'even his maid' could do a better job than the overworked males at the observatory. Fleming became a respected astronomer; she was made an honorary member of the Royal Astronomical Society in London and, amongst many important published works, discovered the Horsehead Nebula in Orion. Buoyed by this successful policy, Pickering continued to expand his 'computers' throughout the later years of the nineteenth century, bringing Henrietta Leavitt into the team in 1893. Pickering assigned her to the study of stars known as variables, whose brightness changes over a period of days, weeks or months. In 1908, Leavitt published a paper based on a series of observations of variable stars in the Small Magellanic Cloud, which we now know to be a satellite galaxy of the Milky Way. It consists of a detailed list of the positions and periods of 1777 variable stars, and towards the end, a brief but extremely important observation: 'It is worthy of note that in Table VI the brighter variables have the longer periods. It is also noticeable that those having the longest periods appear to be as regular in their variations as those which pass through their changes in a day or two.'

This discovery immediately caught the interest of Pickering, and for good reason. If a star's intrinsic brightness is known, then it is a simple matter to calculate its distance. Put very simply, the further away an object is, the dimmer it appears! Leavitt and Pickering published a more detailed study in 1912, in which they proposed a simple mathematical relationship between the period and intrinsic brightness of 25 variable stars. This relationship is known as the period-luminosity relation. All that was required to calibrate the relation was a parallax measurement

LEAVITT'S LEGENDARY PAPER
Henrietta Leavitt's 1908 paper in which she noticed for the first time the relationship between the intrinsic brightness of a Cepheid variable star and the period of its variation in brightness.

ANNALS OF HARVARD COLLEGE OBSERVATORY. Vol. LX. No. IV.

1777 VARIABLES IN THE MAGELLANIC CLOUDS.

By HENRIETTA S. LEAVITT.

In the spring of 1904, a comparison of two photographs of the Small Magellanic Cloud, taken with the 24-inch Bruce Telescope, led to the discovery of a number of faint variable stars. As the region appeared to be interesting, other plates were examined, and although the quality of most of these was below the usual high standard of excellence of the later plates, 57 new variables were found, and announced in Circular 79. In order to furnish material for determining their periods, a series of sixteen plates, having exposures of from two to four hours, was taken with the Bruce Telescope the following autumn. When they arrived at Cambridge, in January, 1905, a comparison of one of them with an early plate led immediately to the discovery of an extraordinary number of new variable stars. It was found, also, that plates, taken within two or three days of each other, could be compared with equally interesting results, showing that the periods of many of the variables are short. The number thus discovered, up to the present time, is 969. Adding to these 23 previously known, the total number of variables in this region is 992. The Large Magellanic Cloud has also been examined on 16 photographic plates with the 24-inch Bruce Telescope, and 808 new variables have been found, of which 152 were announced in Circular 82. As much time will be required for the discussion of these variables, the provisional catalogues given below have been prepared.

The labor of determining the precise right ascensions and declinations of nearly eighteen hundred variables and several hundred comparisons stars would be very great, and as many of the objects are faint, the resulting positions could not readily be used in finding them. Accordingly, their rectangular coordinates have been employed. A reticule was prepared by making a photographic enlargement of a glass plate ruled accurately in squares, a millimetre on a side. The resulting glass measured 11 × 17 inches, the size of the Bruce plates, and was covered with squares measuring a centimetre on a side. Great care was taken to have the scale uniform in all parts of this plate, which was designed to furnish a standard reticule, not only for the Magellanic

SEARCHING FOR PATTERNS

of the distance to a single variable of the type observed by Leavitt. If this could be achieved, then the distance to the Small Magellanic Cloud could be obtained. In 1913, the Danish astronomer Ejnar Hertzsprung, in a spectacularly accurate piece of astronomical observing, managed to measure the distance by parallax to the well-known variable star Delta Cephei. Delta Cephei has a period of 5.366341 days, and lies 890 light years from Earth, according to modern measurements by the Hubble Space Telescope. Because of its historic place as the first of Leavitt's variable stars to have its distance measured, these stars are now known as Cepheid variables. Inexplicably, even though Hertzsprung managed to get the parallax measurement and the distance to Delta Cephei correct, his published paper quotes the distance to the Small Magellanic Cloud as 3000 light years, which is badly wrong; the modern-day measurement is 170,000 light years. There is speculation that Hertzsprung made a simple typographical error in the paper, and for some reason couldn't be bothered to correct it. In any case, the technique had been established, and two years later Harlow Shapley published the first of a series of papers that refined the method and led him to the first measurements of the size and shape of the Milky Way. He concluded that the galaxy is a disk of stars, around 300,000 light years in extent, with the Sun positioned around 50,000 light years from the centre. This is roughly correct – the Milky Way is around 100,000 light years across and the Sun is about 25,000 light years from the centre. This was an important moment in the history of astronomy, because it was the first measurement that relegated the solar system from being the centre of everything. It's true that few if any astronomers would have claimed otherwise by the turn of the twentieth century, but science is a subject that relies on measurement rather than opinion. The journey into insignificance had begun.

BEYOND THE MILKY WAY

With the size and shape of the galaxy measured, the question of our place in creation now shifted from the position of the Sun within the galaxy to the nature of the universe itself. If the progress from Copernicus through Newton to Leavitt and Shapley appears relatively fast, certainly when viewed in the context of the glacial progress throughout the 2000-year dominance of Aristotelian thinking, then the decade that followed Shapley's determination of the size of the Milky Way might be described as an intellectual avalanche. The revolution was fuelled from two sides. A new generation of telescopes and the increasingly sophisticated observational techniques developed by astronomers like Leavitt, Hertzsprung and Shapley provided the data, and in parallel theoretical physics experienced a revolution. Claims of revolutions or paradigm shifts have to be made with great care in science – indeed the terminology is quite unfashionable in certain academic circles. But from a physicist's perspective there is no doubt that physics experienced a revolution in 1915, because in November of that year Albert Einstein presented a new theory of gravity to the Prussian Academy of Science.

The theory is known as General Relativity, and it replaces Newton's law of universal gravitation. Many physicists regard General Relativity as the most beautiful piece of physics yet devised by the human mind, and we will explore why this is so a little later. For now, let us note that the Big Bang, the expanding universe, black holes, gravitational waves and the whole evocative landscape of twenty-first-century cosmological language began, absolutely, with the publication of General Relativity. The parallels with the Newtonian revolution are clear. Without Newton's laws, there is no deep understanding of the solar system and the motions of the planets. Without General Relativity, there is no deep understanding of the large-scale structure and behaviour of the universe. But we are getting ahead of ourselves. As the second decade of the twentieth century dawned, the size and shape of the Milky Way galaxy was established, albeit with rather large errors, but the true extent of the universe beyond our galaxy was still hotly debated. Could we, at least, cling to a sort of token pre-Copernican fig leaf and place our galaxy at the centre of the universe? The desire to be special runs deep. The last intellectual rearguard action against our demotion can, rather theatrically, be said to have played out on a single evening on 26 April 1920 in the Baird auditorium at the Smithsonian Museum of Natural History, Washington DC. This is, of course, an oversimplification, but allow me a minute to enjoy the sound of the outraged shaking jowls of a thousand historians of science before I qualify and partially justify this hyperbolic claim.

CEPHEID VARIABLES

It is interesting to ask what physical processes lead to the relationship between the brightness of a Cepheid variable and its period. The details, as always, are complicated, not least because there are several different types of Cepheid, but the principle is quite simple. Delta Cephei is a yellow giant star, around 4.5 times the mass of the Sun and 2000 times more luminous. Stars of this type have large amounts of helium in their atmospheres. As the atmosphere heats up due to the nuclear fusion reactions in the core, the helium atoms are stripped of both of their electrons, forming what is called doubly ionised helium. In this form, the helium is relatively opaque, meaning that the light from the star is readily absorbed, causing the atmosphere to become hotter and to expand, increasing the stars' luminosity. But as the atmosphere expands further out into space, it cools, and ultimately the temperature drops far enough for the helium atoms to recapture an electron. This causes the gas to become transparent, allowing more light to escape. The rapidly cooling atmosphere then collapses back towards the star, heating up and restarting the cycle. The brighter the star is to begin with, the longer it takes this cycle to play out, and this is the origin of the relationship discovered by Henrietta Leavitt.

CEPHEID VARIABLES
These three images show the Cepheid variable star RZ Velorum at its minimum (left), average (centre) and maximum (right) light phases which occur as part of a cycle. The relationship between a Cepheid variable and its period was discovered by Henrietta Leavitt.

THE GREAT DEBATE

The history of science is littered with crunching moments of conflict, debates and disagreements that divided opinion in the most passionate of battles. The wonderful thing about science, however, is that the debates can be settled when facts become available. Science and 'conservative common sense' famously clashed in 1860 when Thomas Huxley and Samuel Wilberforce fulminated over the new theory of evolution published by Darwin seven months earlier. I imagine Wilberforce's indignant reddening cheeks shaking with righteous outrage as he denied the repugnant possibility that his grandfather was a monkey. None of his relatives was a chimpanzee, by the way; we simply share a common ancestor with them around 6 or 7 million years ago. But the 'unctuous, oleaginous and saponaceous' bishop, as Disraeli once called him, was having none of it. This might be a little unfair to the great Victorian orator and Bishop of the Church of England, but in the case of evolution he was firmly on the wrong side of reality. Few great leaps in knowledge occur without dividing opinion, and this is entirely appropriate. Extraordinary claims require extraordinary evidence, and the great scientific discoveries we are celebrating here are utterly extraordinary. The trick as an educated citizen of the twenty-first century is to realise that Nature is far stranger and more wonderful than human imagination, and the only appropriate response to new discoveries is to enjoy one's inevitable discomfort, take delight in being shown to be wrong and learn something as a result.

The world of astronomy had its moment of intellectual sumo in what has become known as the Great Debate. The year was 1920, and two eminent astronomers found themselves stuck on a train together travelling the 4000 kilometres from California to Washington to discuss the greatest cosmological question of the day. The younger of the two men, Harlow Shapley, we have already met. He had just published his data suggesting that the Milky Way galaxy was much larger than previously suspected. This, however, was where he believed the universe stopped; Shapley was convinced our galaxy was the beginning and end of the cosmos. His travelling companion thought otherwise. Heber Curtis had been studying a misty patch of light known as the Andromeda Nebula. He was convinced that this was not part of our galaxy, but a separate island universe of billions of other stars.

It is not known what they discussed on the train, but the debate itself took place at the Smithsonian Museum of Natural History throughout the day and night of 26 April. At stake was the scale of the universe itself, and both men knew that the question would ultimately be settled by evidence rather than debating skills. The human race had already been shunted from the centre of the universe by Copernicus, and now faced the possibility that the Milky Way galaxy itself was part of a multitude, stretching across millions of light years of space. The question wasn't settled that evening, but the experienced Curtis, perceived as the underdog because of the magnitude of what he was suggesting, landed significant blows. Curtis observed that the Andromeda Nebula contains a number of novae – exploding stars that shine temporarily, but brightly, in the night sky – but he also noted that the novae in Andromeda appeared on average to be ten times fainter than any others. Curtis asserted that Andromeda's novae appear dimmer simply because they are perhaps half a million light years further away than those in the Milky Way. Andromeda is therefore another galaxy, claimed Curtis, which strongly implied that the other so-called nebulae were other galaxies too. This was the very definition of an extraordinary claim, and the extraordinary evidence came only four years later.

HUBBLE AND HOOKER
This, the 100-inch Hooker telescope at Mount Wilson Observatory, California, was the instrument that enabled Edwin Hubble (right) to observe the Cepheid variable stars in the Andromeda Nebula, and by analysis of his findings prove that the galaxy was located outside our own. Hubble is pictured with the then director of the Observatory, Walter Adams (centre), and British astronomer James Jeans (left).

In 1923 a photo of Andromeda, taken by a 33-year-old astronomer called Edwin Hubble, further fuelled the Great Debate. It's only a photograph but, just like Anders' Earthrise, it belongs to a rarefied group of images that have transformed our perspective. Aside from their scientific merit, such images assume great cultural significance because of the ideas they generate and the philosophical and ideological challenges they pose. They also carry with them, in the shadows, personal stories. Someone would have taken a photograph of Andromeda, someday, and discovered what Hubble did. But Hubble took this one, and his story therefore becomes inextricably intertwined with it. Some don't like their history presented in this way, but science is richer when its stories include people as well as ideas; curiosity is, after all, a human virtue. Hubble may never have taken the photograph had he followed through on a promise to his father to practise law. Reading jurisprudence at Queen's College, Oxford, as one of the first Rhodes Scholars, Hubble aimed to fulfil his father's wishes, but John Hubble died before Edwin finished his degree. The death of his father encouraged Edwin to ditch law and revisit his childhood passion for astronomy. He left Oxford for the University of Chicago, joined the Yerkes Observatory and received his PhD in 1917 with a thesis entitled 'Photographic Investigations of Faint Nebulae'. After brief service in the US Army at the end of World War One, Hubble obtained a position at the Mount Wilson Observatory. He found himself at the controls of the largest, most powerful telescope on the planet, and with the knowledge and good sense to point it at the most intriguing and controversial object in the night sky: Andromeda. Just like Curtis before him, Hubble could make out distinct features within the misty patch, but the newly commissioned 100-inch Hooker telescope allowed him to see much more detail. On 5 October 1923 he took a 45-minute exposure, found three unidentified specks that he assumed were new novae and marked them all with an 'N'.

ANDROMEDA
Photographs of Andromeda like this one have transformed our perspective. Such images question long-held beliefs and theories and open up the debate about our history and place in the universe.

To confirm his findings Hubble needed to compare this plate with previous images of Andromeda taken at Mount Wilson. The following day he made the journey down to the basement archive where the observatory's collection of images was catalogued and stored. To Hubble's delight, two of the specks were indeed newly discovered novae – what we now know to be the bright nuclear flares of white dwarf stars as they accrete gas and dust from a nearby companion. But it was the third speck that he found most interesting when he compared it to previous images. As Hubble scanned back through the Mount Wilson catalogue he discovered that the star had been captured before; in some plates it appeared brighter, whereas in others it appeared dim or not present at all. Hubble immediately grasped the importance of his discovery. The third speck was a Cepheid variable, the type of star Henrietta Leavitt had studied two decades earlier. In one of the most famous corrections in scientific history, Hubble crossed out the letter 'N' and replaced it in red ink with the letters 'VAR' followed by a very understated exclamation mark.

Hubble had discovered a cosmic yardstick in Andromeda, and it was a trivial matter to calculate the distance. The new star varied with a period of 31.415 days, which, following Leavitt, implied its intrinsic brightness was 7000 times that of our Sun, and yet it appeared so dim in the night sky that it was invisible to all but the most powerful of telescopes. Hubble's initial calculations revealed that the star was over 900,000 light years away from Earth, a staggering distance when the size of our own galaxy was estimated to be no more than 100,000 light years across. Hubble, with the help of Leavitt's ruler, laid the Great Debate to rest. Andromeda, the distant patch of light in the night sky, is a galaxy; an island, according to current estimates, of a trillion suns. Current measurements put the giant spiral at a distance of 2.5 million light years from the Milky Way, one of around 54 galaxies gravitationally bound together to form our galactic neighbourhood known as The Local Group.

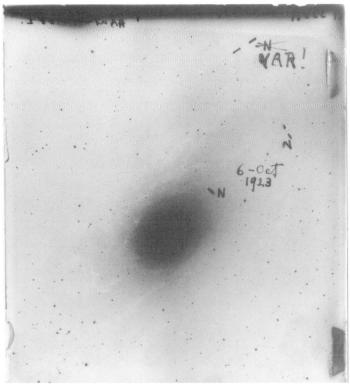

HUBBLE'S EUREKA MOMENT
Edwin Hubble's glass plate from the Hooker telescope very clearly reveals his excitement at his discovery that one of the novae he thought he had previously located was in fact a variable VAR! marks the spot.

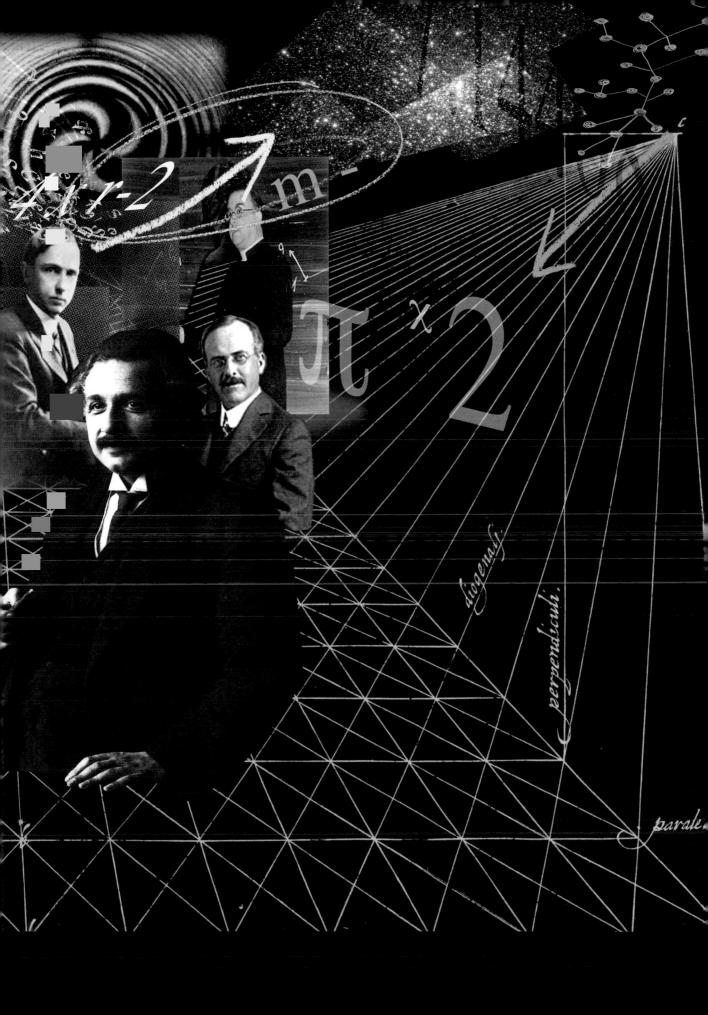

THE POLITICAL RAMIFICATIONS OF REALITY, OR 'HOW TO AVOID GETTING LOCKED UP'

FIRST VIEWS OF THE MOON
Galileo's beautiful watercolours of the Moon, drawn in around November–December 1609, are famous as the first realistic depictions of the Moon viewed through a telescope from Earth, and were revolutionary at the time for suggesting that the lunar surface was not perfectly smooth.

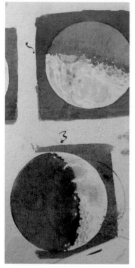

What is science? There are many answers, and whole academic careers are devoted to a complex analysis of the historical and sociological development of the subject. To a working scientist, however, I think the answer is quite simple and illuminating because it reveals a lot about how scientists see themselves and what they do. The great (an overused adjective, but not in this case) physicist Richard Feynman gave a characteristically clear and simple description in his Messenger Lectures delivered at Cornell University in 1964: 'In general, we look for a new law by the following process: First we guess it. Then we – now don't laugh, that's really true – then we compute the consequences of the guess to see what, if this is right, if this law that we guessed is right, to see what it would imply. And then we compare the computation results to nature, or we say compare to experiment or experience, compare it directly with observations to see if it works. If it disagrees with experiment, it's wrong. In that simple statement is the key to science. It doesn't make any difference how beautiful your guess is, it doesn't make any difference how smart you are, who made the guess, or what his name is. If it disagrees with experiment, it's wrong. That's all there is to it.'

Why do I like this so much? The reason is that it is modest – almost humble in its simplicity – and this, in my opinion, is the key to the success of science. Science isn't a grandiose practice; there are no great ambitions to understand why we are here or how the whole universe works or our place within it, or even how the universe began. Just have a look at something – the smallest, most trivial little thing – and enjoy trying to figure out how it works. That is science. In a famous BBC *Horizon* film broadcast in 1982 called 'The Pleasure of Finding Things Out', Feynman went further: 'People say to me, "Are you looking for the ultimate laws of physics?" No, I'm not. I'm just looking to find out more about the world and if it turns out there is a simple ultimate law which explains everything, so be it; that would be very nice to discover. If it turns out it's like an onion with millions of layers and we're just sick and tired of looking at the layers, then that's the way it is.... My interest in science is to simply find out more about the world.'

The remarkable thing about science, however, is that it has ended up addressing some of the great philosophical questions about the origin and fate of the universe and the meaning of existence without actually setting out to do so, and this is no accident. You won't discover anything meaningful about the world by sitting on a pillar for decades and contemplating the cosmos, although you may become a saint. No, a truly deep and profound understanding of the natural world has emerged more often than not from the consideration of much less lofty and profound questions, and there are two reasons for this. Firstly, simple questions can be answered systematically by applying the scientific method as outlined by Richard Feynman, whereas complex and badly posed questions such as 'Why are we here?' cannot. But more importantly, and rather more profoundly, it turns out that the answers to simple questions can overturn centuries of philosophical and theological pontificating quite by accident. Reputations count for naught in the face of observation. The famous story of Galileo's clashes with the Inquisition at the height of the Copernican debate, which he certainly did not expect (nobody does), is the archetypal example.

Galileo began his university career with the study of medicine, but his imagination was captured by art and mathematics. Between studying Medicine in Pisa and returning to his hometown in 1589 to

THE MADONNA ON THE MOON
High up in the dome above the Pauline Chapel in the church of Santa Maria Maggiore in Rome, a spectacular fresco depicts the Madonna on a lunar landscape that is pitted and uneven. In his painting, Lodovico Cardi – better known as Cigoli – reveals the influence of his friend Galileo and his discoveries.

become Professor of Mathematics, Galileo spent a year in Florence teaching perspective and in particular a technique called chiaroscuro. Chiaroscuro is the study of light and shadow, and how it can be used to create a sense of depth by accurately representing the way that light sources illuminate objects. Chiaroscuro was one of the most important new artistic techniques to emerge during Galileo's time, allowing a new sense of realism to be portrayed on canvas.

Although Galileo spent only a brief time in Florence, the skills he acquired had a great impact on his scientific work. In particular, his carefully developed ability to understand the delicate play of light on three-dimensional shapes, when applied to his later astronomical studies, played an important role in undermining the Aristotelian cosmological edifice which formed a cornerstone of the teachings of the Roman Catholic Church.

The small and seemingly innocuous theological thread on which Galileo unwittingly tugged was made available to him on a visit to Venice in 1609, when he purchased the lenses required to build his first telescope. One of the first objects he turned his 'perspective tube' towards was the Moon. With the mind of a mathematician and the eye of an artist, Galileo drew a series of six watercolours representing what he saw.

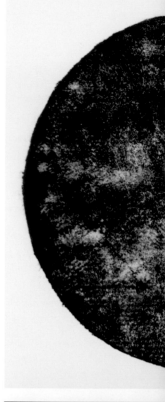

These images are both beautiful and revolutionary. Catholic dogma asserted that the Moon and the other heavenly bodies were perfect, unblemished spheres. Previous astronomers who had viewed the Moon, either with the naked eye or through telescopes, had drawn a two-dimensional blotchy surface, but Galileo saw the patterns of light and dark differently. His training in chiaroscuro revealed to him an alien lunar landscape of mountain ranges and craters.

'I have been led to the conclusion that ... the surface of the Moon is not smooth, even and perfectly spherical – as the great crowd of philosophers have believed about this and other heavenly bodies – but, on the contrary, to be uneven and rough and crowded with depression and bulges. And it is like the face of the Earth itself, which is marked here and there with chains of mountains and depths of valleys.'

GALILEO'S MOON
This sketch of the Moon is one of several made by Galileo in 1610 from observations he made through a telescope he himself had built two years previously.

Galileo shared the watercolours with his long-standing friend from Florence, the artist Cigoli, who was inspired to represent this new and radical view of the Moon in the grandest of settings. Built in the year 430 by Pope Sixtus III, the Pauline Chapel in Rome documents the changing artistic styles and techniques used to represent the natural world across many centuries; a place filled with shifting examples of how the three-dimensional world can be represented on a two-dimensional surface. Covering the dome of the Pauline Chapel is Cigoli's final masterpiece – a striking fresco depicting a familiar scene of the Virgin Mary bathed in a shaft of golden light surrounded by cherubs and angels. The fresco depicts Mary over what was, for the first time, a detailed, textured and cratered moon. The Vatican named it the Assumption of the Virgin, unaware perhaps of the philosophical challenge it represented. Here was art representing scientific knowledge – a type of knowledge radically different to historical or scriptural authority, based on observation rather than dogma and presented unashamedly in a grand setting for all in Rome to see. It is undoubtedly true that Galileo didn't intend to challenge the very theological foundations of the Church of Rome by observing the Moon through a telescope. But scientific discoveries, however innocuous they may seem at first sight, have a way of undermining those who don't much care for facts. Reality catches up with everyone eventually.

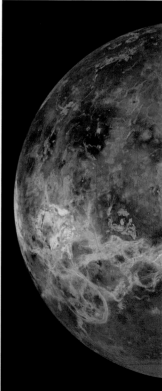

With his depictions of the Moon completed, Galileo turned his ever more powerful lenses to other celestial bodies. Between 7 and 13 January 1610, he became the first human to observe Jupiter's four largest moons – Io, Europa, Ganymede and Callisto – now known as the Galilean

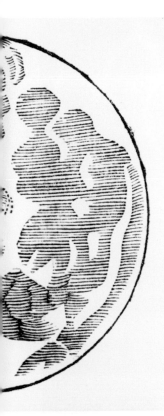

Satellites. For Galileo, this was further evidence to support the work of Copernicus and the physical reality of the heliocentric model. If moons were orbiting Jupiter, Galileo reasoned, it was impossible to argue that the Earth was at the centre of the universe, because heavenly bodies existed that did not circle the Earth.

Galileo published these observations in the spring of 1610 in 'The Starry Messenger', and from his correspondence with Kepler his irritation with the discontent it caused amongst philosophers was clear. 'My dear Kepler, I wish that we might laugh at the remarkable stupidity of the common herd. What do you have to say about the principal philosophers of this academy who are filled with the stubbornness of an asp and do not want to look at either the planets, the Moon or the telescope, even though I have freely and deliberately offered them the opportunity a thousand times? Truly, just as the asp stops its ears, so do these philosophers shut their eyes to the light of truth.'

To Galileo's mind, absolute confirmation of Copernicus's heliocentric model was provided by his studies of Venus. Beginning in September 1610, Galileo observed Venus over the course of months and, like the Moon, he observed that Venus had phases. Sometimes the planet was lit completely by the Sun, but at other times only a crescent appeared to be illuminated. The only plausible explanation for this observation was that Venus was orbiting the Sun. This was surely final compelling evidence of a solar system with the Sun at its heart and the planets orbiting around it.

It wasn't that simple, of course. Galileo, in what was certainly an ill-judged move, decided to move beyond reporting his scientific observations and instead champion a particular theological and philosophical interpretation of the data – namely that the Church was wrong and that the Earth was most definitely not the centre of the universe. This he seems to have done because he wanted to be famous, and famous he became. Copernicus's *De revolutionibus* was banned until 'corrected' (the full version was not removed from the banned list until 1758!) and Galileo ordered not to repeat his 'foolish and absurd' conclusions. Galileo didn't keep quiet, and he achieved his historical notoriety by being put under house arrest in 1633, where he stayed for the remainder of his life.

Many historians characterise Galileo as a bit of an egotistical social climber who brought it all on himself, which is partly true and yet also desperately unfair. He was undoubtedly a great scientist and a supremely talented astronomical observer. In particular, he was the first to clearly state the principle of relativity which lies at the heart of Newton's laws of motion; namely that there is no such thing as absolute rest or absolute motion. This is why we don't feel the movement of the Earth around the Sun, and why Aristotle et al. were misled into reading far too much into their stationary feelings. In the hands of Albert Einstein, the principle of relativity can be generalised to freely falling objects in a gravitational field, and this ultimately leads to modern cosmology and the Big Bang theory. But we are jumping ahead again. The purpose of recounting the story of Galileo is not to attack the easy target of the Inquisition (which nobody expects). Rather, it is to highlight the fact that the smallest and most modest of scientific observations can lead to great philosophical and theological shifts that in turn can have a tremendous impact on society. Galileo, by looking through a telescope, doing some drawings and thinking about what he saw, helped to undermine centuries of autocratic idiocy and woolly thinking. In doing so, he got himself locked up, but also bridged the gap between Copernicus and Kepler, and paved the way for Isaac Newton and ultimately Albert Einstein to construct a complete description of the universe and our place within it.

VENUS
Galileo's observations were not just restricted to the Moon, for he also studied Venus. This false-colour projection shows the western hemisphere of Venus with the North Pole at its apex.

THE HAPPIEST THOUGHT
OF MY LIFE

Scientific progress, then, is often triggered by rather innocuous discoveries or simple realisations. There is a terrible cliché about scientists exhibiting a 'childlike' fascination with nature, but I can't think of a better way of putting it. The sense in which the cliché rings true is that children are occasionally in the habit of focusing on a very small thing and continuing to ask the question 'Why?' until they get an answer that satisfies their curiosity. Adults don't seem to do this as much. Good scientists do, however, and if I have a thesis in this chapter then it is as follows; by focusing on tiny but interesting things with honesty and clarity, great and profound discoveries are made, often by flawed human beings who don't initially realise the consequences of their investigations. The absolutely archetypal example of such an approach can be found at the beginning of Einstein's quest to replace Newton's Theory of Gravity.

Einstein is most famous for his equation $E=mc^2$, which is contained within the special theory of relativity he published in 1905. At the heart of the theory is a very simple concept that dates all the way back to Galileo. Put simply, there is no way that you can tell whether you are moving or not. This sounds a bit abstract, but we all know it's true. If you are sitting in a room at home reading this book, then it feels the same as if you are sitting in an aircraft reading this book, as long as there is no turbulence and the aircraft is in level flight. If you aren't allowed to look out of the window, then nothing you can do in the room or on the plane will tell you whether or not you are 'sitting still' or moving. You might claim that your room is self-evidently not moving, whereas a plane obviously is because otherwise it wouldn't take you from London to New York. But that's not right, because your room is moving in orbit around the Sun, and indeed it is spinning around the Earth's axis, and the Sun itself is in orbit around the galaxy, which is moving relative to other galaxies in the universe. Einstein discovered his famous equation $E=mc^2$ by taking this seemingly pedantic reasoning seriously and asserting that NO experiment you can ever do, even in principle, using clocks, radioactive atoms, electrical circuits, pendulums, or any physical object at all, will tell you whether or not you are moving. Anyone has the absolute right to claim that they are at rest, as long as there is no net force acting on them causing them to accelerate. You are claiming it now, no doubt, if you are reading this book sitting comfortably on your sofa. Pedantry is very useful sometimes, because without Einstein's theory of special relativity we wouldn't have $E=mc^2$, we wouldn't really understand nuclear or particle physics, how the Sun shines or how radioactivity works. We wouldn't understand the universe.

Something important bothered Einstein after he published his theory in 1905, however. Newton's great achievement – the all-conquering Universal Law of Gravitation – did not fit within the framework of special relativity, and therefore one or the other required modification. Einstein's response to this problem was typically Einsteinian; he thought about it very carefully, and, in November 1907, whilst sitting in his chair in the patent office in Bern, he found the right thread to pull. Looking back at the moment in an article written in 1920, Einstein described his idea with beautiful, and indeed child-like, simplicity.

EINSTEIN'S BEAUTIFUL THEORY
Albert Einstein, one of the great minds of science, whose General Theory of Relativity, published in 1916, is often cited as the most beautiful scientific theory of all.

'Then there occurred to me the *"glücklichste Gedanke meines Lebens"*, the happiest thought of my life, in the following form. The gravitational field has only a relative existence in a way similar to the electric field generated by magnetoelectric induction. *Because for an observer falling freely from the roof of a house there exists* – at least in his immediate surroundings – *no gravitational field* [his italics]. Indeed, if the observer drops some bodies then these remain relative to him in a state of rest or of uniform motion, independent of their particular chemical or physical nature (in this consideration the air resistance is, of course, ignored). The observer therefore has a right to interpret his state as "at rest".'

I am well aware that you might object quite strongly to this statement, because it appears to violate common sense. Surely an object falling under the action of the gravitational force is accelerating towards the ground, and therefore cannot be said to be 'at rest'? Good, because if you think that then you are about to learn a valuable lesson. Common sense is completely worthless and irrelevant when trying to understand reality. This is probably why people who like to boast about their common sense tend to rail against the fact that they share a common ancestor with a monkey. How, then, to convince you that Einstein was, and indeed still is, correct?

Most of the time, books are better at conveying complex ideas than television. There are many reasons for this, some of which I'll discuss in a future autobiography when my time on TV is long over. But when done well, television pictures can convey ideas with an elegance and economy unavailable in print. *Human Universe* contains, I hope, some of these moments, but there is one sequence in particular that I think fits into this category.

NASA's Plum Brook Station in Ohio is home to the world's largest vacuum chamber. It is 30 metres in diameter and 37 metres high, and was designed in the 1960s to test nuclear rockets in simulated space-like conditions. No nuclear rocket has ever been fired inside – the programme was cancelled before the facility was completed – but many spacecraft, from the Skylab nosecone to the airbags on Mars landers, have been tested inside this cathedral of aluminium. To my absolute delight, NASA agreed to conduct an experiment using their vacuum chamber to demonstrate precisely what motivated Einstein to his remarkable conclusion. The experiment involves pumping all the air out of the chamber and dropping a bunch of feathers and a bowling ball from a crane. Both Galileo and Newton knew the result, which is not in question. The feathers and the bowling ball both hit the ground at the same time. Newton's explanation for this striking result is as follows. The gravitational force acting on a feather is proportional to its mass. We've already seen this written down in Newton's Law of Gravitation. That gravitational force causes the feather to accelerate, according to Newton's other equation, $F=ma$. This equation says that the more massive something is, the more force has to be applied to make it accelerate. Magically, the mass that appears in $F=ma$ is precisely the same as the mass that appears in the Law of Gravitation, and so they precisely cancel each other out. In other words, the more massive something is, the stronger the gravitational force between it and the Earth, but the more massive it is, the larger this force has to be to get it moving. Everything cancels out, and so everything ends up falling at the same rate. The problem with this explanation is that nobody has ever thought of a good reason why these two masses should be the same. In physics, this is known as the equivalence principle, because 'gravitational mass' and 'inertial mass' are precisely equivalent to each other.

Einstein's explanation for the fact that both the feathers and the bowling ball fall at the same rate in the Plum Brook vacuum chamber is radically different. Recall Einstein's happiest thought. 'Because for an observer falling freely from the roof of a house there exists ... no gravitational field'. There is no force acting on the feathers or the ball in freefall, and therefore they don't accelerate! They stay precisely where they are; at rest, relative to each other. Or, if you prefer, they stand still because we are always able to define ourselves as being at rest if there are no forces acting on us. But, you are surely asking, how come they eventually hit the ground if they are not moving because no forces are

acting on them? The answer, according to Einstein, is that the ground is accelerating up to meet them, and hits them like a cricket bat! But, but, but, you must be thinking, I'm sitting on the ground now and I'm not accelerating. Oh yes you are, and you know it because you can feel a force acting on you. It's the force exerted by the chair on which you may be sitting, or the ground on which you are standing. This is obvious – if you stand up long enough then your feet will hurt because there is a force acting on them. And if there is a force acting on them, then they are accelerating. There is no sleight of hand here. The very beautiful thing about Einstein's happiest thought is that, once you know it, it's utterly obvious. Standing on the ground is hard work because it exerts a force on you. The effect is precisely the same as sitting in an accelerating car and being pushed back into your seat. You can feel the acceleration viscerally, and if you switch off your common sense for a moment, then you can feel

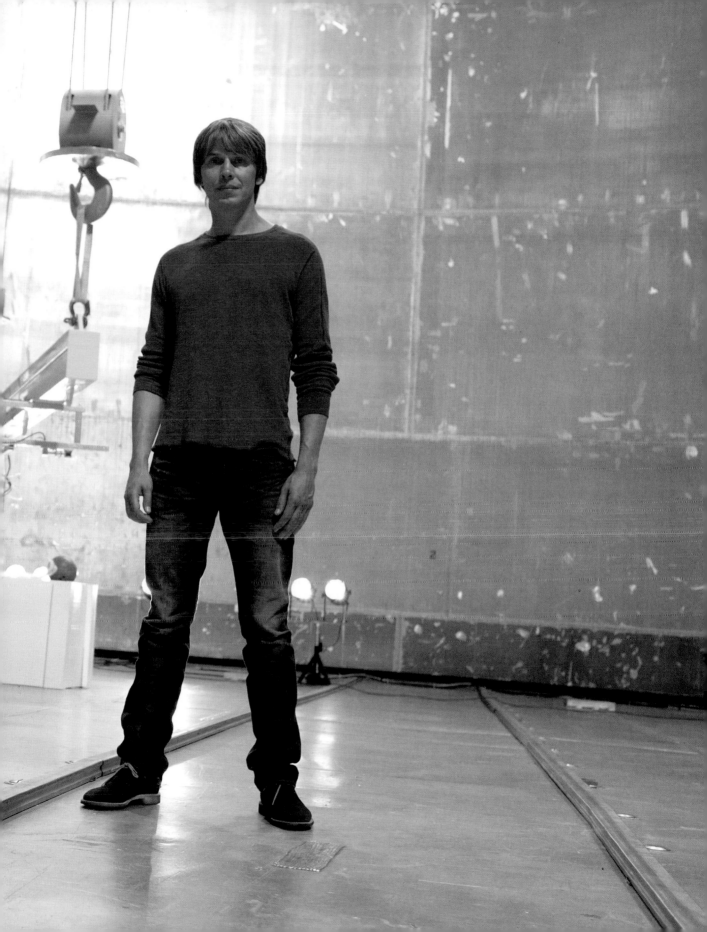

the acceleration now. The only way you can get rid of the acceleration, momentarily, is to jump off a roof.

This is wonderful reasoning, but of course it does raise the thorny question of why, if there is no such thing as gravity, the Earth orbits the Sun. Maybe Aristotle was right after all. The answer is not easy, and it took Einstein almost a decade to work out the details. The result, published in 1916, is the General Theory of Relativity, which is often cited as the most beautiful scientific theory of them all. General Relativity is notoriously mathematically and conceptually difficult when you get into the details of making predictions that can be compared with observations. Indeed, most physics students in the UK will not meet General Relativity until their final year, or until they become postgraduates. But having said that, the basic idea is very simple. Einstein replaced the force of gravity with geometry – in particular, the curvature of space and time.

Imagine that you are standing on the surface of the Earth at the equator with a friend. You both start walking due north, parallel to each other. As you get closer to the North Pole, you will find that you move closer together, and if you carry on all the way to the Pole you will bump into each other. If you don't know any better, then you may conclude that there is some kind of force, pulling you both together. But in reality there is no such force. Instead, the surface of the Earth is curved into a sphere, and on a sphere, lines that are parallel at the equator meet at the Pole – they are called lines of longitude. This is how geometry can lead to the appearance of a force.

Einstein's theory of gravity contains equations that allow us to calculate how space and time are curved by the presence of matter and energy and how objects move across the curved spacetime – just like you and your friend moving across the surface of the Earth. Spacetime is often described as the fabric of the universe, which isn't a bad term. Massive objects such as stars and planets tell the fabric how to curve, and the fabric tells objects how to move. In particular, all objects follow 'straight line' paths across the curved spacetime that are known in the jargon as geodesics. This is the General Relativistic equivalent of Newton's first law of motion – every body continues in a state of rest or uniform motion in a straight line unless acted upon by a force. Einstein's description of the Earth's orbit around the Sun is therefore quite simple. The orbit is a straight line in spacetime curved by the presence of the Sun, and the Earth follows this straight line because there are no forces acting on it to make it do otherwise. This is the opposite of the Newtonian description, which says that the Earth would fly through space in what we would intuitively call a 'straight line' if it were not for the force of gravity acting between it and the Sun. Straight lines in curved spacetime look curved to us for precisely the same reason that lines of longitude on the surface of the Earth look curved to us; the space upon which the straight lines are defined is curved.

This is all well and good, but there may be a question that has been nagging away in your mind since I told you that the ground accelerated up and hit the feathers and the bowling ball at Plum Brook like a cricket bat. How could it possibly be that every piece of the Earth's surface is accelerating away from its centre, and yet the Earth stays intact as a sphere with a fixed radius? The answer is that if a little piece of the Earth's surface at Plum Brook were left to its own devices, it would do precisely the same thing as the feather and the bowling ball; it would follow a straight line through spacetime. These straight lines point radially inwards towards the centre of the Earth. This is the 'state of rest', if you like – the natural trajectory that would be followed by anything. The geodesics point radially inwards because of the way that the mass of the Earth curves spacetime. So a collapsing Earth would be the natural state of things without any forces acting – one in which, ultimately, all the matter

10:35:38:09

TESTING EINSTEIN'S THEORY
In the great vaccum chamber
at Plum Brook Station we
re-created Galileo's simple
experiment by dropping a
heavy object (bowling ball) and
some lighter ones (feathers) to
see which falls faster.

10:35:49:03

10:35:52:10

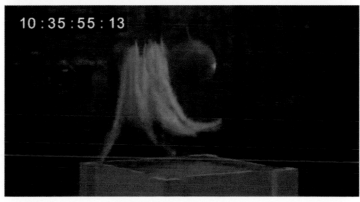

10:35:55:13

THE HAPPIEST THOUGHT

would collapse into a little black hole. The thing that prevents this from happening is the rigidity of the matter that makes up the Earth, which ultimately has its origin in the force of electromagnetism and a quantum mechanical effect called the Pauli Exclusion Principle. In order to stay as a big, spherical, Earth-sized ball, a force must act on each little piece of ground and this must cause each piece of ground to accelerate. Every piece of big spherical things like planets must continually accelerate radially outwards to stay as they are, according to General Relativity.

From what I've said so far, it might seem that General Relativity is simply a pleasing way of explaining why the Earth orbits the Sun and why objects all fall at the same rate in a gravitational field. General Relativity is far more than that, however. Very importantly, it makes precise predictions about the behaviour of certain astronomical objects that are radically different from Newton's. One of the most spectacular examples is a binary star system known rather less than poetically as PSR J0348+0432. The two stars in this system are exotic astrophysical objects. One is a white dwarf, the core of a dead star held up against the force of gravity by a sea of electrons. Electrons behave according to the Pauli Exclusion Principle, which, roughly speaking, states that electrons resist being squashed together. This purely quantum mechanical effect can halt the collapse of a star at the end of its life, leaving a super-dense blob of matter. White dwarfs are typically between 0.6 and 1.4 times the mass of our Sun, but with a volume comparable to that of the Earth. The upper limit of the mass of a white dwarf is known as the Chandrasekhar limit, and was first calculated by the Indian

astrophysicist Subrahmanyan Chandrasekhar in 1930. The calculation is a tour de force of modern physics, and relates the maximum mass of these exotic objects to four fundamental constants of nature – Newton's Gravitational constant, Planck's constant, the speed of light and the mass of the proton. After almost a century of astronomical observations, no white dwarf has ever been discovered that exceeds the Chandrasekhar limit. Almost all the stars in the Milky Way, including our Sun, will end their lives as white dwarfs. Only the most massive stars will produce a remnant that exceeds the Chandrasekhar limit, and the vast majority of these will produce an even more exotic object known as a neutron star. In the PSR J0348+0432 system, quite wonderfully, the white dwarf has a neutron star companion, and this is what makes the system so special.

If the remains of a star exceed the Chandrasekhar limit, the electrons are squashed so tightly onto the protons in the star that they can react together via the weak nuclear force to produce neutrons (with the emission of a particle called a neutrino). Through this mechanism, the whole star is converted into a giant atomic nucleus. Neutrons, just like electrons, obey the Pauli Exclusion Principle and resist being squashed together, leading to a stable dead star. Neutron stars can have masses several times that of our Sun, but quite astonishingly are only around 10 kilometres in diameter. They are the densest stars known; a teaspoon-full of neutron star matter weighs as much as a mountain.

Imagine, for a moment, this exotic star system. The white dwarf and neutron star are very close together; they orbit around each other at a distance of 830,000 kilometres – that's around twice the distance to the Moon – once every 2 hours and 27 minutes. That's an orbital velocity of around 2 million kilometres per hour. The neutron star is twice the mass of our Sun, around 10 kilometres in diameter, and spins on its axis 25 times a second. This is a star system of unbelievable violence. Einstein's Theory of General Relativity predicts that the two stars should spiral in towards each other because they lose energy by disturbing spacetime itself, emitting what are known as gravitational waves. The loss of energy is minuscule, resulting in a change in orbital period of eight millionths of a second per year. In a triumph of observational astronomy, using the giant Arecibo radio telescope in Puerto Rico, the Effelsberg telescope in Germany and the European Southern Observatory's VLT in Chile, astronomers measured the rate of orbital decay of PSR J0348+0432 in 2013 and found it to be precisely as Einstein predicted. This is quite remarkable. Einstein could never have dreamt of the existence of white dwarfs and neutron stars when he had his happiest thought in 1907, and yet by thinking carefully about falling off a roof he was able to construct a theory of gravity that describes, with absolute precision, the behaviour of the most exotic star system accessible to twenty-first-century telescopes. And that, if I really need to say it, is why I love physics.

Einstein's Theory of General Relativity has, at the time of writing, passed every precision test that scientists have been able to carry out in the century since it was first published. From the motion of feathers and bowling balls in the Earth's gravitational field to the extreme astrophysical violence of PSR J0348+0432, the theory comes through with flying colours.

There is rather more to Einstein's magisterial theory than the mere description of orbits, however. General Relativity is fundamentally different to Newton's theory because it doesn't simply provide a model for the action of gravity. Rather, it provides an explanation for the existence of the gravitational force itself in terms of the curvature of spacetime. It's worth writing down Einstein's field equations, because they are (to be honest) deceptively simple.

$$G_{\mu\nu} = 8\pi G T_{\mu\nu}$$

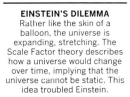

EINSTEIN'S DILEMMA
Rather like the skin of a balloon, the universe is expanding, stretching. The Scale Factor theory describes how a universe would change over time, implying that the universe cannot be static. This idea troubled Einstein.

Here, the right-hand side describes the distribution of matter and energy in some region of spacetime, and left-hand side describes the shape of spacetime as a result of the matter and energy distribution. To calculate the orbit of the Earth around the Sun one would put a spherical distribution of mass with the radius of the Sun into the right-hand side of the equation, and (roughly speaking) out would pop the shape of spacetime around the Sun. Given the shape of spacetime, the orbit of the Earth can be calculated. It's not completely trivial to do this by any means, and the notation above hides great complexity. But the point is simply that, given some distribution of matter and energy, Einstein's equations let you calculate what spacetime looks like. But here is the remarkable point that draws us towards the end of our story. Einstein's equations deal with the shape of spacetime – the fabric of the universe. The first thing to note is that we are dealing with spacetime, not just space. Space is not a fixed arena within which things happen with a big universal clock marking some sort of cosmic time upon which everyone agrees. The fabric of the universe in Einstein's theory is a dynamical thing. Very importantly, therefore, Einstein's equations don't necessarily describe something that is static and unchanging. The second thing to note is that nowhere have we restricted the domain of Einstein's theory to the region of spacetime around a single star, or even a double star system such as PSR J0348+0432. Indeed, there is no suggestion in Einstein's theory that such a restriction is necessary. Einstein's equations can be applied to an unlimited region of spacetime. This implies that they can, at least in principle, be used to describe the shape and evolution of the entire universe.

A DAY WITHOUT YESTERDAY

There were two ways of arriving at the truth;
I decided to follow them both.
Georges Lemaître

Storytelling is an ancient and deeply embedded human impulse; we learn, we communicate, we connect across generations through stories. We use them to explore the minutiae of human life, taking delight in the smallest things. And we tell grander tales of origins and endings. History is littered with stories about the creation of the universe; they seem as old as humanity itself. Multifarious gods, cosmic eggs, worlds emerging from chaos or order, from the waters or the sky or nothing at all – there exist as many creation myths as there are cultures. The impulse to understand the origin of the universe is clearly a powerful unifying idea, although the very existence of many different mythologies continues to be a source of division. It is an unfortunate testament to the emotional power of creation narratives that so much energy is spent arguing about old ones rather than using the increasingly detailed observational evidence available to twenty-first-century citizens to construct new ones. We live in a very privileged and exciting time in this sense, because observational evidence for creation stories was scant even a single lifetime ago. When my grandparents were born in Oldham at the turn of the twentieth century, there was no scientific creation story. Astronomers were not even aware of a universe beyond the Milky Way, which makes it all the more remarkable that the modern scientific approach to the description of the universe emerged almost fully formed from Einstein's Theory of General Relativity before Edwin Hubble published the discovery of his Cepheid variable star in Andromeda and settled Shapley and Curtis's Great Debate.

One of the beautiful things about mathematical physics is that equations contain stories. If you think of equations in terms of the nasty little things you used to solve at school on a damp autumn afternoon, then that may sound like a strange and abstract idea. But equations like Einstein's field equations are much more complex animals. Recall that Einstein's equations will tell you the shape of spacetime, given some distribution of matter and energy. That shape is known as a solution of the equations, and it is these solutions that contain the stories. The first exact solution to Einstein's field equations was discovered in 1915 by the German physicist Karl Schwarzschild. Schwarzschild used the equations to calculate the shape of spacetime around a perfectly spherical, non-rotating mass. Schwarzschild's solution can be used to describe planetary orbits around a star, but it also contains some of the most exotic ideas in modern physics; it describes what we now know as the event horizon of a black hole. The well-known tales of astronauts being spaghettified as they fall towards oblivion inside a supermassive collapsed star are to be found in Schwarzschild's solution. The calculation was a remarkable achievement, not least because Schwarzschild completed it whilst serving in the German Army at the Russian Front. Shortly afterwards, the 42-year-old physicist died of a disease contracted in the trenches.

The most remarkable stories waiting to be found inside Einstein's equations reveal themselves when we take an audacious and seemingly reckless leap. Instead of confining ourselves to describing the spacetime around spherical blobs of matter, why not think a little bigger? Why not try to use Einstein's equations to tell us about all of spacetime? Why can't we apply General Relativity to the entire universe? Einstein noticed this as a possibility very early in the development of his theory, and in 1917 he published a paper entitled 'Cosmological Considerations of the General Theory of Relativity'. It's a big step, of course, from thinking about someone falling off a roof to telling the story of the universe, and Einstein appears to have been uncharacteristically wobbly. In a letter to his friend Paul Ehrenfest a few days before he presented his paper to the Prussian Academy, he wrote 'I have ... again perpetrated something about gravitation theory which somewhat exposes me to the danger of being confined in a madhouse.'

The universe modelled in Einstein's 1917 paper is not the one we inhabit, but the paper is of interest for the introduction of what Einstein later came to view as a mistake. Einstein tried to find a solution to his equations that would describe a finite universe, populated by a uniform distribution of matter, and stable against gravitational collapse. At the time, this was a reasonable thing to do, because astronomers knew of only a single galaxy – the Milky Way – and the stars did not appear to be collapsing inwards towards each other. Einstein also seems to have had a particular story in mind; he felt that an eternal universe was more elegant than one that had a beginning, which left open the thorny question of a creator. He discovered, however, that General Relativity does not allow for a universe with stars, planets and galaxies to be eternal. Instead, his solution told the story of an unstable universe that would collapse inwards. Einstein tried to solve this unfortunate problem by adding a new term in his equations known as the cosmological constant. This extra term can act as a repulsive force, which Einstein adjusted to resist the tendency of his model universe to collapse under its own gravity. Later, he is famously said to have remarked to his friend George Gamow that the cosmological constant was his biggest blunder.

As physicists began to search for solutions to Einstein's equations, more and more possible universes were discovered. None, with the exception of Einstein's universe and a universe without matter and dominated by a (positive) cosmological constant discovered in 1917 by Willem de Sitter, was static. We will return to de Sitter's universe in a moment, but in every other case, Einstein's equations seemed to imply continual evolution, whereas Einstein himself felt that the universe should be unchanging and eternal. As more physicists worked with the equations, things only got worse for Einstein's static, eternal universe.

The first exact cosmological solution of Einstein's equations for a realistic universe filled with galaxies was discovered by Russian physicist Alexander Friedmann in 1922. He reached his result by assuming something that takes us all the way back to the beginning of this chapter; a Copernican universe in the sense that nowhere in space is special. This is known as the assumption of homogeneity and isotropy, and it corresponds to solving Einstein's equations with a completely uniform matter distribution. This may seem to be a gross oversimplification, and in the early 1920s the extent to which this assumption agreed with the observational evidence – a universe seemingly containing just a single galaxy – was tenuous. From a theoretical perspective, however, Friedmann's assumption makes perfect sense. It's the simplest assumption one can make, and it makes it relatively easy to do the sums! So relatively easy, in fact, that Friedmann's work was replicated and extended quite independently by a Belgian mathematician and priest named Georges Lemaître. Lemaître planted his flag firmly in the no-man's-land between religion and science – a strip of intellectual land occupied, whether we like it or not, by cosmology. A student of Harlow Shapley, this deeply religious man never saw a conflict between these two very different modes of human thought. He embodies the much debated and criticised modern notion, introduced by the evolutionary biologist Stephen J. Gould, that science and religion are non-overlapping magesteria, asking the same questions but operating within separate domains. My view is that this is far too simplistic a position to take; questions concerning the origin of the physical universe are of the same character as questions about the nature of the gravitational force or the behaviour of sub-atomic particles, and answers will surely be found by employing the methodology of science. Having said that, I am willing to recognise that romance, or wonder, or whatever the term is for that deep feeling of awe when contemplating the universe in all its immensity, is a central component of both religious and scientific experience, and perhaps there is room for both in providing the inspiration for the exploration of nature.

At least this is what Lemaître felt, and he used his twin perspectives as a guide on his intellectual journey through the cosmos throughout his distinguished career. Ordained a priest in 1923 while studying at the Catholic University in Louvain, Lemaître studied physics and mathematics alongside some of the great physicists and astronomers of the time, including Arthur Eddington and Harlow Shapley, from the University of Cambridge to Harvard and MIT, before returning to Belgium in 1925 to work with Einstein's general relativity.

Lemaître never met Alexander Friedmann, who died from typhoid in 1925. They never spoke or corresponded, and Lemaître was almost certainly unaware of the obscure paper Friedmann had published describing a dynamic and changing universe. He followed the same intellectual path, however, assuming an isotropic and homogeneous distribution of matter in the cosmos, and searching for solutions to Einstein's equations that describe the story of this smooth and uniform universe. And, of course, he came to the same conclusion; such a universe cannot be static – it must either expand or contract. Lemaître met

Einstein at the 1927 Solvay Conference in Brussels, and told him of his conclusions. 'Your calculations are correct, but your physics insight is abominable', snapped the great man. Einstein was wrong. By 1931, Lemaître was writing papers containing wonderfully vivid phrases and making clear his view that Einstein's theory requires a moment of creation – a Big Bang. He writes of 'a day without yesterday', and of the universe emerging from a 'primeval atom'.

In 1934, the Princeton physicist Howard Percy Robertson catalogued all of the possible solutions to Einstein's equations given a uniform distribution of matter throughout the cosmos – a perfect Copernican principle according to which no place in the cosmos is special or significant. The models containing matter tend to describe either an expanding or contracting universe, and therefore suggest a quite wonderful thing; there may have been a day without a yesterday. Einstein's equations contain within them a scientific creation story, even though their author himself resisted it.

The story of Einstein's Theory of General Relativity, and its subsequent application to the whole universe, delivers a compelling narrative illustrating the power of physics. The theory, inspired by thinking about a man falling off a roof, predicts that there was a moment of creation. No experimental measurements are required and no observations need be made other than that things fall at the same rate in a gravitational field. There are multiple layers of irony here! The idea that such progress towards answering the most profound questions

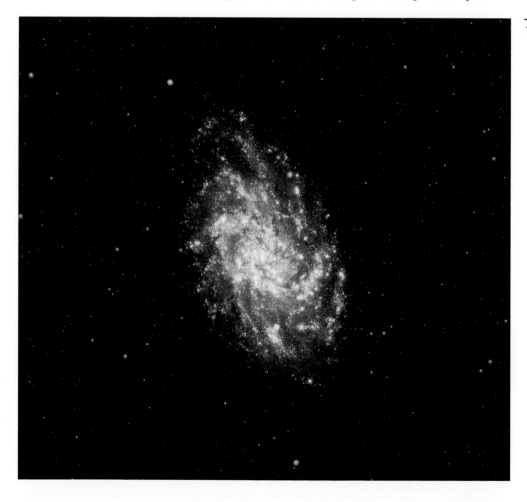

TRIANGULUM GALAXY (M33)
Also known as the Pinwheel galaxy, the Triangulum galaxy is a spiral galaxy which lies about 2.4 million light years from Earth.

about our origins can be made by thinking alone is almost Aristotelian: a partial throwback to the lofty authority of the classical world that Bruno, Copernicus and Galileo did so much to overturn. That the equations seem to describe a universe with a necessary moment of creation, lending support, at least in Lemaître's eyes, to the notion of a creator, would also appear to bring us full circle and back to Borman, Lovell and Anders and the creation stories of old. Indeed, Pope Pius XII, on hearing about the new cosmology, said 'True science to an ever increasing degree discovers God, as though God was waiting behind each door opened by science'. Einstein, to his deep chagrin, having thrown a blanket of rational thought across a landscape of mythology, appeared to have replaced one creation story with another.

To finish the story of our magnificent relegation, let me briefly address these points. The theoretical prediction of an expanding universe does of course require experimental verification, and this came rapidly. On 15 March 1929, Edwin Hubble published a paper entitled 'A relation between distance and radial velocity among extra-galactic nebulae', in which he reported his observation that all galaxies beyond our local group are rushing away from us. Moreover, the more distant the galaxy, the higher its speed of recession. This is precisely what an expanding universe as predicted by Einstein's theory should look like. In 1948, Alpher, Bethe and Gamow published a famous paper (with the coolest author list in the history of physics) which showed how the observed abundance of light chemical elements in the universe could be calculated assuming a very

GALAXIES BEYOND OUR OWN
This Hubble Space Telescope image shows distant galaxies beyond our own which as yet are unidentified and unexplored by scientists on Earth. It is a challenge to our future generations to uncover their secrets.

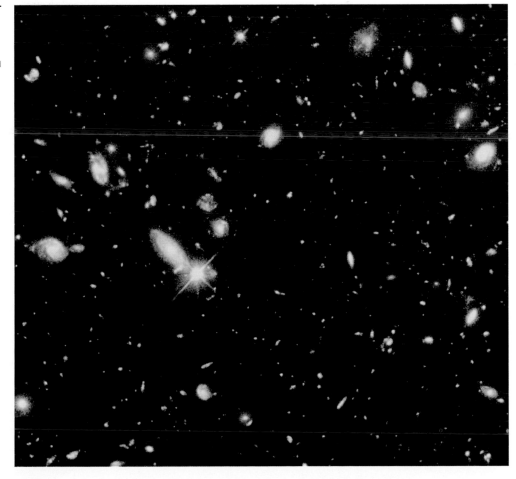

hot, dense phase in the early history of the universe. Modern calculations of these abundances are extremely precise, and agree perfectly with astronomical observations. Perhaps most compellingly of all, the afterglow of the Big Bang, known as the Cosmic Microwave Background Radiation, also predicted by Alpher and Herman in 1948, was discovered by Penzias and Wilson in 1964. We will have much to say about the Cosmic Microwave Background in the following chapters; for now, it is sufficient to say that the discovery that the universe is still glowing at a temperature of 2.7 degrees above absolute zero was the final evidence that convinced even the most sceptical scientists that the Big Bang theory was the most compelling model for the evolution of the universe.

What, though, of the thorny question of the cause of the Big Bang itself? What was the origin of Lemaître's primeval atom? Did God really do it? The standard Big Bang cosmology of the twentieth century has no answer to this question, but twenty-first-century cosmology does. We will address the current scientific understanding of what happened before the Big Bang later on, but let me offer a tantalising hint here. It is now thought that before the Big Bang the universe underwent a period of exponential expansion known as inflation. In this time, the universe behaved in accord with de Sitter's matter-less solution to Einstein's

OUR OLDEST LIGHTS
This snapshot of our universe reveals the oldest lights within it. The tiny temperature fluctuations that ripple through the skies reveal the presence of the stars and galaxies of today and for the future.

equations discovered in 1917. This period of rapid expansion gave us the homogeneous and isotropic distribution of matter we see today on large distance scales, which is the reason why Friedmann and Lemaître's simple Copernican assumptions lead to a description of the evolution of the universe after the Big Bang that fits observational data perfectly. There are no special places in the universe because the early inflationary expansion smoothed everything out. When inflation stopped, the energy contained within the field that drove it was dumped back into the universe, creating all the matter and radiation we observe today. Small fluctuations in the inflation field seeded the formation of the galaxies, uniformly distributed across the sky in their billions, each containing countless worlds, quite possibly without end beyond the visible horizon. In the words of Georges Lemaître, 'Standing on a well-cooled cinder we see the slow fading of the suns and we try to recall the vanished brilliance of the origin of the worlds.' Our cinder is not special; it is insignificant in size; one world amongst billions in one galaxy amongst trillions. But it has been a tremendous ascent into insignificance because, by the virtuous combination of observation and thought, we have been able to discover our place. How Giordano Bruno would have loved what we found.

ARE WE ALONE?

Sometimes I think we are alone in the universe
and sometimes I think we're not.
In either case the idea is quite staggering.

Arthur C. Clarke

SCIENCE FACT OR FICTION?

There are questions to which knowing the answers would have a profound cultural effect. The question of our solitude is one. Are we alone in the universe – yes or no? One of these is true. The question as posed isn't a good one, however, because it is impossible to answer in the affirmative. We have no chance, even in principle, of exploring the entire universe, which extends way beyond the visible horizon 46 billion light years away. The answer can therefore never be yes with certainty. Indeed, if the universe is infinite in extent, we have our answer! No, we are not alone. The laws of nature self-evidently allow life to exist, and no matter how improbable, life must have arisen an infinite number of times. In itself, this is quite a challenging statement, and we will explore it in more detail in later on. But this isn't really what most of us want to know.

I've always been interested in aliens – the ones that fly spaceships around – and I want to talk to one. On a winter afternoon in 1977 I stood in a queue that went around three sides of the Odeon cinema in Oldham with my dad, shuffling through half-frozen puddles to see *Star Wars*, and spent the next decade building Millennium Falcons out of Lego. At some point in 1979 I picked up a magazine about *Alien*, and moved on to *Nostromo*, which required more bricks. To my delight I saw *Alien* when I was 11 years old at Friday Evening Film Society at school, and it didn't put me off. I just realised I really liked the spaceships, and didn't care much about the organic stuff. Everyone should see *Alien* at 11. To hell with the ratings; terror, technology and Sigourney Weaver are good for the soul.

Science fiction was a natural home for my imagination. I'd been interested in astronomy for a while, I'm not sure why, but the study of the stars seemed clean and precise and romantic; something done on cold nights before Christmas with mittens and imagination. *Star Wars, Star Trek, Alien*, Arthur C. Clarke and Isaac Asimov were merged seamlessly with Patrick Moore, Carl Sagan and James Burke, and they remain so; fact and fiction are inseparable in dreams. The superficially orthogonal desires to do science and to imagine distant worlds are closely related: shadows cast by different lights.

So the question 'Are we alone in the universe?' might make good science fiction, but it is not well posed in a scientific sense because the universe is too big for us to explore in its entirety. If we restrict the domain of the question, however, we can address it scientifically. 'Are we alone in the solar system?' is a question we are actively seeking to answer with Mars rovers and future missions to the moons of Jupiter and Saturn, where the conditions necessary for life may be present on multiple worlds. But even here, the use of the word 'alone' in the question is problematic. Would we be alone if the universe were full of microbes? Would you feel alone stranded in a deep cave with no means of escape and a billion bacteria for company? If not being alone means having intelligent beings to communicate with – sophisticated creatures that build civilisations, have feelings, do science and respond emotionally to the universe, then we have our answer in the solar system. Yes – Earth is the only world that is home to a civilisation, and we are alone.

How far might we reasonably expect to extend the domain of our question beyond the solar system? I find it impossible to believe that we'll ever explore the universe beyond our own galaxy. The distance between the Milky Way and our nearest neighbour, Andromeda, is over 2 million light years, and that seems to me to be an unbridgeable distance, at least given the known laws of physics. But that still leaves an island of several hundred billions of stars, 100,000 light years across. We will therefore rephrase our question so that we have a chance of interrogating it in a scientific way, and ask 'Are we the only intelligent civilisation in the Milky Way galaxy?' If the answer is yes, then we are in the cosmic equivalent of an inescapable cave and that would have made my 11-year-old self, gazing up at a dark sky of infinite possibilities, extremely sad. There may be others out there amongst the distant galaxies, but we'll never know. If the answer is 'No', on the other hand, this would have profound consequences. Aliens would exist in a truly science-fiction sense; beings with spacecraft, culture, religion, art, beliefs, hopes and dreams, out there amongst the stars, waiting for us to speak with them. What are the chances of that? We don't know, but at least we have posed a question that can be explored scientifically. How many intelligent civilisations are there likely to be in the Milky Way, given the available evidence today?

CANALS ON MARS?
American amateur astronomer Percival Lowell's map of Mars shows what became popularly known at the time as canals on the planet's surface. Lowell believed these features were created by intelligent life forms.

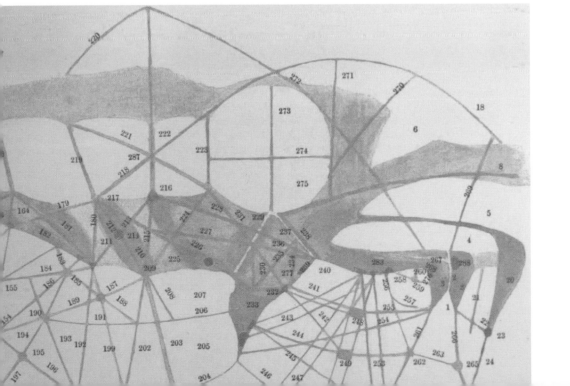

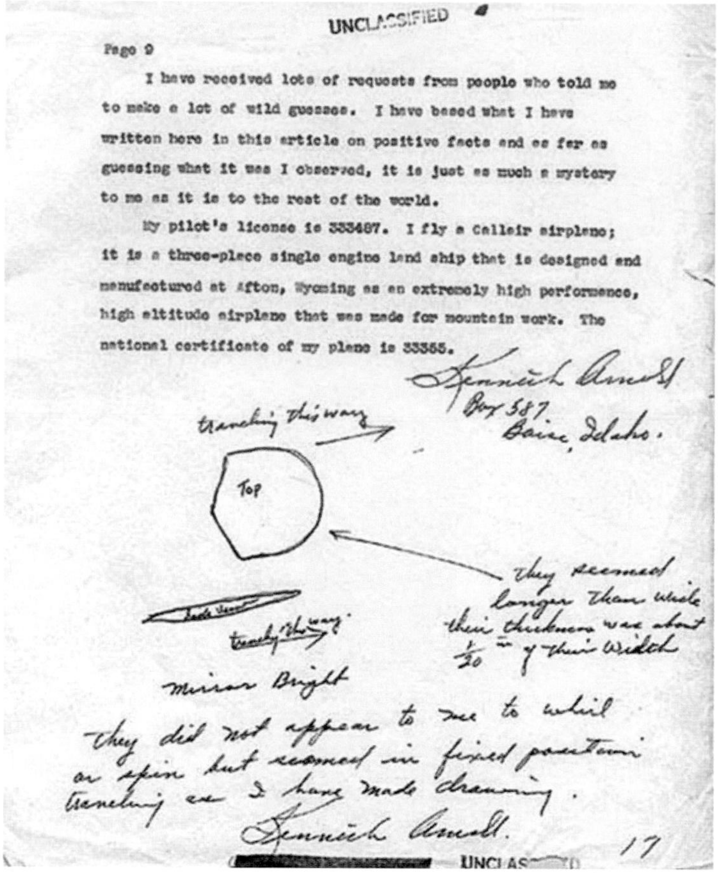

Page 9

I have received lots of requests from people who told me to make a lot of wild guesses. I have based what I have written here in this article on positive facts and as far as guessing what it was I observed, it is just as much a mystery to me as it is to the rest of the world.

My pilot's license is 333487. I fly a Callair airplane; it is a three-place single engine land ship that is designed and manufactured at Afton, Wyoming as an extremely high performance, high altitude airplane that was made for mountain work. The national certificate of my plane is 33355.

Kenneth Arnold
Box 387
Boise, Idaho.

travelling this way

Top

travelling this way

mirror bright

they seemed longer than wide their thickness was about $\frac{1}{20}$ of their width

they did not appear to me to whirl or spin but seemed in fixed position travelling as I have made drawing.

Kenneth Arnold.

17

THE FIRST ALIENS

On 24 June 1947, Ken Arnold, an amateur pilot from Scobey, Montana, was flying over Mount Rainier, one of the most dangerous volcanoes in the world. Arnold was an experienced pilot with thousands of flying hours, and this implied he was a trustworthy observer. On returning to the airfield, he claimed to have seen nine objects flying in the mountain skies, describing them as 'flat like a pie pan' and 'like a big flat disc'. He estimated the discs were flying in formation at speeds of up to 1920 kilometres per hour. The press jumped on the story – coining the term 'flying saucer' – and within weeks hundreds of similar sightings were reported from all over the world. On 4 July a United Airlines crew reported seeing another formation of nine discs over the skies of Idaho, and four days later, the mother of all UFO stories exploded at Roswell, New Mexico, with the confirmation and then rapid retraction by the United States Air Force of a recovered 'flying disc' – an alien craft crash-landed on Earth.

I'll put my cards on the table here; I believe in UFOs. That is to say, I believe that there have been sightings of flying things in the sky that the observers were unable to identify, some of which were objects. But I do not believe for a moment that these were spacecraft flown by aliens. Occam's razor is an important tool in science. It shouldn't be oversold; nature can be complex and bizarre. But as a rule of thumb, it is most sensible to adopt the simplest explanation for an observation until the evidence overwhelms it.

My favourite response to the criticism that dismissing the possibility of alien visitations to Earth is unscientific was provided by physicist and

THE FIRST FLYING SAUCERS
Ken Arnold's original letter about sightings of UFOs, as he sent it to Army Air Force Intelligence on 12 July 1947.

Nobel Laureate Richard Feynman in his Messenger Lectures at Cornell University in 1964: 'Some years ago I had a conversation with a layman about flying saucers — because I am scientific I know all about flying saucers! I said "I don't think there are flying saucers". So my antagonist said, "Is it impossible that there are flying saucers? Can you prove that it's impossible?" "No", I said, "I can't prove it's impossible. It's just very unlikely". At that he said, "You are very unscientific. If you can't prove it impossible then how can you say that it's unlikely?" But that is the way that is scientific. It is scientific only to say what is more likely and what less likely, and not to be proving all the time the possible and impossible. To define what I mean, I might have said to him, "Listen, I mean that from my knowledge of the world that I see around me, I think that it is much more likely that the reports of flying saucers are the results of the known irrational characteristics of terrestrial intelligence than of the unknown rational efforts of extraterrestrial intelligence." It is just more likely. That is all.'

Irrespective of the veracity of the stories of mutilated cows, crop circles and violated Mid-Westerners at the hands of these alien visitors, the cultural impact of these early sightings was very real. America quickly entered into a media-fuelled love affair with alien invaders in shiny discs brandishing anal probes (why didn't they use MRI scanners, a non-Freudian would surely ask?). Of all the hundreds of thousands of references to flying saucers that began to appear in the media, a cartoon by Alan Dunn published in the *New Yorker* magazine on 20 May 1950 found its way into the lunchtime conversation of a group of scientists at the Los Alamos National Laboratory in New Mexico.

A LOAD OF RUBBISH?
Alan Dunn's cartoon in the *New Yorker* on 20 May 1950 blamed the aliens who had been increasingly 'seen' in New York for stealing city residents' rubbish bins.

Form 125L

S[IGN]AL CORPS, UNITED STATES ARM[Y]

WASHINGTON-ALASKA MILITARY CABLE AND TELEGRAPH SYSTEM

TELEGRAM

RECEIVED AT 1308 1ST AVENUE, SEATTLE, WASH.

18RD B 78 GOVT DUPE

RD PUGETSOUND WN AUG 22 1924

GOVT COMDT 13 NAV DIST   158

SEATTLE WN

7021 ALNAVSTA EIGHT NAVY DESIRES COOPERATE ASTRONOMERS WHO BELIEVE POSSIBLE THAT MARS MAY ATTEMPT COMMUNICATION BY RADIO WAVES WITH THIS PLANET WHILE THEY ARE NEAR TOGETHER THIS END ALL SHORE RADIO STATIONS WILL ESPECIALLY NOTE AND REPORT ANY ELECTRICAL PHENOMENON UNUSUAL CHARACTER AND WILL COVER AS WIDE BAND FREQUENCIES AS POSSIBLE FROM 2400 AUGUST TWENTY FIRST TO 2400 AUGUST TWENTY FOURTH WITHOUT INTERFERRING WITH TRAFFIC 1800

SECNAV WASHN DC

257P

RADIO SILENCE DAY

Edward W. Eberle, then Chief of US Naval Operations, instructed all naval stations to clear the airwaves on 22 August 1924 in order to monitor them for any signs of transmissions that could be made by Martians.

Enrico Fermi was one of the greatest twentieth-century physicists. Italian by birth, he conducted his most acclaimed work in the United States, having left his native country with his Jewish wife Laura in 1938 as Mussolini's grip tightened. Fermi worked on the Manhattan Project throughout World War Two, first at Los Alamos, and then at the University of Chicago, where he was responsible for Chicago Pile 1, the world's first nuclear reactor. In a squash court underneath a disused sports stadium in December 1942, Fermi oversaw the first man-made nuclear chain reaction, paving the way for the Hiroshima and Nagasaki bombs.

After the war Fermi settled as a professor in Chicago, but he often visited Los Alamos. During one of these visits, in the summer of 1950, Fermi settled down for lunch with a group of colleagues including Edward Teller, the architect of the hydrogen bomb, and fellow Manhattan Project alumni Herbert York and Emil Konopinski. At some point, talk turned to the recent reports of UFO sightings and the *New Yorker* cartoon, stimulating Fermi to ask a simple question that turned a trivial conversation into a serious discussion: 'Where are they?'

FERMI'S PARADOX

The Fermi Paradox is the apparent contradiction between the high probability of extraterrestrial civilisations' existence and humanity's lack of contact with, or evidence for, such civilisations.

Fermi's question is a powerful and challenging one that deserves an answer. It has become known as the Fermi Paradox. There are hundreds of billions of star systems in the Milky Way galaxy. Our solar system is around 4.6 billion years old, but the galaxy is almost as old as the universe. If we assume life is relatively common, and on at least some of these planets intelligent civilisations arose, it follows that there should exist civilisations far in advance of our own somewhere in the galaxy. Why? Our civilisation has existed for around 10,000 years, and we've had access to modern technology for a few hundred. Our species, Homo sapiens, has existed for a quarter of a million years or so. This is a blink of an eye in comparison to the age of the Milky Way. So if we assume we are not the only civilisation in the galaxy, then at least a few others must have arisen billions of years ahead of us. But where are they? The distances are not so vast that we cannot imagine travelling between star systems in principle. It took us less than a single human lifetime to go from the Wright Brothers to the Moon. What might we imagine doing in the next hundred years? Or thousand years? Or ten thousand years? Or ten million years? Even with rocketry technology as currently imagined, we could colonise the entire galaxy on million-year timescales. The Fermi Paradox simply boils down to the question of why nobody has done this, given so many billions of worlds and so many billions of years. It is a very good question.

LISTEN VERY CAREFULLY

LISTENING TO THE NEIGHBOURS
The invention of the radio led many people to think that we would soon be communicating with our neighbours – Mars being considered the most likely planet to harbour intelligent life.

For three days in 1924, William F. Friedman had a very important job. As chief cryptographer to the US Army, Friedman was used to dealing with National Security responsibilities, but from 21–23 August he was asked to search for an unusual message. On these dates Mars and Earth came within 56 million kilometres of each other, the closest the two planets had been since 1845, and they would not be so close again until August 2003. This offered the best opportunity since the invention of radio to listen in on the neighbours.

To make the most of the planetary alignment, scientists at the United States Naval Observatory decided to conduct an ambitious experiment. Coordinated across the United States, they conducted a 'National Radio Silence Day', with every radio in the country quietened for five minutes on the hour, every hour, across a 36-hour period. With this unprecedented radio silence and a specially designed radio receiver mounted on an airship, the idea was to make the most of the Martian 'fly-by' and listen in for messages, intentional or otherwise, from the red planet.

Conspiracy theories notwithstanding, William F. Friedman didn't decipher the first message from an alien intelligence, and the American public soon tired of the disruption to their news bulletins, but the principle of the experiment was sound. The idea that we might listen in to aliens had first been proposed 30 years earlier by the physicist and engineer Nikola Tesla. Tesla suggested that a version of his wireless electrical transmission system could be used to contact beings from Mars, and subsequently presented evidence of first contact. He wasn't right, but in 1896, one year before the publication of *War of the Worlds*, it was certainly a plausible claim. Tesla wasn't alone; other luminaries of the time shared his optimism, including the pioneer of long-distance radio transmission, Guglielmo Marconi, who believed that listening to the neighbours would become a routine part of modern communications. By 1921 Marconi was publicly stating that he had intercepted wireless messages from Mars, and if only the codes could be deciphered, conversation would soon begin.

The failure of the National Radio Silence Day brought a temporary halt to the organised search for extraterrestrial signals, and the idea dropped out of scientific fashion until the post-war flying saucer boom. One of the first scientists to make the search for ET scientifically acceptable again was Philip Morrison, a contemporary and colleague of Fermi. It is not known whether they discussed the Fermi Paradox directly, but the idea of answering it certainly played on Morrison's mind throughout the 1950s. At the end of the decade Morrison published a famous and influential paper with another of Fermi's collaborators, Giuseppe Cocconi, laying out the principles of using radio telescopes to listen for signals. 'Searching for Interstellar Communications' was published in the prestigious journal *Nature*, and proposed a systematic search of the nearest star systems on a very specific radio frequency – the so-called 21cm hydrogen line.

Morrison and Cocconi chose the hydrogen line because it is a frequency that any technological civilisation interested in astronomy will be tuned in to. Hydrogen is the most abundant element in the universe, and hydrogen atoms emit radio waves at precisely this frequency. If we could see these wavelengths with our eyes, the sky would be aglow, and this is why astronomers tune their radio telescopes to the 21cm line to map the distribution of dust and gas in our galaxy and beyond. If a technological civilisation wants to be heard, then under the assumption that anyone with any sense does radio astronomy, the 21cm line would be the most obvious choice for a message.

Morrison and Cocconi's paper inspired the birth of one of the most widely debated and controversial astronomical projects of modern

21CM LINE

Hydrogen atoms consist of two particles – a single proton bound to a single electron. Protons and electrons have a property called spin, which for these particular particles (known as spin ½ Fermions, named after Enrico Fermi himself) can take only one of two values, often called spin 'up' and spin 'down'. There are therefore only two possible configurations of the spins in a hydrogen atom; the spins can be parallel to each other – both 'up' or both 'down', or anti-parallel – one 'up' and one 'down'. It turns out that the parallel case has slightly more energy than the anti-parallel case, and when the spin configuration flips from parallel to anti-parallel, this extra energy is carried away as a photon of light with a wavelength of 21cm.

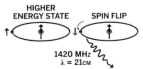

HIGHER ENERGY STATE · SPIN FLIP · 1420 MHz · $\lambda = 21$cm

times. Within a year of its publication, the 85-foot radio telescope at the National Radio Astronomy Observatory in Green Bank, West Virginia, was pointing towards two nearby stars – Tau Ceti and Epsilon Eridani – listening in to the 21cm hydrogen line for any signs of unnatural order in the signals from the stars. The project, known as Ozma after a character from L. Frank Baum's *Land of Oz,* was the brainchild of Frank Drake, a young astronomer from Cornell University. Drake chose Tau Ceti and Epsilon Eridani as the first target star systems because of the stars' similarity to our own Sun and their proximity, just 10 and 12 light years away from Earth. In 1960 Drake had no idea if these stars harboured planetary systems, because no planets had been detected outside our solar system at that time. We now know that Drake's guess was a good one. Tau Ceti is thought to have five planets orbiting the star, with one of them in the habitable zone (see page 84). Epsilon Eridani is also thought to have at least one gas giant planet with an orbital period of around 7 years. After 150 hours of observation, Drake heard nothing, but for him this was the beginning of a lifetime dedicated to the search for extraterrestrial intelligence, a search commonly known by its acronym, SETI.

Today SETI is a global scientific effort, analysing data from telescopes used primarily for radio astronomy. The organisation also has a dedicated collection of telescopes designed specifically to detect signals from extraterrestrial civilisations at the Hat Creek Radio Observatory near San Francisco. The Allen Array, named after Microsoft founder Paul Allen who donated over $30 million to fund the construction of the project, consists of 42 radio antennae able to scan large areas of the sky at multiple radio frequencies, including the 21cm hydrogen line. If there are any civilisations making a serious attempt to contact us with technology at least as advanced as our own within a thousand light years, the Allen Array will hear them.

In the early 1960s, the scientific community was sceptical about such endeavours and Frank Drake was perceived as a maverick. It's important to be sceptical in science, but as Fermi understood, a back-of-the-envelope calculation with some plausible assumptions suggests that the search for ET may not be futile. Indeed, the alternative view that our civilisation is unique or extremely rare in a galaxy of a hundred billion suns appears outrageously solipsistic, and the sceptical finger might as easily be pointed at the cynics. There was, however, a handful of scientists who understood the importance of asking big questions, and together with Peter Pearman, a senior scientist at America's prestigious National Academy of Sciences, Drake organised the first SETI conference in November 1961. The Green Bank meeting was small, but the list of attendees, who named themselves The Order of the Dolphin, was impressive.

Philip Morrison was there, as was his co-author of the seminal 1959 *Nature* paper, Giuseppe Cocconi. I have a professional connection with Cocconi, who was a noted particle physicist and director of the Proton Synchrotron accelerator at CERN in Geneva. Cocconi was instrumental in discovering early experimental evidence for the pomeron, an object in particle physics known as a Regge trajectory that I have spent most of my career studying. The eminent, highly respected astronomer Otto Struve also attended. Struve publicly stated his belief in the existence of intelligent extraterrestrial life, perhaps because he had recently suggested a method for detecting alien planets outside our solar system (See page 85). Nobel Laureate Melvin Calvin, most famous for his work on photosynthesis, was present, along with future Hewlett Packard vice president for R&D Barney Oliver, astronomer Su-Shu Huang, communications specialist Dana Atchley and the colourful neuroscientist and dolphin researcher John Lilly. The most junior attendee was a 27-year-old postdoc. called Carl Sagan. I would love to have been there, although I'd have spent the whole time chatting with Cocconi about pomerons.

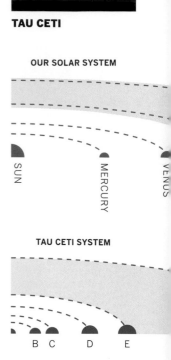

TAU CETI

OUR SOLAR SYSTEM

SUN   MERCURY   VENUS

TAU CETI SYSTEM

B   C   D   E

In preparation for the meeting, Drake drew up an agenda designed to stimulate a structured conversation amongst the group. If the search for intelligent extraterrestrial life was to be taken seriously, it was clear in Drake's mind that the discussion should be rigorous and provide a framework for future research. The way to do that is to address the problem quantitatively rather than qualitatively; to break it down into a series of probabilities that can be estimated, at least in principle, using observational data.

Drake focused on a well-defined question – the one we discussed above: how many intelligent civilisations exist in the Milky Way galaxy that we could in principle communicate with? Drake's brilliant insight was to express this in terms of a simple equation containing a series of probabilities. What is the fraction of stars in the galaxy that have planets? What is the average number of planets around a star that could support life? What is the fraction of those planets on which life begins? What is the probability that, given the emergence of simple life, intelligent life evolves? Given intelligence, how likely is it that the intelligent beings build radio telescopes and are therefore capable of communicating with us? Multiply all these probabilities together, and multiply by the number of stars in the Milky Way, and you get a number – the number of intelligent civilisations that have ever existed in the Milky Way.

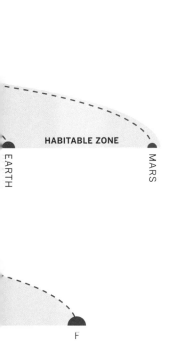

HABITABLE ZONE

EARTH

MARS

F

This isn't all Drake did, however, because he was interested in the number of civilisations that we might be able to speak to now, and that requires the addition of a rather thought-provoking term – the average lifetime of civilisations from the moment they develop the technology to communicate. If a civilisation arose a billion years ago and vanished shortly afterwards, then we would never be able to talk to them. The question of the lifetime of a civilisation may have been more vivid in the early 1960s than it is today. The Manhattan Project had been the training ground for many of the great physicists, and the Cuban missile crisis was less than a year away, propelling the world, in Soviet Premier Khrushchev's words to President Kennedy, towards '... the abyss of a world nuclear-missile war'. To me, and to the participants at the Green Bank conference, the idea that a civilisation might destroy itself is both ludicrous and likely. We are pathetically inadequate at long-term planning, idiotically primitive in our destructive urges and pathologically incapable of simply getting along. More of this later! Putting the lifetime term into the equation was therefore scientifically valid and a political masterstroke, merely confronting the question should give us pause for thought at the very least.

To complete the equation with the lifetime term included – recall that it should give the number of currently contactable civilisations in the Milky Way – a little thought will convince you that the whole lot must be multiplied by the current rate of star formation in the galaxy. That might not be immediately obvious, but I have confidence you can demonstrate to yourself that it's the correct thing to do. Homework is good.

The completed equation, which is known as The Drake Equation, is shown to the right.

When Drake wrote down his equation, only R was known with precision. Star formation had been closely studied in parts of our galaxy and the data suggested a value of around one new star per year. The rest of the terms were unknown in the 1960s, and we will spend the majority of this chapter exploring them, given over 50 years of astronomical and biological research. Despite the lack of experimental data, however, the Green Bank participants spent the meeting debating each one of the terms in the Drake Equation. This is the power of Drake's formulation. It's not yet possible to make a measurement of the fraction of planets on which life emerges with any sort of precision, but it is possible to look at the experience we have on Earth, and increasingly in the wider solar

THE DRAKE EQUATION

$$N = R_* \times f_s \times f_p \times n_e \times f_l \times f_i \times f_c \times L$$

where:

N
the number of civilisations in our galaxy with which radio communication might be possible (i.e. which are on our current past light cone)

R_*
the average rate of star formation in our galaxy

f_p
the fraction of those stars that have planets

n_e
the average number of planets that can potentially support life per star that has planets

f_l
the fraction of planets that could support life that actually develop life at some point

f_i
the fraction of planets with life that actually go on to develop intelligent life (civilisations)

f_c
the fraction of civilisations that develop a technology that releases detectable signs of their existence into space

L
the length of time for which such civilisations release detectable signals into space

system, and make an informed guess. The probability of the emergence of intelligence given simple life is also a difficult question, but we do know that it took over 3 billion years on Earth, and that may give us a clue. Drake's equation is valuable therefore because it provides a framework for discussion and debate, focuses the mind and suggests a direction for future research, just as Drake intended.

The Green Bank meeting did produce a consensus number, based on the not inconsiderable expertise of the participants; there are of the order of 10,000 civilisations present now in the Milky Way with whom we could communicate if we had enough radio telescopes and the will to conduct a systematic search. Interestingly, Philip Morrison, veteran of the Manhattan Project, felt that the lifetime of technological civilisations may be so short that this number could well be zero, although he observed that '... if we never search, the chance of success is zero.'

I had the privilege of meeting Frank Drake during the filming of *Human Universe*. In my view he is one of the greatest living astronomers. Frank collects and cultivates orchids, and by complete coincidence I arrived at his house when his Stanhopea orchid was flowering. These delicate and complex flowers bloom for only two days every year, and the chance of seeing one on a random visit is therefore small. Frank turned to me and said 'well, so it is with SETI – we've learned that we must search over and over and over through the years, until we are in the right place at the right time to make the discovery'. There is 'hope' in its name, and there is nothing wrong at all with admitting a dash of hope.

Throughout the 1960s and 1970s, SETI projects both big and small continued to develop across the planet. Soviet scientists joined their American contemporaries in pointing radio receivers to the sky in the hope of detecting a signal in the noise. NASA considered funding Project Cyclops, a $10-billion-dollar super-array of 1500 dishes that could listen for signals originating up to 1000 light years from Earth. It never progressed beyond the planning stage, but the scale of the project demonstrates that SETI was considered to be a serious scientific endeavour. By the mid-1970s, various projects had come and gone but none had detected the faintest hint of a significant signal. This failure, combined with a lack of progress in pinning down any of the terms in the Drake Equation – it was not even certain that planets existed in large numbers beyond our solar system – made the search look increasingly futile. Not only was there a deafening silence, no one had much idea where to look or how hard to listen. NASA didn't lose faith, however, and in 1973 Ohio University's ten-year-old Big Ear telescope was optimised for a SETI survey and began taking data.

Four years later, on 18 August 1977, Jerry R. Ehman, then a volunteer at the Big Ear, received a knock on the door of his house. It was a Thursday morning and, as usual, standing at the door was a technician carrying reams of paper printouts. This was an age when a state-of-the-art hard disk could hold only a couple of megabytes, and every few days someone had to visit the telescope, print out the data and wipe the disks clean. Ehman put the three-days' worth of printed data onto his kitchen table and began searching. He was confronted with dozens of pages covered in hundreds of letters and numbers.

The list of numbers and letters depicts the strength of the signal hitting the telescope at different times. A space denotes low intensity, and higher intensities are registered as numbers from 0 to 9. For stronger signals still, letters between A and Z are used. Most of the data the 'Big Ear' recorded contained no letters; a stream of 1s and 2s signified sweeps across the general radio hiss of the sky. That morning, however, Ehman stumbled across something different. At approximately 10.16pm Eastern Standard Time on 15 August, a radio pulse of extreme intensity entered the antennae, recorded with the alphanumeric code 6EQUJ5. The signal lasted for

WOW! SIGNAL
Ehman's now-famous printout which illustrates the strongest signal ever recorded by the Big Ear – known as the Wow! signal because of his annotation.

72 seconds, precisely the length of time a transmission of distant origin would register as the rotation of the Earth swept the telescope past the source. This is extremely important. If the signal had been caused by some kind of Earth-based interference, it would be highly unlikely to rise and fall in this manner, precisely and coincidently simulating the rotation of the Earth and the telescope's field of view on the sky. The peak was marked by the letter U, the strongest signal ever recorded by the Big Ear, denoting an intensity over 30 times that of the background emission of the galaxy. And equally strangely, the signal had a wavelength of 21cm – the hydrogen line favoured by Morrison and Cocconi in their 1959 *Nature* paper. A smoking gun for extraterrestrial communication?

With a now-famous flourish, Ehman circled the six characters and scribbled 'Wow!' on the printout. He then continued as a research scientist should, and looked to see if it happened again. He flicked through page after page, but the event of 10.16pm on 15 August was a solitary blip in the background noise. This presented a problem, because it should have happened again. The Big Ear telescope scans each part of the sky twice, separated by 3 minutes, so there should have been a similar Wow! signal in the data 3 minutes afterwards. None was present. This doesn't rule out an intelligent extraterrestrial origin; perhaps ET just turned the transmitter off a minute or so after it was first detected. Who knows?

The origin of the Wow! signal was narrowed down to a point in the sky in the direction of the constellation Sagittarius. Tau Sagittarii, a stable orange star twice the mass of our Sun and around 122 light years away, is the closest bright star to the source. Since August 1977 multiple attempts have been made to recover the signal using the world's most sensitive radio telescopes. Many hours have been spent listening, but nothing unusual has ever been detected again. Today, over 35 years later, there is no satisfactory explanation, but no serious scientist, no matter how embedded in SETI, would claim it as definitive evidence of intelligent extraterrestrial communication. Scientific results have to be repeatable, and the observation has never been repeated. For the moment, the Wow! signal remains an interesting anomaly in an otherwise silent sky. It is the stuff of dreams; the faintest of whispers in a great silence.

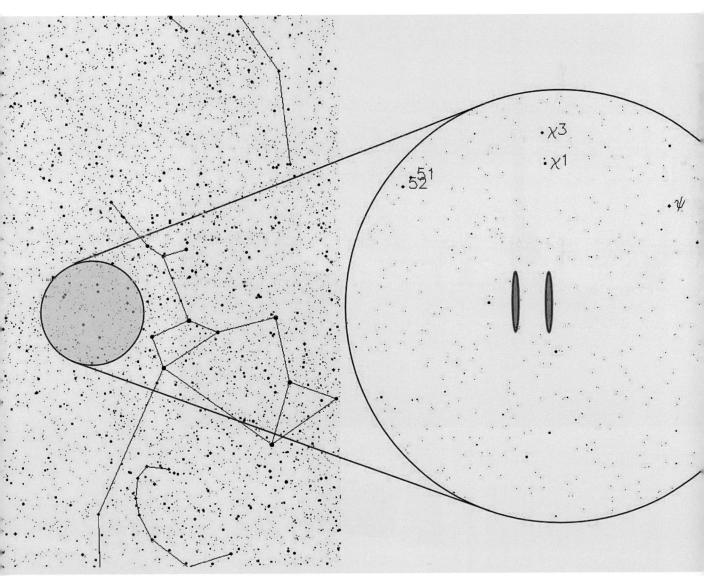

PROTOTYPE PROBE

This prototype of the two Voyager space probes launched in 1977 was created at NASA's Jet Propulsion Laboratory in Pasadena, California. In March 1977 the probe underwent a series of tests designed to see if the probe would survive launch. It passed all the tests and work began on the Voyager space probes which were to be sent out to explore the outer solar system gas giants, Jupiter, Saturn, Uranus and Neptune.

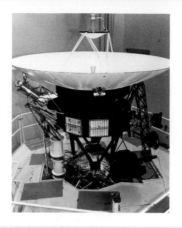

HIGH-GAIN ANTENNA

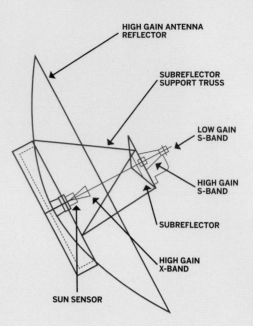

HIGH GAIN ANTENNA REFLECTOR

SUBREFLECTOR SUPPORT TRUSS

LOW GAIN S-BAND

HIGH GAIN S-BAND

SUBREFLECTOR

HIGH GAIN X-BAND

SUN SENSOR

PROBES ON TOUR

The Voyager probes have visited most of the outer planets on their way out of the solar system. Each visit has also used the planets' gravitational pull to slingshot the probes on their journey.

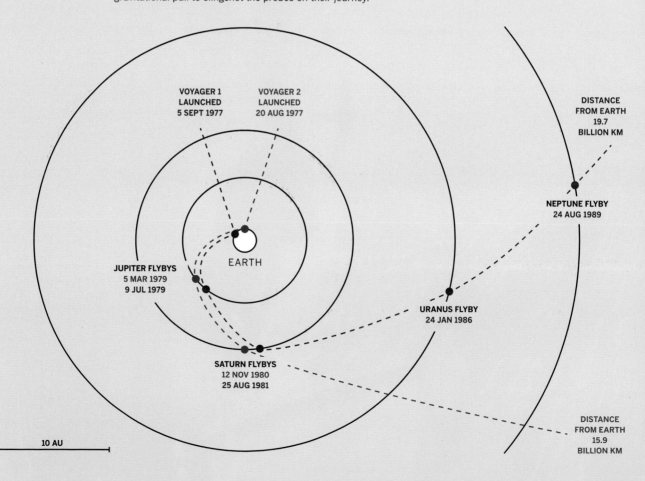

VOYAGER 1
LAUNCHED
5 SEPT 1977

VOYAGER 2
LAUNCHED
20 AUG 1977

DISTANCE
FROM EARTH
19.7
BILLION KM

NEPTUNE FLYBY
24 AUG 1989

EARTH

JUPITER FLYBYS
5 MAR 1979
9 JUL 1979

URANUS FLYBY
24 JAN 1986

SATURN FLYBYS
12 NOV 1980
25 AUG 1981

DISTANCE
FROM EARTH
15.9
BILLION KM

10 AU

THE GOLDEN VOYAGE

*This is a present from a small, distant world, a token of our sounds,
our science, our images, our music, our thoughts and our feelings.
We are attempting to survive our time so we may live into yours.*
US President Jimmy Carter

Two days after Jerry Ehman spotted the Wow! signal, the human race responded with a long-planned contribution to the interstellar conversation. In an explosive, serendipitous moment, the Voyager 2 spacecraft blasted into the sky above Space Launch Complex 41 at Kennedy Space Centre, followed two weeks later by its twin Voyager 1.

The Voyager missions were designed to take advantage of a rare planetary alignment to study the outer solar system gas giants Jupiter, Saturn, Uranus and Neptune. I remember the launch – I had collected a series of PG Tips tea cards called 'The Race Into Space', in which the Grand Tour mission was described as 'the most ambitious unmanned space project known'. Using the newly proposed gravity assist, a spacecraft could accelerate around Jupiter, Saturn and Uranus to encounter Neptune only a decade from launch. The Voyagers delivered, I suspect, way beyond their designers' wildest dreams, returning the first detailed pictures of the esoteric moons of Jupiter and Saturn, and in the case of Voyager 2, sweeping onwards to become the only spacecraft to date to visit Uranus and Neptune, where it photographed the distant ice moon Triton in the summer of 1989.

At the time of writing, on 8 July 2014, Voyager 1 is the most distant man-made object at over 127 astronomical units from Earth, so distant that radio waves take over 17½ hours to reach it. This puts Voyager 1 at the very edge of the solar system, on its way into interstellar space. The bus sized spacecraft has enough electrical power to continue to communicate with its home world until around 2020, at which point it will fall silent. In 40,000 years it will drift within 1.6 light years of the red dwarf star Gliese 445 in the constellation of Camelopardalis. Voyager 2 will reach Sirius, the brightest star in the night sky, in 296,000 years.

The Voyagers are accompanied on their lonely flights out of our solar system by a dream – an unusually sentimental and hopeful afterthought to a scientific mission bolted to their sides almost 40 years ago.

The Voyager Golden Record is our message in a bottle. An old fashioned phonograph record constructed of gold-plated copper floating through the universe, it contains what some would term a surreal mixture of sound recordings, images and information. It was designed to provide an alien civilisation with information about who we are, what we know and what our planet is like. There are 116 images on the disc; the first 30 or so are scientific, illustrating our solar system, our home world, the

THE GOLDEN DISC
Our message to worlds beyond our own. The Voyager probes carried this phonograph on which were recorded sounds and images that would reflect life on Earth.

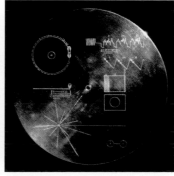

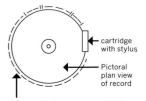
WHAT THE DIAGRAM MEANT

cartridge with stylus
Pictoral plan view of record

Binary code defining proper speed to turn the record (3.6 seconds) (| = Binary 1, — = Binary 0) Expressed in 0.70 x 10-9 seconds, the time period associated with the fundamental transition of the hydrogen atom

Elevation view of record — Elevation view of cartridge

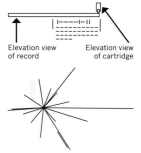
The location of our Sun utilising 14 pulsars of known directions from our Sun. Binary code defines frequency of pulses

VIDEO PORTION OF RECORDING

Wave form of video signals on recording
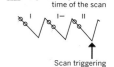
Binary code tells time of the scan

Scan triggering

Video image frame showing direction of scan. Binary code indicates time of each scan sweep (512 vertical lines per complete picture)

If properly decoded, the first image which will appear is a circle

Two lowest states of hydrogen atom. Vertical lines with dots indicate spin moments of proton and electron. Transition time from one state to the other provides the fundamental clock reference used in all the cover diagrams and decoded pictures

structure of DNA, the anatomy of our bodies, our reproduction and our birth. Anatomy takes up more room than any other subject, perhaps reflecting our own fascination with what aliens might look like. In the most magnificently colloquial and futile gesture towards the alien's moral sensibilities, no nudity was allowed! I find it hard enough to imagine the inner workings of alien brains, but I cannot begin to fathom what it must be like inside the mind of a person who raised such an objection to the depiction of the human body. 'How do these beings reproduce? Perhaps they use those ten dangly things on the ends of their arms? Disgusting!'

The illustrations go on to detail our planet's landscapes and the variety of life on Earth, before dedicating 50 images to our lives and the civilisation we've constructed – from the Great Wall of China to a supermarket. Finally, there are images of the scientific instruments we have used to explore the universe from microscopes to telescopes, including the Titan rocket that launched the Voyagers into space. Chosen by a committee chaired by Carl Sagan, the disc also contains music and sounds, including human greetings in 55 languages, recordings reflecting 'the sounds of the Earth', and the ultimate 1977 mix tape featuring 90 minutes of music from Beethoven to Chuck Berry. Sagan wanted the Beatles' 'Here comes the Sun' on the disc, but EMI refused copyright permission for the universe. I like to imagine that Carl Sagan put the song on the record anyway in a great cosmic two-fingered salute to corporate Earth. That would have been pure Sagan – 'You're most welcome to go fetch it'.

The outside cover of the golden disc is more functional. As well as instructions on how to play back the images and sounds at precisely 16⅔ revolutions per minute for the audio, and how to build a record player, it also contains a map so that any extraterrestrial civilisation will be able to trace the record back to our planet. The map uses the position of 14 pulsars whose precise locations are marked relative to the Sun. The pulsars are identified by their fingerprints – each has a unique and unvarying rate of rotation. The most important piece of content on the cover is the key to unlock the information – a diagram illustrating the spin configurations of a hydrogen atom. The 21cm hydrogen emission line is a fundamental and universal property of nature, a Rosetta Stone that will allow an alien scientist to unlock the secrets of Earth. The disc also contains one last invisible source of information; electroplated onto the surface of the cover is an ultra-pure sample of uranium 238, an isotope with a half-life of 4.468 billion years. This is Voyager's clock, a way for any civilisation to determine the age of the record, assuming that they aren't creationists who disagree with radiometric dating. Perhaps these are the sorts of aliens that would also be offended by nudity.

For all the thought and care that went into these discs, neither Voyager spacecraft is heading towards any particular star; these tiny craft constructed by human hands will almost certainly never be found. The vastness of space swallows travellers, and of course Voyager's scientists and engineers knew this. That, however, is not the point; the act of launching these gilded emissaries into space expresses something important. It's my childhood science fiction dream of living in a *Star Wars* galaxy filled with life and possibilities. It is a desire to reach out to others, to attempt contact even when the chances are vanishingly small; a wish not to be alone. The golden discs are futile and yet filled with hope; the hope that we may one day know the boundaries of our loneliness and lay to rest the unsettling internal noise that accompanies the enduring silence.

Friends of space, how are you all? Have you eaten yet?
Come visit us if you have time.
Margaret Sook Ching, Voyager Golden Record

THE 1977 PLAYLIST

Brandenburg Concerto No. 2 in F
First Movement, Bach

'Kinds of Flowers'
Court gamelan, Java

Percussion
Senegal

Pygmy girls' initiation song
Zaire

'Morning Star' & 'Devil Bird'
Aborigine songs, Australia

'El Cascabel'
Mexico

'Johnny B. Goode'
Chuck Berry

Men's House Song
New Guinea

'Tsuru No Sugomori'
('Crane's Nest'), Shakuhachi, Japan

'Gavotte en rondeaux'
from the Partita No. 3, Bach

Queen of the Night aria, no. 14.
The Magic Flute, Mozart

'Tchakrulo'
Chorus, Georgian S.S.R.

Panpipes & Drum
Peru

'Melancholy Blues'
Louis Armstrong

Bagpipes
Azerbaijan S.S.R.

Rite of Spring
Stravinsky

The Well-Tempered Clavier
Book 2, Bach

Fifth Symphony
Beethoven

'Izlel je Delyo Hagdutin'
Bulgaria

Night Chant
Navajo Indians

'The Fairie Round'
Holborne, Paueans, Galliards, Almains and Other Short Aeirs

Panpipes
Solomon Islands

Wedding Song
Peru

'Flowing Streams'
Ch'in, China

'Jaat Kahan Ho'
Raga, India

'Dark Was the Night'
Blind Willie Johnson

String Quartet No. 13 in B flat
Beethoven

ALIEN WORLDS

An intrinsically improbable event may become highly probable if the number of events is very great.... [I]t is probable that a good many of the billions of planets in the Milky Way support intelligent forms of life. To me this conclusion is of great philosophical interest. I believe that science has reached the point where it is necessary to take into account the action of intelligent beings, in addition to the classical laws of physics.
Otto Struve

Let us now return to Frank Drake's equation and use it as intended as a framework to address in a systematic manner the question of our solitude. Recall that the equation consists of a series of terms which, when multiplied together, give an estimate of the number of currently contactable civilisations in the Milky Way galaxy. At the 1961 Green Bank meeting only the first term – the rate of star formation in the Milky Way – was known with any precision. Over half a century later, we can do much better. The next term in the equation is the fraction of stars in the Milky Way that have planets orbiting around them – most definitely a prerequisite for an intelligent civilisation to emerge. It's true that the civilisation may not have remained confined to its home world, and we will discuss this possibility later on. But it must be true that for life to emerge and evolve to the point where it can build spacecraft, a planet of some sort is required.

This space we declare to be infinite...
In it are an infinity of worlds of the same kind as our own.
Giordano Bruno, 1584

KEPLER-62

OUR SOLAR SYSTEM

SUN

MERCURY

KEPLER-62 SYSTEM

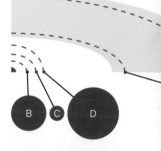

B   C   D

HABITABLE ZONE

EARTH

MARS

E F

The existence of alien worlds has been speculated about for many centuries. Ever since Copernicus began the process of demoting our solar system from its preferred place in the cosmos, it has been natural to assume that at least some of the stars in the sky must have planetary systems. Yet despite this seemingly common-sense conclusion, reached by virtually every right-thinking astronomer from Giordano Bruno onwards, the existence of other planets remained nothing more than an educated guess well into my lifetime. The vast distances between the stars and the limitations of technology locked us inside our own solar system with no way of seeing beyond. Throughout the nineteenth century a number of astronomers claimed to have detected distant planets, but all these observations proved to be flawed.

Today the picture couldn't be more different; the night sky is known to be awash with worlds. One of the more enticing of the known solar systems is located around a slightly smaller, cooler version of our Sun called Kepler-62. About 1200 light years from Earth in the constellation of Lyra, the system has been widely studied because it has at least five planets. Two of them, Kepler 62-e and Kepler 62-f, are particularly interesting because they are Earth-like in both size and distance from the star. Bathed in Kepler-62-shine, these worlds may, if they have the right atmospheric conditions, support oceans of liquid water on their surfaces. We will discuss the significance of this in the context of life later on.

The discovery of extra-solar planets has been possible due to the rapid development of precision astronomical instruments, both space-based and terrestrial, that allow us to see beyond the bright glare of stars to the worlds that lie in the shadows. Imagine looking at our solar system from the nearest star system to Earth, Alpha Centauri. The system is 4.37 light years away, and consists of two sun-like stars – one slightly more massive than the other – orbiting each other with a period of approximately 80 years. The red dwarf Proxima Centauri is probably a distant gravitationally bound component of the system, making it a loosely bound triple star. Looking back towards Earth from 40 trillion kilometres with the naked eye, our sun would look like any other solitary star. Detecting exoplanets is no easy task because planets are vanishingly small and faint, masked by the brightness of their parent stars, and directly imaging them remains a major technical challenge.

To step out of the glare has required the development of indirect methods of detection based on surprisingly sensitive technologies. On 21 April 1992 the first conclusive detection of an exoplanet was made by radio astronomers Aleksander Wolszczan and Dale Frail, working at the Arecibo Observatory in Puerto Rico. They were hunting for planets around a pulsar known as PSR 1257+12, located 1000 light years from Earth, using a delicate method of indirect observation known as pulsar timing. Pulsars are spinning neutron stars, some of the most exotic objects in the universe. PSR 1257+12 is 50 per cent more massive than our Sun, but has a radius of just over 10 kilometres. It is, in effect, a giant atomic nucleus, spinning on its axis every 0.006219 seconds – that's 9,650 rpm. As you may gather from this rather precise statement, it is possible to measure the spin-rates of pulsars with great precision by timing the interval between pulses of radio waves emitted from the stars like a lighthouse. Wolszczan and Frail reasoned that if a large enough planet was orbiting a pulsar, the gravitational tug should shift the arrival times of the radio pulses by enough to be detectable. And sure enough, they found two planets orbiting PSR 1257+12, and measured their masses and orbits. Planet A has a mass of 0.020 times the mass of Earth and orbits the star once every 25.262 days. Planet B is 4.3 times the mass of Earth, and orbits once every 66.5419 days. Subsequently, a third planet has been discovered, with a mass of 3.9 times that of Earth and orbiting every 98.2114 days. Pulsar astronomy is indeed a precision science.

KEPLER-62F WITH 62E AS MORNING STAR
An artist's impression of the smallest habitable planet. Like our solar system, Kepler-62 has two habitable zone worlds. Kepler-62f is approximately 40 per cent larger than Earth; Kepler-62e, 60 per cent larger than Earth, orbits the inner edge of the habitable zone.

THE HABITABLE ZONE

The most important requirement for the evolution of life as we know it is liquid water. This can only exist on the surface of a planet if that planet is far enough away from the star at the centre of its planetary system: too close and the surface is too hot, resulting in any water boiling off into space; too far away and the surface is too cold and the water will exist only as ice. The too hot/too cold scenario is what is known as the Goldilocks Zone. The distance and width of the Goldilocks Zone also depend on the size and temperature of the central star – it is further away from large, hot stars and closer in systems with small, cold stars. Using the Hertzsprung-Russell diagram (see page 97) and the known size of the star allows the calculation of each system's Goldilocks Zone, thus allowing us to determine whether the observed planets are likely to have liquid water and are therefore candidates for the evolution of life.

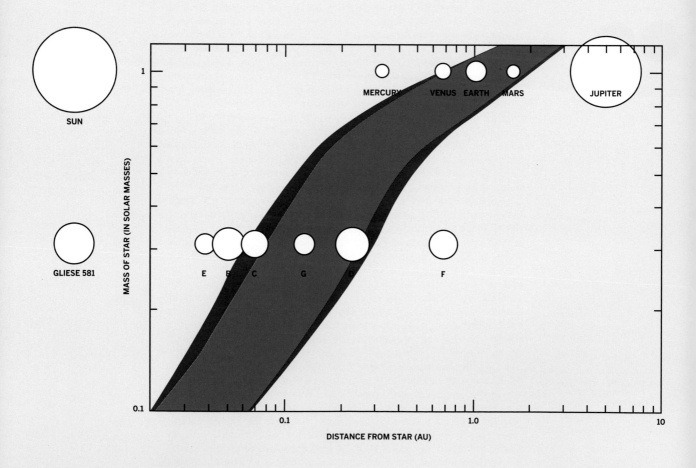

HABITABLE ZONE

POSSIBLE EXTENSION OF ZONE DUE TO VARIOUS UNCERTAINTIES

This was an historic observation, but of limited direct interest to SETI since there is absolutely no chance that life could survive the hostile environment around such a violent astronomical object. It was, however, an existence proof – the first discovery of planets beyond our solar system, and a surprising one at that.

To search for Earth-like planets around Sun-like stars required the development of different but equally beautiful methods of observation. The first of these to be deployed was the radial velocity method. A star doesn't sit still at the centre of a solar system with planets orbiting around it. Rather, the star and planets orbit around their common centre of mass. The centre of mass of a solar system with a single star will always be inside the star itself, because it carries virtually all of the mass, but the star will still wobble around the centre of mass of the system as seen from Earth.

This planetary-induced wobble is small but measurable. In our solar system Jupiter causes our Sun to wobble backwards and forwards with a velocity change of approximately 12.4 m/s across a period of twelve years. The Earth's effect is minute in comparison, inducing a velocity change of just 0.1 m/s over a period of a year.

In the 1950s, future Green Bank pioneer Otto Struve suggested that such a planetary-induced wobble could be detected using the Doppler Effect. When a star moves towards the Earth, its light is shifted towards the blue part of the spectrum, and when it moves away from the Earth its light is shifted towards the red part of the spectrum. By making measurements of the specific frequencies (i.e. colours) of light absorbed by chemical elements in the star's atmosphere, and measuring how much

THE DOPPLER METHOD
Otto Struve (1897–1963) was a member of an astronomical dynasty. His father, uncle, grandfather and great-grandfather were renowned astronomers. He was awarded the Gold Medal of the Royal Astronomical Society in 1944, the fourth member of his family to be honoured in this way, for his work on stellar spectroscopy.

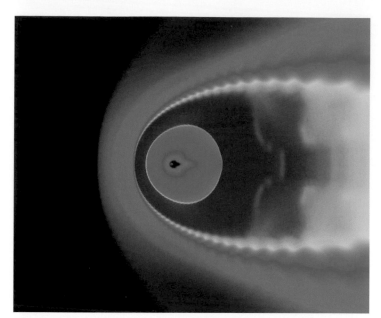

HELIOSPHERE MODEL
This Magnetohydrodynamical (MHD) model illustrates the interaction of the Sun's heliosphere (within the central blue dot) with the local interstellar medium (ISM), which traverses left to right.

these are shifted relative to the known frequencies as measured here on Earth, the motion of the star backwards and forwards can be determined over a period of time, and this can be used to calculate the orbital period of the planet and to estimate its mass. If there is more than one planet, the motion of the star will be more complicated, but since the orbital periods of the planets are regular, the contributions of the different planets to the star's wobble can be figured out.

Struve was one of the first respected scientists to publicly state his belief in extraterrestrial life. In the 1950s, however, the spectrographs used to measure red and blue shift were only able to detect velocity changes of a few thousand m/s, and at the Green Bank meeting he could only speculate that his technique would one day confirm his prejudice that planetary systems are common. Struve didn't live long enough to see his method applied, dying just two years after Green Bank, long before technology caught up with his ambition. It took until 1995 for two Swiss astronomers, Michel Mayor and Didier Queloz, to detect a planetary-induced Doppler shift using the Observatoire de Haute-Provence in France. The team discovered a planet orbiting the Sun-like star 51 Pegasi, located 50.9 light years from Earth.

This planet is named 51 Pegasi b, but its nickname is Bellerophon, after the mythological Greek hero who rode Pegasus, the winged stallion. Since its historic discovery, Bellerophon has been observed and examined in quite some detail, and it is no second Earth. It is a deeply hostile world, orbiting its parent star every four Earth days on a trajectory that takes it far closer than Mercury approaches our own Sun. Unlike Mercury, Bellerophon is a gas giant planet with a mass 150 times that of the Earth and a surface temperature approaching 1000 degrees Celsius. Although only half the mass of Jupiter, it may have a greater radius because the high surface temperature causes it to swell. Such exoplanets are known as Hot Jupiters – big enough and close enough to cause a significant wobble in their parent stars, which is why these types of worlds were discovered first by the early planet hunters.

The first evidence of a potential Earth-like planet arrived in 2007, when Stephan Audrey and his team at the European Southern Observatory in Chile announced the discovery of a planet around the red dwarf star Gliese 581, just over 20 light years from Earth. This was

RADIAL VELOCITY METHOD

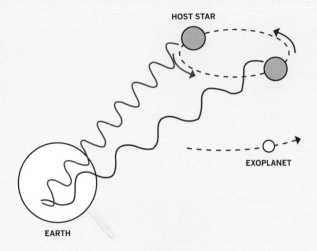

HOST STAR

EXOPLANET

EARTH

FINDING EXOPLANETS

One of the most exciting areas of current astronomical research is the hunt for planets around other stars – known simply as exoplanets – which are potential homes for extraterrestrial life. Until recently, such a search would have been impossible, as planets are too faint to see over interstellar distances. However, thanks to new instrumentation, we are now able to detect the telltale signals of exoplanets using two main techniques: the radial velocity method and the transit method. With these techniques, individual planets and even planetary systems have been discovered around hundreds of stars. Masses of these extrasolar planets range from a few times that of Earth to the size of 25 Jupiters.

TRANSIT METHOD

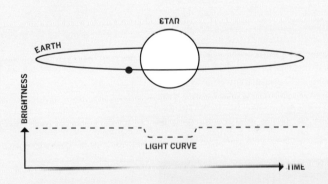

EARTH

STAR

BRIGHTNESS

LIGHT CURVE

TIME

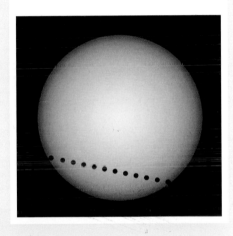

	KEPLER-4B	KEPLER-5B	KEPLER-6B	KEPLER-7B	KEPLER-8B
FLUX / PHASE (HOURS)					
ORBITAL PERIOD (EARTH DAYS)	3.2 DAYS	3.5 DAYS	3.2 DAYS	4.9 DAYS	3.5 DAYS
EARTH MASS	4.31	18.8	15.0	16.9	18.3

the second planet to be discovered in this system, but Gliese 581-c made headline news around the world because of its apparent Earth-like qualities. This planet is a rocky world, about five times as massive as Earth, and possibly the right distance away from its parent star to support liquid water on the surface: the stuff out of which science-fiction dreams are made. Further research has cast doubt on the idea that Gliese 581-b might have the necessary conditions to support life, but in March 2009 the second-Earth hunters got their own dedicated scientific instrument, and with it a cascade of new data became available.

The Kepler Space Telescope has transformed our knowledge of the distribution of planets in the Milky Way. Kepler is not a general-purpose instrument with multiple detectors and myriad ambitions; the telescope was designed for one purpose: to look for Earth-like planets. Free of the distorting effects of the Earth's atmosphere, Kepler carries a high-precision photometer, an instrument that has measured the light intensity from over 100,000 stars considered stable enough to support life on planets around them. Kepler searches for planets using a technique known as the transit method. If a planet passes across the face of a star as seen from Earth, the observed brightness of the star will drop by the tiniest of margins. Kepler's photometer is so sensitive it can measure changes in brightness (to use precise astronomical language we should say changes in the apparent magnitude) of less than 0.01 per cent. Observing repeated dips in brightness allows the orbital period of the planet to be measured, and the details of the changes in the brightness, combined with knowledge of the orbit, allows the size and mass of the planetary candidate to be estimated. The transit method has been extremely successful in the hunt for exoplanets, but the technique is not entirely reliable, often throwing up false positives. Once a promising candidate is found, the location is passed to ground-based telescopes for further analysis, and, if confirmed, the planets are classified as discoveries. Kepler has used the transit method of planet hunting on a quite extraordinary scale since it became fully operational in May 2009. As I write in July 2014, NASA's Exoplanet Archive lists 1,737 confirmed planets, over 50 per cent of which have been discovered using the Kepler data. This number is all the more staggering because Kepler is only capable of detecting a very small number of the planetary systems in our

STELLAR NURSERY
Stars come in all sizes and a range of colours. On location in Peru, we replicated a galaxy to help us understand which stars might be able to support life.

GLIESE 581-C
Gliese 581-c (right) made headline news because of its Earth-like qualities. Five times as massive as Earth, as this comparative computer artwork shows, it lies about 20.3 light years away from our planet.

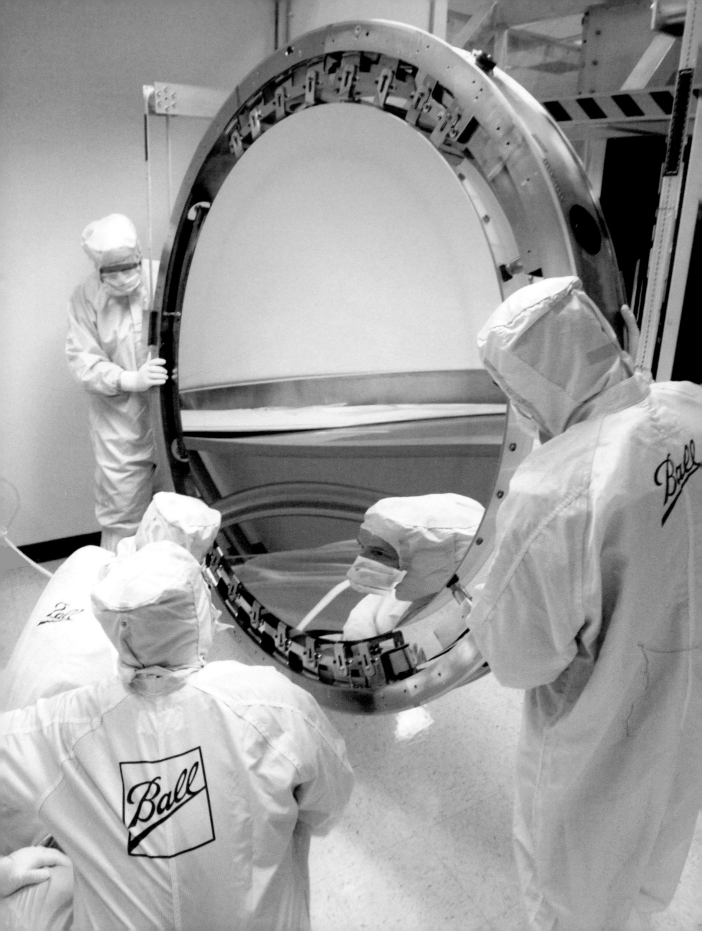

galaxy. Kepler views around 0.3 per cent of the sky in the constellations of Cygnus, Lyra and Draco, and even in this small patch, the telescope can only detect planets that pass directly in between their parent star and Earth. If the plane of the planetary orbits is orientated at the wrong angle, which is more likely than not, Kepler will not see any planets. Furthermore, Kepler only observed for four years, and because it has to see more than one transit to measure an orbit, it is blind to planets that orbit with periods greater than four years – which is the case for all the outer planets in our solar system. And finally, Kepler only sees stars out to a distance of approximately 3000 light years, whilst our galaxy has a diameter of 100,000 light years. Kepler's data set, then, contains only a tiny fraction of the planetary systems out there. All of these losses can be corrected for in a statistical sense, and when the numbers are crunched we have a reliable observation-based number to put into the Drake Equation. The fraction of stars that have planetary systems is close to 100 per cent! On average, there is at least 1 planet per star in the Milky Way galaxy, and we can insert the second term with confidence: $f_p = 1$.

The extraordinary Kepler mission was expected to last until 2016, but technical malfunctions may mean the telescope has now finished its planet-hunting activity. Even so, the huge volume of data is still being worked through and indications suggest it may have captured evidence for up to 3000 more planets circling distant stars.

This is encouraging for SETI enthusiasts, but in the hunt for civilisations, it's not the number of planets out there that really matters; rather, it is how many of these planets are capable of supporting life. This is the next term in the Drake Equation – the average number of planets per star that has planets that can support life – n_e. This is sometimes referred to as the Goldilocks question; how many of those billions of planets are not too hot and not too cold, but just right to allow life to exist on their surface?

**KEPLER SPACE TELESCOPE
FIELD OF VIEW**
This star map shows the
constellations of Cygnus and
Lyra. The area marked with
boxes indicates the telescope's
field of view, which includes
over 100,000 stars.

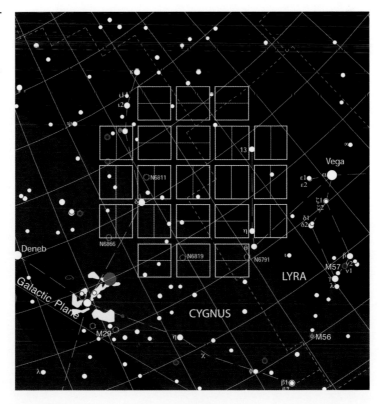

THE RECIPE FOR LIFE

*Extended regions of liquid water, conditions favourable for
the assembly of complex organic molecules, and energy sources
to sustain metabolism.*
NASA, 2008

Why Earth? What is it about our planet that makes it a home for life? In 2008 NASA brought together a team of scientists to define in the most basic terms the properties a planet needs to have a chance of supporting life, given our current scientific knowledge. Top of the list was liquid water – an ingredient virtually every biologist would agree is necessary for life. Water is a uniquely complex liquid, with its simple H_2O molecules forming great complexes held loosely together by hydrogen bonds. It forms the scaffolding around which biology happens, holding molecules and orientating them in just the right way for chemical reactions to take place. It is a superb solvent, and remains a liquid over an unusually large range of temperatures and pressures. It has been said that we will never truly understand biology until we understand water, such is its role in the chemistry of life on Earth. Fortunately, water is abundant in the universe. Hydrogen is the most common element, making up 74 per cent of the matter in the universe by mass. Oxygen is the third most abundant, at around 1 per cent, and these two reactive atoms combine to form water whenever they can. Water has been present in the universe for over 12 billion years, which we know because we've seen it. In July 2011, a giant reservoir of water was detected around an active galaxy known as APM 08279+5255. The cloud contains over 140 trillion times the amount of water in Earth's oceans, and is over 12 billion light years away, having formed less than 2 billion years after the Big Bang. So water is necessary for biology and, fortunately, extremely common throughout the universe.

Earth is unique in the solar system, however, because it is currently the only place where the surface conditions are right for water to exist in all three of its states: solid, liquid and gas. There are ice sheets at the poles and on the summits of the highest mountain peaks. In the atmosphere, clouds of water vapour form and fall as rain and snow, flowing back through rivers into the oceans that cover over 70 per cent of the surface. Mars has water, but on the cold red planet it can only be found as ice trapped in the poles and deep below ground and, just possibly, as sub-surface liquid lakes. Venus may once have been wet, but its proximity to the Sun and runaway greenhouse effect boiled any primordial oceans off into space long ago. This appears to suggest that it is Earth's distance from the Sun that defines its suitability for life. Drag the Earth closer to the Sun and the temperatures would rise, the oceans would evaporate into the atmosphere, and if things got too hot the water molecules would escape into space, leaving Earth a dry, Venusian world. Drag the Earth further out towards Mars, and temperatures would drop until eventually the surface water would freeze.

It might appear tempting, therefore, to look for planets at roughly the same distance from their stars as Earth in the search for living worlds. This would be oversimplistic, because things are a lot more complicated. The conditions on the surface of a planet depend on many factors, the distance to the star being only one. The mass of the planet determines the gravitational pull it exerts on the molecules in its atmosphere, and this determines which atmospheric molecules it can hang on to at a given temperature. This is important because the atmosphere plays a critical role in setting the surface temperature of a planet. Venus has the hottest surface in the solar system other than the Sun because of its greenhouse gas-laden atmosphere, despite being much further away from the Sun

THE HOTTEST STEP
A natural sinkhole, cut out of the limestone of the High Andes. Around 500–600 years ago, the Inca modified it by creating the circular steps. It is thought that it was a rudimentary agricultural research station, with every step having a range of microclimates, each of which was a habitable zone for their crops. An ideal TV location.

HYDROLOGICAL CYCLE
Ancient salt mines in an Incan Valley. The water comes from melting snow, which then evaporates leaving the salt. An example of water in its three states –solid ice, liquid water and water vapour.

than Mercury. The Moon, on the other hand, has very little atmosphere due to its small mass, and even though it is the same distance from the Sun as the Earth, its surface temperatures range from over 120°C in direct sunlight to below -150°C at night. NASA's Lunar Reconnaissance Orbiter measured the coldest temperature ever recorded in the solar system, -247°C, in the limb of a crater at the Moon's North Pole, which never receives sunlight because the Moon's spin axis is almost perpendicular to its orbital plane. The composition of the atmosphere is determined in part by the geology of the planet; on Earth, plate tectonics play an important role in regulating the amount of carbon dioxide in the atmosphere. CO_2 is a greenhouse gas, and higher concentrations of such gases raise the temperatures. The presence of sulphur dioxide in the atmosphere from volcanic eruptions can cool the surface of a planet, however, because sulphate aerosols reflect sunlight back out into space. The Mount Pinatubo eruption in June 1991 cooled the Earth's surface by up to 1.3 degrees for the three years following the eruption. And we shouldn't forget that life itself alters the composition of planetary atmospheres quite radically. Earth's atmosphere today is a product of the action of living things; before photosynthesis evolved, there was very little free oxygen in the atmosphere, and plants play an important role in removing CO_2 and locking it up in biomass. The planet's mass, spin axis, orbit, geology and atmospheric composition all conspire in a complex way to set the average surface temperature and atmospheric pressure, which ultimately determine whether liquid water can exist on the surface. And if life gets going, its effects have to be folded in as well.

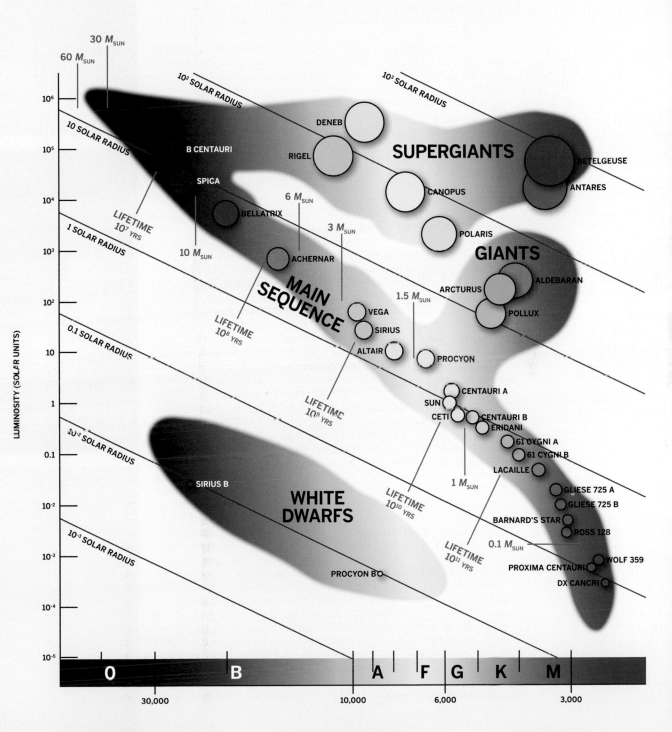

THE HERTZSPRUNG-RUSSELL DIAGRAM

The size and surface temperature of a star are the key components in calculating the distance that planets have to orbit the star to allow liquid water to exist. The size and surface temperature also vary over the lifetime of the star, resulting in the Goldilocks Zone moving closer to the star because older stars tend to burn at lower temperatures.

Beyond the planet, a vitally important ingredient for producing a potentially living world is, of course, the parent star itself, and all stars are most definitely not alike. There are over two hundred billion stars in the Milky Way galaxy. The largest known supergiant stars are over 1500 times the diameter of our Sun. If such a star were located at the centre of our solar system, it would engulf Jupiter. At the other end of the spectrum are tiny red dwarfs, with diameters from around half that of our sun to as small as a tenth of it. The smallest known star at the time of writing goes by the name of 2MASS JO5233822-1403022, which shines eight thousand times less brightly than our sun and is smaller (but denser) than Jupiter.

As with virtually everything in physics, a good way to make sense of this stellar menagerie is to draw a graph. The most famous graph in all of astronomy is known as the Hertzsprung-Russell diagram (on the previous page), after astronomers Ejnar Hertzsprung and Henry Norris Russell, who drew it independently in 1911. They plotted the surface temperature of the stars (which is directly related to their colour – hot stars are blue or white hot, cool stars are red) against their brightness. It is immediately obvious that the stars are not distributed randomly on the diagram. Most lie on a sweeping line ascending from the bottom right to the top left. This line is known as the Main Sequence. Our yellow sun lies around the middle of the main sequence, and all the stars on this line are generating their energy in the same way – by fusing hydrogen into helium in their cores. These are the 'standard stars', if you like, although their masses, lifetimes and suitability for the support of living solar systems are very different.

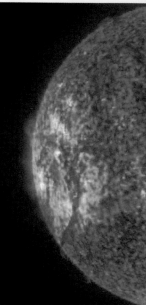

The basic physics underlying the Main Sequence line is simple. Stars are clouds of hydrogen and helium, which is pretty much all there is in the universe to a good approximation, collapsing under their own gravity. As the cloud collapses, it heats up. This is not surprising – all gases get hot when they are compressed – try pumping up a bicycle tyre. Eventually, the collapsing ball of gas gets so hot that the positively charged hydrogen atoms overcome their mutual electromagnetic repulsion and fuse together in a nuclear reaction to make helium. This releases a tremendous amount of energy, which further heats up the gas, increasing the rate of nuclear reactions and continuing to heat the gas. Hot gases want to expand, and so ultimately a balance will be reached between the crushing force of gravity and the outward pressure exerted by the nuclear-heated gas. This is the current state of our Sun, happily converting 600 million tonnes of hydrogen every second into helium to counteract the inward pull of gravity. For less massive stars, the equilibrium will be reached at a lower temperature because the inward pull of gravity is weaker. Having a lower surface temperature, these stars will be redder than our sun, and also less luminous. These are the dim, red stars at the bottom right of the diagram, known as red dwarfs. We've already met an example of a red dwarf – our nearest stellar neighbour, Proxima Centauri. Red dwarfs also have the longest lifetimes of the stars on the Main Sequence, simply because they have to burn their fuel at a lower rate in order to reach a stable equilibrium with gravity.

At the other end of the Main Sequence are the massive blue stars. Ten times the mass of our Sun or more, the inward pull of gravity is strong, and they have to burn their hydrogen fuel at a profligate rate to resist collapse. This makes them hot, and therefore blue, but also short-lived. The largest Main Sequence stars will use up their nuclear fuel in ten million years or less, at which point they will move off the Main Sequence to become red giant stars. The red giants, like the famous Betelgeuse in the constellation of Orion, are stars nearing the end of their lives. Starved of hydrogen in their cores, they begin to fuse helium into heavier elements like carbon and oxygen. These stars are the origin of

most of the heavy elements in your body. Their cores become superheated in their ultimately futile battle against gravity, causing their outer layers to expand and cool. This is why the red giants sit at the top right of the Hertzsprung-Russell diagram. They are vast, and therefore bright, but their cool surfaces cause them to glow a deep red. Red giants will last for only a few million years before they run out of nuclear fuel, at which point they shed their outer layers, forming one of the most beautiful sights in nature – a planetary nebula. It is these clouds, rich in carbon and oxygen, which ultimately distribute the building blocks of life into the galaxy. Your building blocks are likely to have been part of a planetary nebula at some point over five billion years ago. Cooling at the heart of the nebula is the fading core of the star, exposed as a white dwarf. These stars populate the bottom left of the Hertzsprung-Russell diagram.

There are a handful of other exotic stars out in the Milky Way. The vast blue supergiant stars like Deneb are extremely hot and extremely luminous. Deneb, the brightest star in Kepler's field of view in the constellation of Cygnus, is almost 200,000 times more luminous than our Sun, and 20 times more massive. It burns its nuclear fuel at a ferocious rate, and will probably explode in a supernova explosion within a few million years, leaving a black hole behind.

The Hertzsprung-Russell diagram, then, is the key to understanding stellar evolution, and also contains vital information for planet hunters. Stars that do not lie on the Main Sequence are highly unlikely to support planetary systems with the right conditions for life. They are either short-lived and ferociously bright, or have had a life history fraught with violence and change. The Main Sequence, containing the stable, hydrogen-burning stars, is where we should look for stability. But even there, the more massive, brighter stars are likely to be too short-lived for complex life to emerge. On Earth, life existed for over three billion years before complex organisms emerged in the Cambrian Explosion just 550,000 years ago. We will discuss the history of life on Earth in more detail a little later, but for now we might venture an educated guess that stars with lifetimes significantly shorter than a billion years or so are unlikely to preside over planets with intelligent civilisations. This rules out the blue stars at the top left of the Main Sequence. Even familiar stars like Sirius, the brightest star in the night sky and only twice the mass of the Sun, can probably be ruled out as its lifetime on the Main Sequence is expected to be a billion years at most. We are therefore left with stars on the Main Sequence with masses within a factor of two or less of our Sun as candidates for solar systems that could support complex life.

There may also be a lower limit on the masses of life-supporting stars, although this is very much an active area of research. Around 80 per cent of the stars in the Milky Way are red dwarfs, and many are known to have solar systems. Red dwarfs have potential lifetimes measured in the trillions of years, so there is no issue with their longevity. Despite their frugal use of fuel, however, red dwarfs tend to be volatile and variable in their light output. Sunspots can reduce their brightness by a factor of two for long periods of time, and violent flares can increase their brightness by a similar factor over time periods of days or even minutes. Planets in orbit around red dwarfs are therefore subject to significant and rapid changes in the amount of light and radiation they receive. Furthermore, because of their low light output, planets must be extremely close to the star if they are to be warm enough for liquid water to exist on the surface, irrespective of the details of their atmospheres. When planets orbit close to stars, they become tidally locked, with one hemisphere permanently facing the star and the other always facing into the darkness of space. We only see one face of our Moon for the same reason – tidal locking is inevitable for moons orbiting close to planets or planets orbiting close to stars. This results in a strange kind of climate for potentially habitable

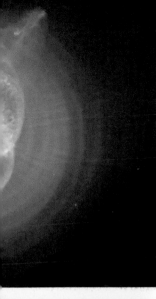

THE CAT'S EYE NEBULA
Taken by NASA's Hubble Space Telescope, this image shows the sheer beauty of a dying star shedding its outer layers.

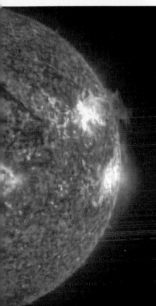

LIFE-GIVING STAR
The stable stars within the Main Sequence supply the heat and light that is required to sustain life on a planet such as Earth.

SUPERGIANT STAR
Antares – the white star in the bottom left of the picture – is one of the best-known examples of a supergiant star.

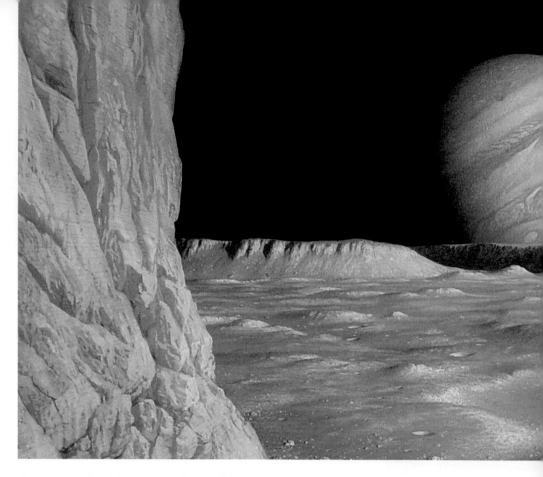

planets around red dwarf stars; there will be regions of permanent day, and regions of permanent night.

Despite all these problems, however, recent computer modelling suggests that red dwarf planets may be able to maintain stable surface conditions if they have thick, insulating atmospheres and deep oceans, and life has plenty of time to evolve in these unfamiliar (to us) conditions. The jury is still out as to whether the red dwarfs that populate the low-mass region of the Hertzsprung-Russell diagram could be candidates for living solar systems.

Where does all this leave us? If we take the conservative path, and focus our attentions on the Sun-like orange and yellow stars on the main sequence, we can look at the Kepler data to estimate how many of these so-called F, G and K-type stars in the Milky Way have rocky planets in the right orbits to allow liquid water to be present on the surface, at least in principle. These planets orbit within what is known as the habitable zone, and this is the number we want to measure and insert into the Drake Equation. This has been done, and the results are surprising. In a recent study, ten planets were identified as Earth-like in the Kepler data set, in the sense that they have the right mass and composition, and are in the right orbits around their parent Main Sequence F, G or K stars, to support liquid water on their surfaces for long periods of time. Applying all the statistical corrections to account for the alignment of the solar systems relative to Earth, the lack of ability to see planets with longer orbital periods, and so on, we can estimate with a reasonable degree of certainty that there are around 10,000 Earth-like planets capable of supporting life in Kepler's field of view. This in turn suggests that around a quarter of F, G and K stars in the Milky Way have potentially life-supporting planets in orbit around them, corresponding to ten billion habitable planets.

If we allow the possibility that planets around red dwarfs may also be habitable, then we can more than double that number.

There is one final point worth making about habitable zones around stars. In our solar system, Venus, Mars and Earth are within the habitable zone as commonly defined, but there are other places where life may exist. Several of the moons of Jupiter and Saturn are planet-sized worlds, and it is known that the Jovian satellites Europa and Ganymede, and quite possibly Saturn's giant moon Titan and the small but active Enceladus, have sub-surface oceans or lakes of liquid water. Europa in particular is considered to be one of the most likely places beyond Earth that may support life, even though it is outside the more commonly defined habitable zone around the Sun. If we admit the possibility that planet-sized moons may extend the habitable zone around stars, then the number of potentially life-sustaining worlds in the Milky Way increases significantly.

Over 50 years after the Green Bank meeting, the first three astronomical terms in the Drake Equation are now known from experimental data, and they are encouraging for SETI. There are, of course, large uncertainties, and one can find differing interpretations of the data in the academic literature. What is absolutely clear, however, is that the number of potential homes for life in the Milky Way is measured in hundreds of millions at the very least – most likely billions. From an astronomical perspective, the Milky Way could be teeming with life. The next three terms in the Drake Equation are biological; they concern the probability that life will emerge spontaneously on a planet that could support it, and the probability that the necessarily simple life that first appears evolves into complex, intelligent beings capable of constructing a technological civilisation. It is to these difficult questions that we now turn.

ORIGINS

Earth formed 4.54 +/- 0.07 billion years ago out of the flattened disc of dust orbiting our young Sun. The planet was far from hospitable for the first few hundred million years of its life; it was an intensely hot and volcanic world, bombarded by asteroids and comets and, at least once, it collided with another planet, which resulted in the 23.5-degree tilt of our spin axis and the formation of the Moon.

Slowly, the solar system became a more ordered place, and Earth cooled to the point where liquid water could exist on its surface. There is evidence that liquid water existed as far back as 4.4 billion years, but it is certain that our planet was blue by the end of the late heavy bombardment 3.8 billion years ago, and around this time we find the first evidence of life. Structures known as microbially induced sedimentary structures were discovered in 2013 at a remote site in the Pilbara region of Western Australia. They were found in a sedimentary rock layer laid down in the early Archean period, 3.48 billion years ago. Similar structures are found today along ocean shorelines and in rivers and lakes, formed by the interaction of microbial mats with sediments carried through them by water currents. They indicate the presence of a complex microbial ecosystem, most likely a purple layer of slime that thrived in the warm, wet, oxygen-free environment of the early Earth, filling the atmosphere with the sulphurous stench of anaerobic breath. Early Earth would not appear welcoming to our eyes or noses.

Beyond 3.5 billion years, there is indirect evidence for the existence of life as far back as 3.7 billion years. Geologists studying some of the oldest sedimentary rocks on Earth in the Isua Supracrustal Belt in Western Greenland analysed the ratio of carbon isotopes in sedimentary rocks. The ratio of the heavier carbon 13 isotope to the more common carbon 12 can be used as a biomarker, because organisms preferentially use the lighter carbon 12 isotope in metabolic processes. Around 98.9 per cent of naturally occurring carbon is carbon 12, and if the concentration is significantly higher in a particular rock deposit then this is taken as evidence that the carbon was laid down by biological processes.

What can this evidence tell us about the probability of life emerging spontaneously on other worlds? The problem is that Earth is a sample size of one, so it would be erroneous to draw firm conclusions. It is interesting to observe that life emerged very early in the Earth's history – probably as soon as the conditions were right. The first half a billion years after Earth's formation is known as the Hadean Eon, named after the Greek god of the underworld. It is likely that the carbon dioxide atmosphere, volcanism and frequent bombardment from space made life impossible on the surface during the Hadean. From the start of the Archean Eon 4 billion years ago, and certainly after the violent period of the solar system's history known as the Late Heavy Bombardment – which is known from analysis of lunar rocks to have ended 3.8 billion years ago – Earth became a more stable planet, and this date coincides with the earliest evidence for life. It is tempting, therefore, to suggest that life began on Earth pretty much as soon as it could have done after the violence of its formation. If this is taken as a working hypothesis, then we might venture that the probability of life arising on a planet that could support it – the term f_l in the Drake Equation – is close to 100 per cent. This is, of course, speculative to say the least, and we would know this number with much greater certainty if we found that life arose independently on Mars, Europa, or one of the many bodies in the solar system that had or still have large bodies of liquid water on or below the surface. This is one of the most important motivations for the exploration of Mars and the moons of the outer solar system.

ARCHEAN LANDSCAPE
Earth as it would have appeared during the Archean period, 3.48 billion years ago.

A BRIEF HISTORY OF LIFE ON EARTH

At this stage in the analysis of the Drake Equation, it's looking promising for the alien hunters. There are billions of potentially habitable worlds in the Milky Way galaxy, and it is possible to interpret the early emergence of life on Earth as a hint (evidence would be too strong a word) that simple life may be inevitable, given the right conditions. The next term in the equation turns out to be more problematic for the optimist, however. We need to estimate f_i, the fraction of planets with life that go on to develop intelligent life, and f_c, the fraction of those worlds on which civilisations develop the technology to be contactable. As for the origin of life, the only evidence we have can be found in the history of life on Earth, so let us briefly summarise what we know.

The first population of living things whose ancestors survived to the present day is commonly known as LUCA – the Last Universal Common Ancestor. These four words mean something very specific; because all living things on the planet today share the same basic biochemistry, including DNA, we may assert that all living things are related and share a common origin. Specifically, if you trace your personal lineage back – to your parents, grandparents, great-grandparents and so on – you will find an unbroken line stretching all the way back to LUCA. It is possible that life emerged more than once on Earth, with different biochemistry, but we have no evidence of it. LUCA may have been unrecognisable when compared to today's life – they may not even have been cellular in nature, but rather a collection of biochemical reactions involving proteins and self-replicating molecules, possibly contained inside rocky chambers around deep-sea hydrothermal vents. They would certainly have been simpler than the earliest known microbial mats, but somewhere in your genome there will be sequences of DNA that have been faithfully passed down across the great sweep of geological time, and if you have children, you'll pass these four-billion-year-old messages on to them.

Our task is to try to estimate how likely it is that, given enough time, LUCA will evolve into organisms capable of building a civilisation. This is, of course, not precise; no accurate scientific statements can be made with a sample size of one! All we know for sure is that it happened here. The best we can do is trace our lineage back through time and try to identify potential bottlenecks along the way.

Our species, Homo sapiens, emerged around 250,000 years ago in the Great Rift Valley of East Africa. Given that Homo sapiens is the only species to have built a civilisation, the probability of our evolution from earlier hominin species is what we need to know to estimate f_c. To summarise, the emergence of Homo sapiens was undoubtedly fortuitous, dependent on many factors including, it appears, the geology of the Rift Valley itself and the details of cyclical changes in the Earth's orbit. But given enough time and the existence of large numbers of relatively intelligent animals on Earth, it is at least possible to imagine that some other creature may have made the long journey towards civilisation at some point in the future had we not emerged when we did. This is, of course, simply my opinion, and you should make up your own mind after reading further. Incredibly fortunate as we are to exist, therefore, I don't think the ascent from primates to humans is the most important evolutionary bottleneck in the road to technological civilisation, given the pre-existing biological diversity on Earth and a few tens or hundreds of millions of years of stability into the future. Rather, I think we should direct our attention back over the much longer time periods between the origin of life on Earth and the emergence of the first intelligent animals. We are mammals, which first appeared 225 million years ago in the Triassic era. Dinosaurs also appeared around this time, a subgroup of

RIFT VALLEY
Lake Natron, in the East African Rift, Tanzania. Birthplace of Homo sapiens.

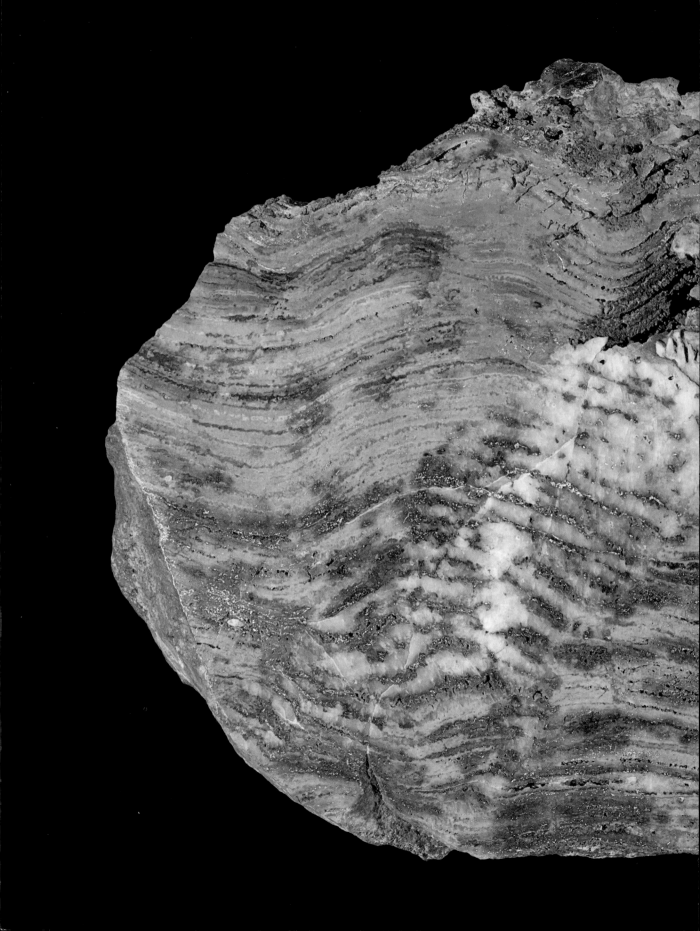

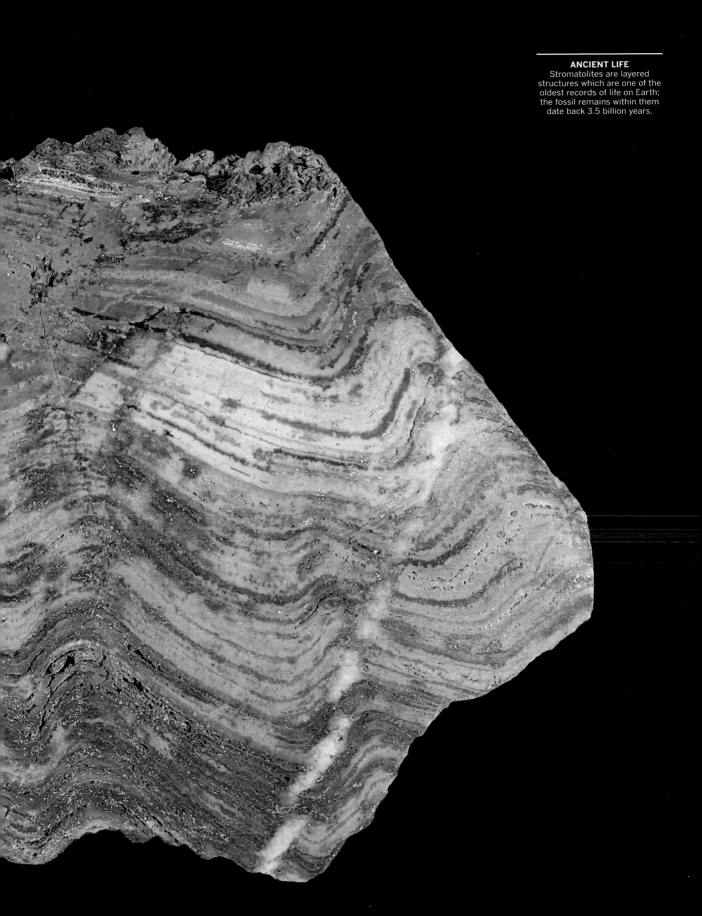

archosaurs to which birds and crocodiles are related. The first evidence of large numbers of complex animals can be found around 530 million years ago, during a period of rapid biological diversification known as the Cambrian explosion. The earliest fossils of multicellular organisms, known as Ediacaran biota, have been identified as far back as 655 million years. Many of these organisms appear sponge-like or quilted, and nothing like them survives today. There is evidence of animal-like body plans in some Ediacaran fossils, with a clearly differentiated head, but because of their soft bodies fossils are rare and relatively little is known about them. Beyond 655 million years ago, there is no evidence of multicellular life on Earth.

The half a billion years or so from the Cambrian explosion to the present day is, in geological terms, relatively short, and life seems to have marched towards greater complexity ever since. This is a gross oversimplification, and we certainly do not suggest that evolution can be viewed as an inevitable march towards intelligence. One might be tempted to assert, however, that given something akin to a Cambrian explosion, the probability of developing intelligent life may be non-negligible, although there are scientists who will strongly disagree.

There is a significantly longer stretch of time between LUCA and the Cambrian explosion – over 3 billion years – and if we are looking for potential barriers to the emergence of intelligence we should investigate the vast expanse of time before complex, multi-cellular life appeared. Why did single-celled organisms remain 'simple' on Earth for so long? Most biologists would point to at least two crucial evolutionary innovations that were necessary, though not sufficient, to trigger the Cambrian explosion. The first was oxygenic photosynthesis. An oxygen atmosphere is probably a necessary precursor for the development of

complex living things. All multicellular animals today breathe oxygen. This is not a coincidence or a biological fluke; it is chemistry. We release the stored energy from our food by oxidising it – a chemical reaction that is around 40 per cent efficient in the presence of oxygen. Food can be oxidised by other elements such as sulphur, but these reactions typically have an efficiency of 10 per cent or less. If a food chain is to be supported, with predators eating prey that eat plants and so on, then oxygen is probably essential. Without it, the energy available for predators would diminish by 90 per cent at each step in the food chain. This wouldn't simply mean that an oxygen-starved planet could be full of grazing animals like sheep and cows but no predators such as cats or sharks or humans. The arms race between predators and prey was a vital evolutionary driver towards living complexity on Earth; eyes, ears and brains offer a survival advantage whether you are the hunter or the hunted, and if predation had been impossible for energetic reasons it is far less likely or perhaps impossible that complex animals would have evolved.

Photosynthesis has been around for a long time. The 3.5-billion-year-old Western Australian microbial mat structures are bacterial and they were probably early photosynthesisers, using light from the Sun to grab electrons off hydrogen sulphide and force them onto carbon dioxide to form sugars. They would not have used a pigment as complex as the green chlorophyll that colours the landscapes of Earth today; more likely they would have used simpler molecules from the same family known as porphyrins, which occur naturally and whose precursors have been found in Moon rocks and in interstellar space. Living things are like electrical circuits – they need a flow of electrons to power their metabolism, and given the ready availability of sunlight and naturally occurring molecules that can be assembled into machines to capture it and deliver electrons, it is not too difficult to see how primitive photosynthesis might have appeared very early in the history of life on Earth.

STROMATOLITES: A RARE SIGHTING
The number of stromatolites around the world is fast declining, having fallen prey to grazing. These specimens have been preserved in the Hamelin Pool Marine Nature Reserve in Western Australia.

Given the obvious advantage of using the light from the Sun to power the processes of life, it's not surprising that some early bacteria used photosynthesis for a different purpose – to synthesise a molecule known as adenosine triphosphate, or ATP, the energy storage system for life. ATP is one of the molecules that all living things share, and must therefore be very ancient, perhaps dating back to LUCA and the origin of life.

The type of photosynthesis found in modern plants, trees and algae is a hybrid of these two processes, with an important twist. Crucially, the electrons are no longer taken from hydrogen sulphide, but from water. The fusion of these two slightly different types of photosynthesis, and the use of sunlight to grab input electrons off water, was the great evolutionary leap that led to the oxygenation of the Earth's atmosphere. Known as oxygenic photosynthesis, it evolved at some point earlier than 2.5 billion years ago. We know this because at this time Earth started to rust, forming great orange iron oxide layers known as banded iron formations, and this requires the presence of large amounts of free oxygen in the atmosphere. Molecular oxygen is an unstable and highly reactive gas, and must be constantly replenished. Astronomers in search of life on exoplanets would consider the detection of an oxygen atmosphere as a smoking gun for the presence of photosynthesis. Oxygenic photosynthesis is a terrifically complicated process, though; the molecular machinery is known as the Z-scheme, and its operation has only been understood in detail in the last few years. The sugar-manufacturing part alone, known as photosystem 2, consists of 46,630 atoms. The structure of the part that holds water molecules in place ready for their electrons to be harvested, known as the oxygen-evolving complex, was discovered in 2006. It is perhaps not surprising, therefore, that the more primitive forms of photosynthesis were not combined together into the oxygen-releasing Z-scheme for well over a billion years.

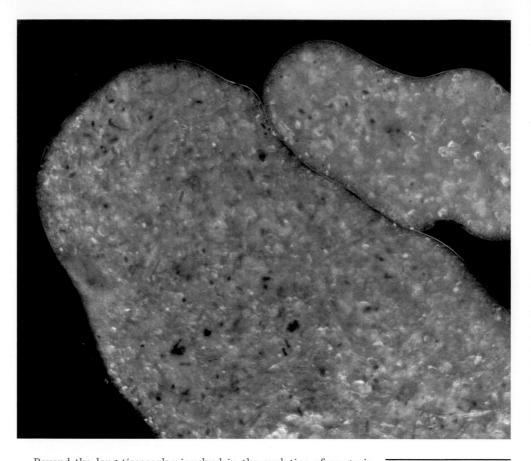

ENDOSYMBIOSIS IN ACTION
Visible inside this Giant
Amoeba (*Pelomyxa palustris*)
are the endosymbiotic bacteria.

Beyond the long timescales involved in the evolution of oxygenic photosynthesis, however, there is another piece of circumstantial evidence that may suggest an evolutionary bottleneck. All the green plants and algae that fill our atmosphere with oxygen today perform their photosynthesis inside structures called chloroplasts. Chloroplasts look for all the world like free-living bacteria, and that is because they were, long ago. The story is that a bacterium, most likely one of the great family of early photosynthesisers known as cyanobacteria, was swallowed up by another cell and became co-opted to perform the complex task of grabbing electrons off water and using them to manufacture ATP and sugars, releasing the waste product oxygen in the process. This engulfing of one cell by another, and the merging of their properties, is known as endosymbiosis, an ability possessed by some cells that allows for step-changes in living things through the wholesale merger of capabilities that evolved separately and over vast periods of time in different organisms. But here is the key point; everything on the planet today that performs oxygenic photosynthesis does it using the Z-scheme, and this strongly implies that it only evolved once, most probably in a population of cyanobacteria over 2.5 billion years ago. This tremendously advantageous innovation was so useful that it became co-opted into every plant, every tree, every blade of grass and every algal bloom on the planet, flooding the atmosphere with the oxygen necessary for the Cambrian explosion to populate Earth with endless forms most beautiful. If there were ever a smoking gun for a bottleneck, this is it.

But how on earth does a cell 'learn' how to engulf another one and survive? How did endosymbiosis arise? A clue, and perhaps an even more significant bottleneck, may be found in another pre-requisite for the

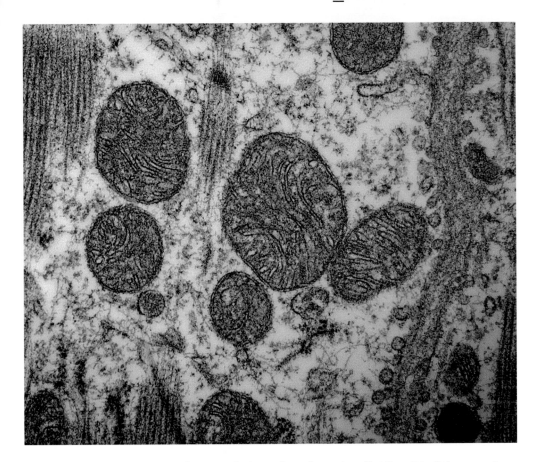

MITOCHONDRIA
These innocuous-looking circles form the power stations of cells, providing around 80 per cent of your energy through the ATP they produce.

Cambrian explosion – the eukaryotic cell. All multicellular organisms are made up of cells known as eukaryotes – cells with a nucleus and a host of specialised structures each charged with performing specific tasks. The eukaryotic cells in every living thing look so similar that an alien biologist, knowing nothing about planet Earth, would immediately recognise that human eukaryotes are closely related to those from a blade of grass. The earliest known eukaryotic cells date from around two billion years ago. Beyond this, simpler cells known as prokaryotes were the only living things on the planet. Bacteria and archaea, the two single-celled kingdoms of life that still flourish today, are prokaryotes. They are simple in the sense that they lack the vast, specialised machinery of the eukaryotes, although as we've seen they do possess some vital and extremely complex abilities – photosynthesis being a very good example.

The most striking difference between eukaryotes and prokaryotes is the eukaryotes' cell nucleus, which contains most of its DNA. In the story of evolution of life on Earth, however, it is the small amount of DNA stored outside the nucleus that is most revealing. Almost all eukaryotic cells contain structures called mitochondria. The word 'almost' is used a lot in biology. Unlike physics, there always seem to be one or two exceptions that ruin sentences in books like this. Most biologists believe that even the eukaryotes that don't possess mitochondria did so at some point in the past, however, so we can take it that these structures are ubiquitous. Mitochondria are the power stations of the cell, and their job is to produce ATP. Around 80 per cent of your energy comes from the ATP produced in mitochondria, and without them you certainly wouldn't exist. A clue as to their evolutionary origin is contained in their DNA, which is stored

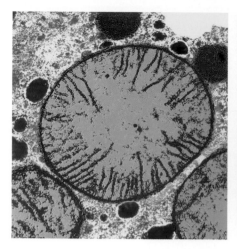 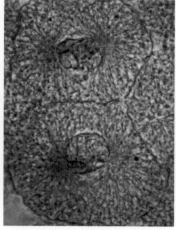 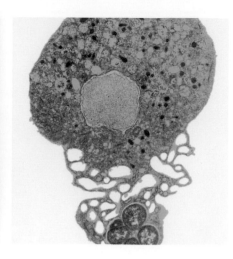

BUILDING BLOCKS OF LIFE
Life on Earth comes in an amazing array of different forms, but essentially all are built from the same basic cells, each of which contains very similar structures. From left to right: mammalian mitochondria; whitefish daughter cells after mitosis; neutrophil and trapped bacteria; cell division; red blood cells; mitosis cell division.

in loops and kept separate from the genetic material in the cell nucleus. Bacteria also store their DNA in loops, and this is not a coincidence. The mitochondria were once free-living bacteria.

The obvious question is, how did the bacterial mitochondria get inside the cells of every complex organism on the planet? The answer is through endosymbiosis, just as for the chloroplasts, but there is not universal agreement on the detail, and the detail matters a great deal. What is not in question is that the mitochondria are bacterial in origin. The debate surrounds the nature of the original host cell. One camp of biologists believes that the host cell was already a eukaryote, which over many millions of years had evolved an ability called phagocytosis – the ability to ingest other cells. This is a traditional Darwinian explanation – one in which complex traits evolve gradually over time via mutations and natural selection. If this is true, then it is possible to view the eukaryotic cell as just another evolutionary innovation, albeit a very important one, that might crop up anywhere given enough time. The other possibility, which is favoured by many biologists, has different implications. The idea is that the swallowing of the proto-mitochondrial cell was the origin of the eukaryotic cell itself. There was no such thing as phagocytosis or the eukaryotic cell before this singular event, and this 'fateful encounter' changed everything. Recent DNA evidence suggests that the host cell was probably an archaeon, one of the two great prokaryotic domains. Somewhere, in some primordial ocean, this simple prokaryote managed to swallow a bacterium – a trick that neither cell possessed before – and against terrific odds the pair survived and multiplied. The archaeon gained a huge advantage – a previously unimaginable energy supply from the bacterium's sophisticated ATP factory. The bacterium also gained an advantage – it was protected and, over aeons, could specialise and concentrate entirely on producing energy for its host. If this theory is correct, the origin of complex life on Earth was a complete accident. Without access to the energy supply from the mitochondria, all the complexities of the eukaryotic cell, which are absolutely necessary for complex multicellular life, would never have evolved. Earth would be a living planet today, but a planet of prokaryotes, and certainly not home to a civilisation.

I cannot tell you which of these two theories is true. If it were obvious, then all academic biologists would agree. But my impression is that the fateful encounter is currently the more widely accepted theory, and if it is correct then this has very important consequences for estimating the probability of the evolution of intelligent life. Eukaryotes are absolutely essential for intelligence. There is no biologist who

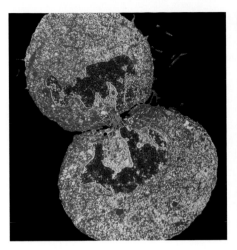 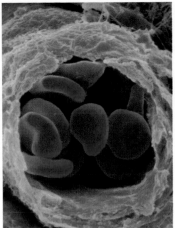 

would suggest that the prokaryotes, for all their ingenuity in developing photosynthesis and mitochondrial machinery, would have managed to construct radio telescopes given enough time and a following wind. Without eukaryotes, there would be only slime.

I think these are very important points to consider in the Drake Equation. If it is correct that at least two of the necessary foundations for the emergence of complex multicellular life on Earth arose from barely credible accidents, then they might be seen as potential bottlenecks in the evolution of intelligence elsewhere in the Milky Way.

So where are we in our attempt to estimate the chances that, given the origin of life on a planet, intelligence will arise? This is where we move from science to speculation and opinion, and with these caveats, let me give you my personal view.

Given the eukaryotic cell and an oxygen atmosphere, life on Earth became diverse and complex relatively quickly. It is almost certainly no coincidence that the Cambrian explosion followed soon after a rapid rise in the oxygen content of the atmosphere. Whether it is possible to claim that intelligence on the scale necessary to build a civilisation is likely given the right biological building blocks and enough time – half a billion years, let's say – is another question. We simply don't know, and the very specific conditions in the African Rift Valley that led to the emergence of early modern humans only 250,000 years ago might suggest that civilisation-level intelligence is a rare development, even given animals as sophisticated as primates, never mind a eukaryote and an oxygen atmosphere.

An optimist would assert that there are billions of potential homes for life in the Milky Way, and that since life emerged on Earth pretty much as soon as it could at the end of the violence of the Hadean, then the Milky Way must be teeming with life and therefore civilisations. I would agree that the Milky Way must be teeming with life – I think there is a sense of chemical inevitability about it. Even accepting this line of argument, however, a pessimist would surely point to the evolution of the eukaryotic cell and oxygenic photosynthesis as being potential bottlenecks. On Earth, it took life over three billion years to get to the eve of the Cambrian. That's three billion years of planetary stability – a quarter of the age of the universe. If just one of the necessary steps – the fateful encounter, let's say – was at the fortunate end of a probability distribution, then one can easily imagine that the 20 billion Earth-like worlds in the Milky Way could all be covered in prokaryotic slime. A living galaxy, yes, but a galaxy filled with intelligence? Given what we know about the ascent from prokaryote to civilisation on Earth, I'm not so sure.

A BRIEFEST MOMENT IN TIME

Let's take one final journey back to Green Bank in 1961. Drake and his colleagues, with far less evidence than we have today, concluded that our galaxy seems remarkably conducive to life, full of Earth-like worlds warmed by the glow of benign stars. They too believed that a good fraction of these billions of worlds must be home to life, and given that Darwin's law of evolution by natural selection must apply across the universe, they concluded that intelligence must have emerged on at least some of these planets. As I've argued above, I'm not so sure about intelligence, but we must at least consider the possibility that potential evolutionary bottlenecks like the eukaryotic cell and oxygenic photosynthesis aren't as bad as they might appear. In this case, the final term in the Drake Equation

becomes all-important. Perhaps it is L, the lifetime of civilisations, that is the fundamental reason for the great silence. This is a sobering thought. The reason we have made no contact with anyone is not because of a lack of stars, or planets, or living things; it's because of the in-built and unavoidable stupidity of intelligent beings.

This might seem a bit strong, but it is a view shared at Green Bank by Manhattan Project veteran Philip Morrison. Morrison was intimately involved in the design and development of the first atomic bomb, and he helped load Little Boy onto *Enola Gay* destined for Hiroshima. The fact that human beings had deployed a potentially civilisation-destroying weapon twice, against civilian targets, and that Morrison had personally loaded one of the bombs, must have never left him, and on the eve of the Cuban missile crisis, it must have seemed likely that we would do it again on a much grander scale.

Drake realised this as well, which is certainly one of the reasons why he introduced the time that a technological civilisation can endure into his equation: we can after all only communicate with nearby civilisations if they exist at the same time as us. This is a possible resolution to the Fermi Paradox. Civilisations inevitably blow themselves up soon after acquiring radio technology, and therefore the Milky Way will remain forever silent apart from the briefest, non-overlapping flickers of intelligence. This might seem like a solipsistic conceit; how can we possibly assume that human stupidity is universal? We can't, of course. But just as for the biological arguments we made against the inevitable emergence of complex life on an otherwise living world, we only have the Earth as a guide, and extrapolating from our own experience is the best we can do. On Earth, Rutherford discovered the atomic nucleus in 1911 and we destroyed two cities and killed over 200,000 of our fellow human beings with nuclear technology 34 years later. About 17 years after that, having seen the devastation nuclear weapons can cause, Khrushchev and Kennedy came close to ending it all, and to this day we don't know how close we came to eliminating the fruits of almost four billion years of evolution. Here on Earth it appears that sanity, perspective and an appreciation of the rarity and value of civilisation emerges after, and not before, the capability to build big bombs. We have the bombs, but I don't think enough of us have the rest. Why should other young civilisations be any different? If this is the reason for the Great Silence, then I suppose we might take comfort in the fact that we are not the only idiots to have existed in the Milky Way, but that's the coldest comfort I can imagine.

The above might be seen as a naïve rant, of course. One could argue that mutually assured destruction, the guiding principle of the Cold War, did act to stabilise our civilisation and is still doing so today. Perhaps no intelligent beings will knowingly destroy their civilisation, which is what global nuclear war on Earth would surely do; after all, Kennedy and Khrushchev ultimately took this view. Similarly, one assumes that the submersion of Miami and Norwich by rising sea levels would silence the so-called climate change sceptics (I'd call them something different) and trigger a change of policy that will avert catastrophic, civilisation-threatening climate change in good time. It seems to me, however, that a small planet such as Earth cannot continue to support an expanding and flourishing civilisation without a major change in the way we view ourselves. The division into hundreds of countries whose borders and interests are defined by imagined local differences and arbitrary religious dogma, both of which are utterly irrelevant and meaningless on a galactic scale, must surely be addressed if we are to confront global problems such as mutually assured destruction, asteroid threats, climate change, pandemic disease and who knows what else, and flourish beyond the twenty-first century. The very fact that the preceding sentence sounds hopelessly utopian might provide a plausible answer to the Great Silence.

**MELTING ICEBERG
IN GREENLAND**
The melting icecaps of Greenland are a reminder to us of the catastrophic threat we face from climate change and our wilful destruction of our planet.

SO, ARE WE ALONE?

What, then, is the range of estimates for the number of civilisations in the Milky Way, given the limited evidence we have at our disposal? During the filming of *Human Universe*, Frank Drake told me that the Green Bank meeting came up with a number of around 10,000, and he sees no reason to change that estimate. This would be wonderful, and makes the search for signals from these civilisations one of the great scientific quests of the twenty-first century. I strongly support SETI, because contact with just one alien civilisation would be the greatest discovery of all time, and it's worth the investment on that basis alone.

There is, however, one piece of evidence that might suggest a more lonely position for us on our little home world. In 1966 the mathematician and polymath John von Neumann published a series of lectures entitled 'Theory of Self Reproducing Automata' in which he analysed in great detail the possibility of constructing machines capable of building copies of themselves. Such machines exist in nature, of course – all living things do this routinely. In principle, therefore, one might imagine a sufficiently advanced civilisation building a self-replicating Von Neumann space probe and launching it out to explore the galaxy. On reaching a solar system, the probe would mine the planets, moons and asteroids, extracting the materials necessary to build one or more copies of itself. The newly minted probes would launch themselves out to neighbouring solar systems and repeat the process, spreading across the Milky Way. Even given the vast distances between the stars, computer models assuming currently envisioned rocketry technology suggest that such a strategy could result in the exploration of the entire Milky Way galaxy within a million years.

Science fiction? It certainly sounds like it, but if there is no objection in principle to the construction of a Von Neumann probe, then one has to develop an argument as to why we don't see any. The reason that this is difficult to do is due to timescales. The Milky Way has been capable of supporting life for over ten thousand million years. It is possible to envisage many millions of civilisations rising and falling over such vast expanses of time, and if only one had developed a successful Von Neumann probe, then the galaxy should be filled with its progeny; there should be at least one Von Neumann probe operating in our solar system today. Carl Sagan and the astronomer William Newman noticed a flaw in this line of argument. If the probes multiply exponentially and unchecked, then one can show that they consume the resources of the entire galaxy relatively quickly, and we'd certainly have noticed that! Or more accurately, we wouldn't be here to notice that. Sagan reasoned that this obvious risk would be sufficient to prevent any civilisation intelligent enough to build Von Neumann probes from actually doing so. They would be doomsday machines. Other astronomers have countered that it wouldn't be beyond the wit of such an advanced intellect to build in some fail-safe mechanism that guaranteed, for example, only one probe per solar system, or a finite lifetime for each probe. Others have argued that there may indeed be a Von Neumann probe operating in our solar system today, with appropriate fail-safe mechanisms installed to stop it eating everything. If such a probe were relatively small, perhaps sitting amongst the asteroids or even in the Kuiper Belt of icy comets beyond the orbit of Neptune, then we'd almost certainly be unaware of its presence.

Von Neumann probes wouldn't be the only signatures of ultra-advanced civilisations. Imagine a civilisation many millions of years ahead of us, carrying out engineering projects on galactic scale. Imagine interstellar starships or great space colonies constructed in otherwise uninhabitable solar systems. Why not? As I said at the start of this

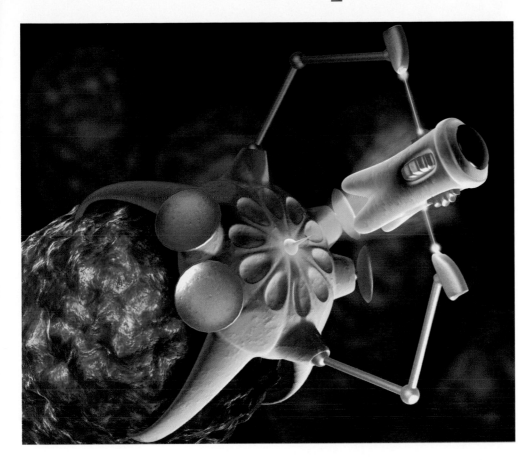

ENCOUNTERS WITH ROBOTS
Theoretically the first encounter of a space-faring civilisation is more likely to be with a self-replicating robot than with the actual life form. This computer artwork shows a nanorobot assembler using a claw to attach itself to a bacterium. One goal of nanotechnology like this is to design self-replicating systems, which would allow large manufacturing projects to become economically viable.

chapter, we went from the Wright Brothers to the Moon in a single human lifetime, so, I ask again, how far will we travel, if the laws of physics allow, given another thousand years? Or ten thousand? Or a million? What signature will we leave on the sky if we survive and prosper that long? None of these questions is trivial, because the sheer immensity of the timescales available for life to evolve in the Milky Way galaxy forces us to consider them. Why should we be the most advanced civilisation in the galaxy when we've only been building spacecraft for half a century in a 13-billion year-old universe? I don't have an answer to this. It bothers me. Perhaps the distances between the stars are indeed too great, or perhaps there are insurmountable difficulties in building self-replicating machines or starships, but I can't think what they might be.

I am tempted, therefore, to make the following argument for the purposes of debate. I think that advanced, space-faring civilisations are extremely rare, not because of astronomy, but because of biology. I think the fact that it took almost four billion years for a civilisation to appear on Earth is important. This is a third of the age of the universe, which is a very long time. Coupled with the remarkable contingency of the evolution of the eukaryotic cell and oxygenic photosynthesis – not to mention the half a billion years from the Cambrian explosion to the very recent emergence of Homo sapiens and civilisation – I think this implies that technological civilisations are stupendously rare, colossally fortuitous accidents that happen on average in much fewer than one in every two hundred billion solar systems. This is my resolution to the Fermi Paradox. We are the first civilisation to emerge in the Milky Way, and we are alone. That is my opinion, and given our cavalier disregard for our own safety, it terrifies me. What do you think?

WHO ARE WE?

But why, some say, the moon?
Why choose this as our goal?
And they may well ask why climb the highest mountain?
Why, 35 years ago, fly the Atlantic? ...
We choose to go to the moon.

President John F. Kennedy

SPACEMAN

Astronaut John Young was once asked how he would feel if his epitaph read 'John Young: The Ultimate Explorer'. Young smiled, and in a test pilot's drawl replied, 'I'd feel sorry for the guy who wrote it'. Young was, and still is, a hero of mine. My first vivid memory of live space exploration was watching Space Shuttle Columbia climb on a tower of bright vapour into a blue Cape sky on 12 April 1981. It was midday in Manchester, the Easter holidays, and I was 13 years old. Because of a two-day launch delay, Columbia's test flight took place precisely 20 years to the day after Yuri Gagarin made his black-and-white voyage into orbit on 12 April 1961, but Young and his co-pilot, Bob Crippen, in their orange spacesuits, were astronauts from the colour age, the future – as distant from the Russian hero as gleaming white-winged Columbia was from *Vostok 1*. Equidistant from both was Apollo, which Young flew to the Moon. Twice. It was the age of optimism, the age of wonder, the golden age when the ape went into space. When unflappable aviator Young, whose pulse rate did not increase during the launch of NASA's only manned spacecraft ever to have flown without an un-manned test flight, piloted Columbia back for a flawless manual landing at Edwards Air Force Base two days later, he turned to Crippen and said 'We're not too far away – the human race isn't – from going to the stars'.

In 2014 the stars feel further away than they did in 1981; the International Space Station is a wonderful piece of engineering that has allowed us to learn how to live and work in near-Earth orbit, but it is no closer to the stars than Columbia. Its construction is no mean achievement; one of the most important things to realise about engineering at the edge is that the only way to learn is to actually do it. You can't think your way into space; you have to fly there. But I can't help but feel, in the words of Billy Bragg, that the space race is over and we've all grown up too soon.

It was different in Gagarin's day. Nobody is born to be a spaceman. We're apes, honed by natural selection to operate in the Great Rift Valley. Gagarin's father was a carpenter and his mother was a milkmaid. Both worked on a collective farm. Gagarin's first job at the age of 16 was in a steel mill, but after showing an aptitude for flight as an air cadet he joined the military when 21 and was posted to the First Chkalovsk Air Force Pilots School in Orenburg. Rising through the ranks, he made a name for himself as a skilled and intelligent aviator, and in early 1960 he was chosen along with 19 other elite pilots for the newly established space programme. Standing just 5 foot 2 inches tall, Gagarin had the right stuff and was perfect for the tiny *Vostok* spacecraft, whose single-seat crew compartment was only 2.3m in external diameter. After a year of training, Nikolai Kamanin, head of the cosmonaut programme, chose Gagarin ahead of his rival, Gherman Titov, just four days before the flight. The history books are filled with the names of great men and women whose presence in the collective memory of humanity was assured by the slimmest of margins. Gagarin, alongside Armstrong, will be remembered for as long as there are humans in the cosmos; the name of the equally brilliant Titov, Russia's second cosmonaut, has faded away.

Gagarin's flight was a true journey into the unknown. Strapped on top of the Vostok-K rocket, which flew 13 times and made it into space on 11 occasions, the 27-year-old performed like a true test pilot. Despite a two-hour delay during which every component of the spacecraft hatch was taken apart and rebuilt while Gagarin remained strapped into his seat, his heart rate was recorded at 64 beats per minute just before launch. This is not to say that Gagarin wasn't fully aware of what he was about to do. Before boarding, Gagarin made one of the great speeches of the age.

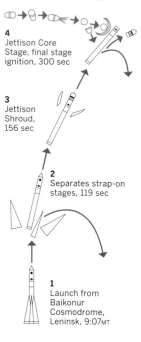

VOSTOK'S ORBIT OF EARTH

6 Begin orientation for retro burn at 800km from landing site, 9:51MT

7 Retro burn and instrument module separation, 10:25MT. Begin re-entry, 10:35MT

4 Jettison Core Stage, final stage ignition, 300 sec

3 Jettison Shroud, 156 sec

2 Separates strap-on stages, 119 sec

1 Launch from Baikonur Cosmodrome, Leninsk, 9:07MT

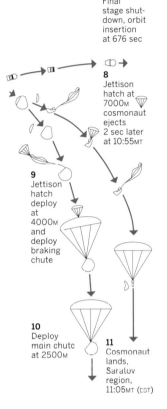

5
Final stage shut-down, orbit insertion at 676 sec

8
Jettison hatch at 7000м cosmonaut ejects 2 sec later at 10:55мт

9
Jettison hatch deploy at 4000м and deploy braking chute

10
Deploy main chute at 2500м

11
Cosmonaut lands, Saratov region, 11:05мт (ЕST)

THE SPACE RACE BEGINS
Vostok 1 ensured the Soviets and spaceman Yuri Gagarin secured a place in the history books. On 12 April 1961, *Vostok* and Gagarin successfully made the first manned flight into space. The race was on in space exploration.

'Dear friends, both known and unknown to me, fellow Russians, and people of all countries and continents, in a few minutes a mighty spaceship will carry me into the far-away expanses of space. What can I say to you in these last minutes before the start? At this instant, the whole of my life seems to be condensed into one wonderful moment. Everything I have experienced and done till now has been in preparation for this moment. You must realise that it is hard to express my feeling now that the test for which we have been training long and passionately is at hand. I don't have to tell you what I felt when it was suggested that I should make this flight, the first in history. Was it joy? No, it was something more than that. Pride? No, it was not just pride. I felt great happiness. To be the first to enter the cosmos, to engage single-handed in an unprecedented duel with nature – could anyone dream of anything greater than that? But immediately after that I thought of the tremendous responsibility I bore: to be the first to do what generations of people had dreamed of; to be the first to pave the way into space for mankind. This responsibility is not toward one person, not toward a few dozen, not toward a group. It is a responsibility toward all mankind – toward its present and its future. Am I happy as I set off on this space flight? Of course I'm happy. After all, in all times and epochs the greatest happiness for man has been to take part in new discoveries. It is a matter of minutes now before the start. I say to you, "Until we meet again", dear friends, just as people say to each other when setting out on a long journey. I would like very much to embrace you all, people known and unknown to me, close friends and strangers alike. See you soon!'

HERO OF HIS TIME
Yuri Gagarin's flight into space made headline news in the Soviet Union and internationally, and his name and fame have endured through history in his home country and across the world.

ТРИУМФ ЭРЬ

Весь мир восхищен бесприме

It's too easy to attach trite labels to human actions – magnificent, horrific and everything in between – based on a simplified view of their causes. One can argue that the rockets carried aloft the egos of the superpowers alongside the astronauts, and this is surely right. But Gagarin spoke these words, and I challenge anyone to read them and not detect sincerity. All our actions mask a morass of motivations, worthy and less so, and the greatest human adventures are no less noble for that.

At 9.07am local time, Gagarin blasted off from Baikonur Cosmodrome in Kazakhstan, as every Russian cosmonaut has done since. Within 10 minutes, he was orbiting Earth at an altitude of 380 kilometres. His route took him across the Siberian wastes and the Pacific Ocean above the Hawaiian islands, past the tip of South America and into the South Atlantic, where he was greeted by a second sunrise before a 42-second de-orbit burn over the Angolan coast slowed *Vostok 1* into a parabolic orbit and an 8-g deceleration inside Earth's thickening atmosphere. The journey once around his home world took 1 hour and 48 minutes. Gagarin ejected from the capsule 7 kilometres above ground and, as planned, cosmonaut and spacecraft completed the final descent apart. Gliding back to Earth by parachute, Gagarin landed 280 kilometres away from the intended landing site near the Russian city of Engels. Dressed in orange spacesuit and white helmet, a farmer and his daughter bore sole witness to his historic return. 'When they saw me in my space suit and the parachute dragging alongside as I walked, they started to back away in fear,' recollected Gagarin later. 'I told them, don't be afraid, I am a Soviet citizen like you, who has descended from space and I must find a telephone to call Moscow!'

EVOLUTION OF HOMINIDS

These hominid evolutionary trees trace our genetic history as humans to the Old World monkeys that roamed Earth 25 million years ago. Discoveries of various remains, including those of the famous *Australopithecus afarensis* skeleton, commonly called Lucy, have helped us piece together an idea of our ancestry. It is believed that around 7 or 8 million years ago we split from the chimpanzees and the process of evolution onto bipedal Homo sapiens began as these monkeys started to spend more time on the ground than in the trees.

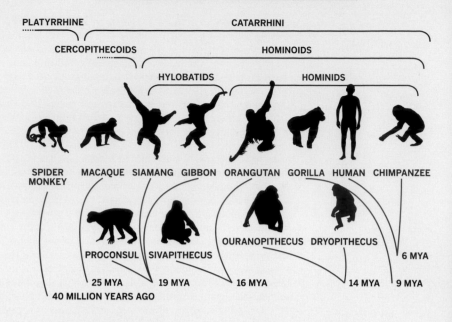

HOMINID EVOLUTION

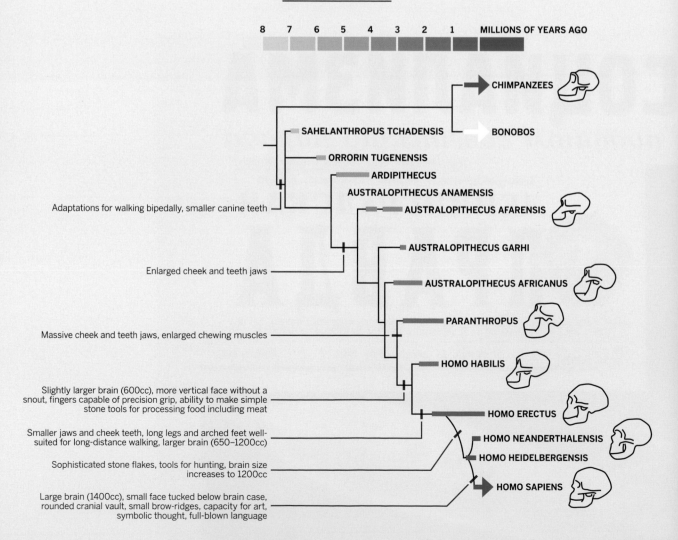

APEMAN

Primates appeared relatively recently in the history of life on Earth. Studies of mitochondrial DNA suggest the Strepsirrhini suborder, containing the ancestors of Madagascar's lemurs, diverged from our own Haplorhini suborder approximately 64 million years ago, which implies that a common ancestor was present before this time, but not a great deal earlier. The first complete primate fossil found to date is that of a tree-dwelling creature known as *Archicebus achilles*, dated at 55 million years old. Discovered in the fossil beds of central China in 2013, this tiny creature would have been no bigger than a human hand, making it not only the oldest but also one of the smallest known primates.

Our family, known as the Hominidae, or more commonly the great apes, share a common ancestor with Old World monkeys around 25 million years ago, and during the making of *Human Universe* we filmed a rare species of these distant cousins in the Ethiopian Highlands. The road out of Addis towards the 3000-metre Guassa Plateau is excellent to a point, and then not excellent. The scenery, on the other hand, improves with altitude. Golden grasses illuminated by shifting lambent light through dark clouds cling to near-vertical mountainsides framing pristine villages along the high valley floors. It is fresh, cold and insect-less on the peaks above the Rift; a place to drink tea and eat *shiro*, a spiced Ethiopian stew of chickpeas and lentils. After a night in the cold but magnificently desolate Guassa community lodge, we set off at dawn to intercept the gelada baboons on their way back to their caves and ledges from early-morning foraging expeditions on the higher slopes.

The gelada baboons are a species of Old World monkey found only in the Ethiopian Highlands. They are the only surviving species of the genus Theropithecus that once thrived across Africa and into Southern Europe and India. The males in particular are powerful, long-haired animals, weighing over 20 kilograms with a bright red flash of skin on their white chests. I was told not to look them in the eye, so I didn't. Fifty thousand years ago, as our planet emerged from the last ice age, the gelada retreated into the highlands above the Rift where they still live, uniquely amongst extant primates, as graminivores, on a diet made up almost entirely of the tough high-altitude grasses and occasional herbs.

EARTH'S EARLIEST PRIMATE
Found within a rock in the Hubei Province of central China, this is the oldest complete fossil of a tree-dwelling primate found to date.

They approach with nonchalant agility in small groups, which reflect the most complex social structure of any non-human primate. Most of the groups I saw contained one or two males and perhaps eight or ten females and their young. These are referred to as reproductive units, and clearly defined hierarchies exist within them. Females usually remain in the same unit for life, but males move between them every four or five years. There are also male-only units of ten or fifteen individuals. These social units are arranged into higher groupings known as bands, herds and communities. The community we encountered numbered several hundred individuals who wandered past in their little tribes, females and young pausing to eat, groom and play whilst the larger males eyed us closely.

Despite the 25-million-year separation in evolutionary time, the gelada are very easy to anthropomorphise, especially from a vantage point amongst them, probably because their behaviour seems reminiscent of

our own and their babies are cute. Like us, they spend most of their time on the ground and operate in social groups. Some researchers familiar with the geladas claim they exhibit the most sophisticated communication behaviour of any non-human primate, employing gestures and a range of different vocalisations strung together into sequences communicating reassurance, appeasement, solicitation, aggression and defence. For all their sophistication, however, the gelada are a long way from possessing anything more complex than the simplest of human characteristics and abilities. This is, of course, an utterly obvious observation – they are monkeys! But what isn't obvious is why. The gelada separated from our common ancestor at the same time, but that self-evident statement leads to a deeper question: what is it that happened to our ancestors during those 25 million years that led us to the stars and left them on the hillsides of the Guassa Plateau eating grass?

OLD WORLD MONKEYS
The gelada baboons (*Theropithecus gelada*) are found in the grassland areas of the Ethiopian Highlands. They are the only surviving species of the genus Theropithecus that once thrived across Africa and into Southern Europe and India.

LUCY IN THE SKY

I am an aviation geek. I love aircraft. As I set off to film the African scenes for 'ApeMan SpaceMan', I noticed that the Ethiopian Airlines Boeing 787 I boarded at London Heathrow, bound for Addis Ababa, registration ET-AOS, was named 'Lucy'.

On the morning of 24 November 1974, Donald Johanson and a team of archaeologists were searching for bone fragments at a site near the Awash River in Ethiopia. The area was known to be a site rich in rare hominid fossils, but on that particular morning, Johanson and his graduate student Tom Gray found little to inspire them. As is often the way in science, however, a dash of serendipity coupled with an experienced scientist who understands how to increase the chances of receiving its benefits, made a seminal contribution to the understanding of human evolution. Johanson shouldn't even have been there – he had planned to spend time back at the camp updating his field notes – but as they prepared to leave, Johanson decided to wander over to a previously excavated gully and have one last look. Even though they'd surveyed the area before, this time Johanson's eye was drawn to something lying partially hidden on the slope. Closer inspection revealed it to be an arm bone and a host of other skeletal fragments – a piece of skull, a thigh bone, vertebra, ribs and jaw all emerged from the ground and, crucially, they were all part of a single female skeleton. The find triggered a three-week excavation, during which every last scrap of fossil AL 288-1 was recovered. They named it Lucy, after track 3, side one, of *Sgt. Pepper's Lonely Hearts Club Band*, because this was 1974 and they played it a lot on their tape recorder. 'Home taping kills music', they used to say back then, but it also names airliners.

Lucy lived 3.2 million years ago in the open savannah of Ethiopia's Afar Depression. Standing just over 1 metre tall and weighing less than 30 kilograms, she would have looked more ape like than a human. Her brain was small, about one-third of the size of a modern human's and not much larger than a chimpanzee's. The anatomy of her knee, the curve of her spine and the length of her leg bones suggest that Lucy regularly walked upright on two legs, although there are a handful of scientists who would disagree. What is generally agreed upon, however, is that Lucy was a member of the extinct hominin species *Australopithecus afarensis*, and she was either one of our direct ancestors, or very closely related to them. Her bipedalism was probably an evolutionary adaptation caused by climate change in the Rift. As the number of trees reduced and the landscape became more savannah-like, the arboreal existence of our more distant ancestors became less favoured, and the increasing distances between trees selected for Australopithecus's upright gait made travel across the ground more efficient.

In 'Who Speaks for Earth?', the thirteenth chapter of Carl Sagan's *Cosmos*, there are two pictures set side by side. One is of footprints covered by volcanic ash 3.7 million years ago near Laetoli, in Tanzania, probably made by an Australopithecus afarensis like Lucy. Some 400,000 kilometres away and 3.7 million years later, another hominin footprint was left in the dust of the Sea of Tranquility. Together, they speak eloquently of our unlikely, magnificent ascent from the Rift Valley to the stars. The remainder of this chapter deals with the 3 million years between Lucy and the Moon. The timescale is ridiculously small; less than a tenth of one per cent of the period of time during which life has existed on Earth. Lucy was little more than an upright chimpanzee; an animal, a genetic survival machine. We bring art, science, literature and meaning to the Earth; we are a world away, and yet separated by the blink of an eye. 'Our obligation to survive is owed not just to ourselves but also to that Cosmos, ancient and vast, from which we spring,' wrote Sagan. I'd like to add that we owe it to Lucy as well.

FROM THE NORTH STAR
TO THE STARS

Before astrology was consigned to the status of trifling funfair entertainment by science, it was believed that the position of the planets against the distant stars had a profound effect on people's daily lives. If you don't know what the stars or planets actually are, this is at least within the bounds of reason, but as our understanding of physics improved, so it became clear that there is no way that the position of a distant planet relative to the fixed stars can have any effect on the behaviour of a human being on the surface of the Earth. The planets can and do affect the Earth's motion through the Solar System over timescales far greater than those of human lifetimes, though, and recent research suggests that long-term changes in Earth's orientation and orbit may have played a crucial role in hominid evolution.

Polaris is a true giant, almost 50 times the diameter of our sun. It is also a Cepheid variable, one of the valuable standard candles upon which the astronomical distance scale rests. At a distance of only 434 light years, it is both the closest Cepheid and one of the brighter stars in the sky, dominating the constellation Ursa Minor. Polaris also happens to be aligned directly with the Earth's spin axis, and this special position on the celestial North Pole makes it invaluable to navigators. As the Earth spins on its axis, Polaris sits serenely as all other stars rotate around it. At any point in the northern hemisphere, your latitude is the angle between Polaris and the horizon; zero degrees north at the Equator, where Polaris is on the horizon, and 90 degrees north at the Pole where Polaris is directly overhead. As viewed from Oldham, Lancashire, UK, Polaris sits at an angle of 53.54 degrees above the horizon.

Christopher Columbus and Ferdinand Magellan relied on Polaris as they crossed the oceans and explored new worlds. Perhaps more surprisingly, on board Apollo 8 Jim Lovell carried a sextant as a back-up navigational device. Designed by the MIT instrument laboratory in Cambridge, Massachusetts, it may not have looked traditional but it operated in exactly the same manner as the one constructed by instrument maker John Bird in 1757. Polaris was one of Apollo's key navigational stars. It was paired with Gamma Cassiopeia on Lovell's charts, which was known in Apollo jargon as 'Navi'. The name was coined by Gus Grissom on Apollo 1 as a prank – it was his middle name 'Ivan' backwards. Two other navigational stars, Gamma Velorum and Iota Ursa Major, were named 'Regor' after Roger Chaffee and 'Dnoces' after Ed White the 'Second'. Using the stars for navigation might seem hopelessly old-fashioned, but if you think about it for a moment, you'll realise that there is no other way that a spacecraft in deep space can orient itself, other than relative to the fixed stars on the celestial sphere.

A spacecraft will often shift its position relative to the stars, but on Earth, things feel different because our orbit around the Sun is relatively stable from year to year. There are wobbles on relatively short timescales associated with changes in the speed of Earth's rotation, and these lead to the insertion of leap seconds to keep our atomic clocks synchronised with the heavens. Between 1972 and 1979, nine leap seconds had to be inserted, whilst none was needed between the beginning of 1999 and the end of 2005. Earth's rotation rate is noticeably chaotic when compared to the accuracy of atomic clocks.

The largest short-term contribution to changes in Earth's rotation comes from the gravitational influence of the Moon, which acts to slow down the rate of spin by around 2.3 milliseconds per century due to friction between the tidal bulges in the oceans and the rotating solid Earth beneath, but there are also longer-term changes. The most pronounced of

NAVIGATING THE STARS
Frank Borman, spacecraft commander on the Apollo 8 mission, relied on the latest technology to explore new worlds, but knowing that colleague Jim Lovell had brought his sextant with him if technology failed them!

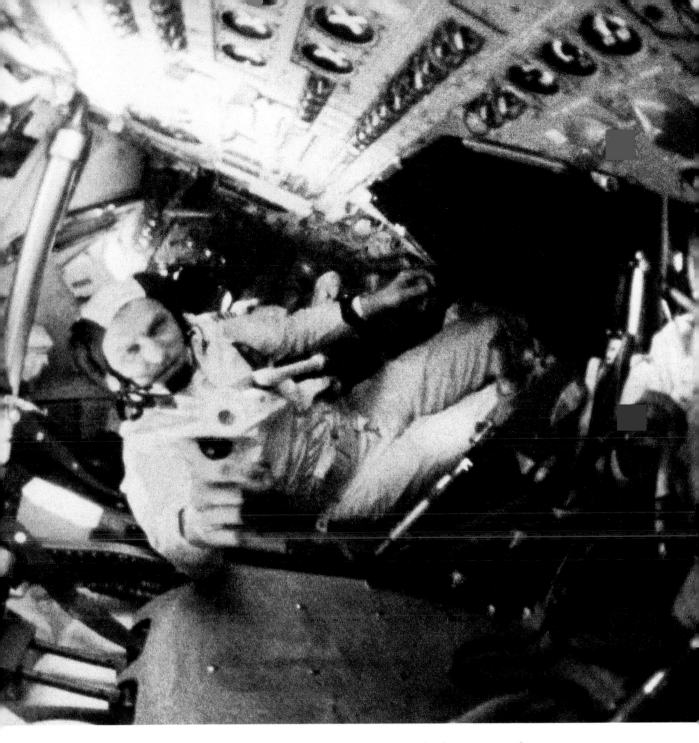

these is known as axial precession or, more commonly, the precession of the equinoxes. The Earth spins on its axis like a gyroscope, and because it spins, it bulges out at the Equator. Because the Earth isn't a perfect sphere, the gravitational influence of the Sun and Moon exerts a torque on the Earth that causes its spin axis to sweep around in a circle once every 26,000 years. This is not subtle, because the spin axis itself is tilted at 23 degrees relative to the plane of Earth's orbit, and precession therefore has a large effect on the night sky that was first documented by the Greek astronomer Hipparchus, around 150 BCE. Precession manifests itself as a shift in the position of the celestial pole relative to the fixed stars. There will come a time in the not too distant future when Polaris will no longer sit above the celestial North Pole as our spin axis traces out a circle in the sky. In about 3000 years' time, navigators of the future will rely on Gamma Cephei as a back-up for their GPS systems as they sail across the seas of our planet, and in 8000 years it will be the bright star Deneb. The identity of the North Star has altered many times throughout human history. As the Egyptians finished building the Great Pyramid of Giza in 2560 BCE, Alpha Draconis lay closest to the celestial pole. Two and a half thousand years later, as the Romans did things for us, Kochab, the second-brightest star in Ursa Minor, and its neighbour Pherkad were known as the 'Guardians of the Pole'. Precession therefore affects navigation, but more importantly it also affects our climate.

The 23-degree tilt of Earth's spin axis is responsible for the seasons; summer in the northern hemisphere occurs when the North Pole is tilted towards the Sun, leading to constant daylight within the Arctic Circle. Half a year later and the geometry is reversed, with the South Pole receiving 24-hour daylight and the southern hemisphere experiencing summer. Precession alone would have no effect on the climate if the Earth's orbit were a perfect circle, but it isn't; it is elliptical, with the Sun at one focus. At the turn of the twenty-first century, it happens to be the case that the Earth is at its closest approach to the Sun (known as perihelion) in January, just after the winter solstice when the North Pole is pointing away from the Sun. This makes northern winters slightly milder than they would otherwise be, because the Earth receives a little bit more solar radiation during the northern winter. In around 10,000 years' time, however, precession will have carried the Earth's spin axis around by a half-turn, and it will be the North Pole that points towards the Sun at perihelion, making northern hemisphere summers slightly warmer and winters cooler. The more elliptical the Earth's orbit, the more pronounced this effect.

This is where things get a little more complicated, but it's the complication that matters for our story. The planets are significantly further away than the Moon, but also significantly more massive, and their constantly shifting positions induce periodic changes to our orbit over long timescales. Jupiter has the most pronounced effect due to its large mass and relative proximity. The largest of these changes occurs on a timescale of 400,000 years. Picture the Earth's orbit becoming periodically more elliptical and more circular, stretching back and forth with a period of 400,000 years. This oscillation modulates the effect of precession on the climate; at the times when the Earth's orbit is at its most elliptical, the changes due to precession will be at their most pronounced. This effect is known as astronomical or orbital forcing of the climate.

There are many such resonances in Earth's orbit – another important change in the eccentricity of the ellipse occurs every 100,000 years. Furthermore, the tilt of the axis itself swings back and forth between around 22 and 25 degrees on a 41,000-year cycle. The whole solar system is like a giant bell, ringing with many hundreds of harmonics driven by the gravitational interactions between the Sun, planets and moons.

Over many thousands of years, these shifts in the Earth's orbit and orientation relative to the Sun have led to dramatic changes in climate, and are certainly one of the key mechanisms that drive the Earth into and out of ice ages. It is perhaps obvious that these long-term shifts in climate should have had an effect on the evolution of life; ice ages present a significant challenge to animals and plants and this will provoke an evolutionary response via natural selection. More surprisingly, recent research has suggested a direct link between precession, the 400,000-year eccentricity cycle, and the evolution of early modern humans.

ASTRONOMICAL SEASONS

The Milankovitch theory describes the collective effects of changes in the Earth's movements upon its climate. They are named after Serbian geophysicist and astronomer Milutin Milankovitch, who worked on it during his internment as a prisoner in World War One. Milankovitch mathematically theorised that variations in eccentricity, axial tilt and precession of the Earth's orbit determined climatic patterns on Earth. The Earth's axis completes one full cycle of precession approximately every 26,000 years. At the same time, the elliptical orbit rotates over a much longer timescale. The combined effect of the two precessions leads to a 21,000-year period between the astronomical seasons and the orbit. In addition, the angle between Earth's rotational axis and the normal to the plane of its orbit (obliquity) oscillates between 22.1 and 24.5 degrees on a 41,000-year cycle. It is currently 23.44 degrees and decreasing.

THE PRECESSION OF EARTH'S SPIN AXIS

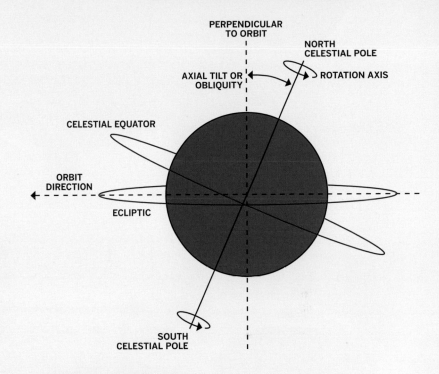

PERPENDICULAR TO ORBIT

NORTH CELESTIAL POLE

AXIAL TILT OR OBLIQUITY

ROTATION AXIS

CELESTIAL EQUATOR

ORBIT DIRECTION

ECLIPTIC

SOUTH CELESTIAL POLE

THE PRECESSION OF THE EQUINOXES

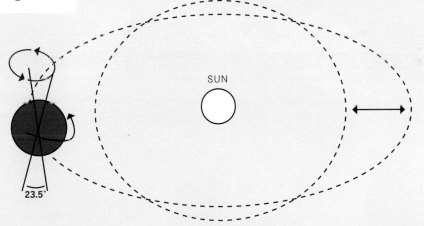

The Earth wobbles like a top on its axis over a 20,000-year cycle

SUN

The tilt of the Earth's axis changes over a 40,000-year interval

23.5°

The shape of its orbit changes the Earth's distance from the Sun over a period of 100,000 years

MILANKOVITCH CYCLES

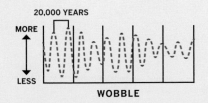

20,000 YEARS

MORE

LESS

WOBBLE

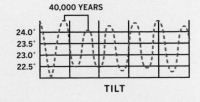

40,000 YEARS

24.0°
23.5°
23.0°
22.5°

TILT

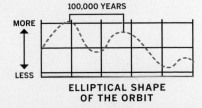

100,000 YEARS

MORE

LESS

ELLIPTICAL SHAPE OF THE ORBIT

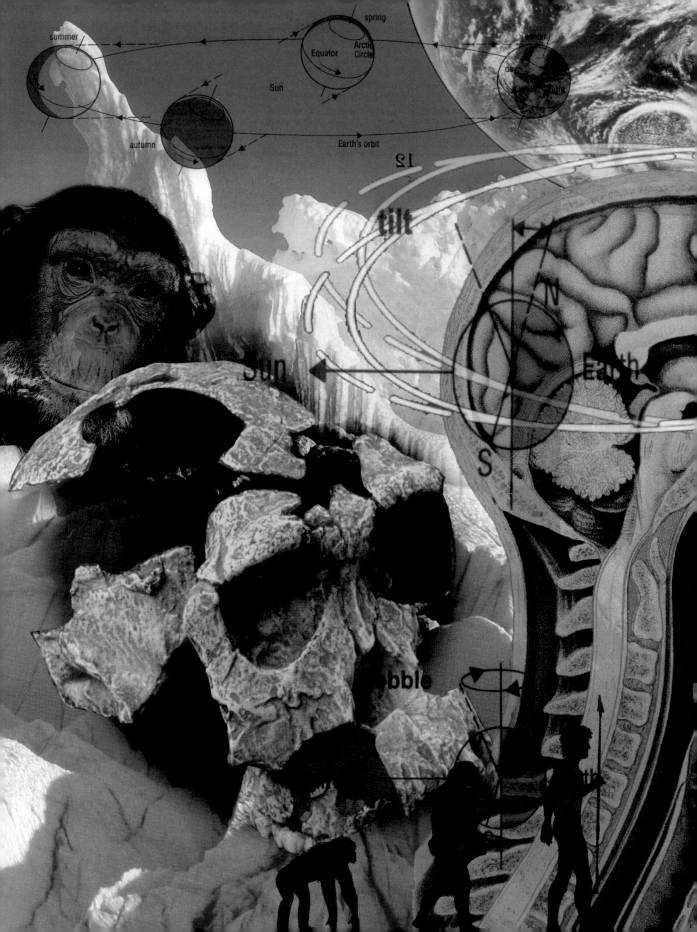

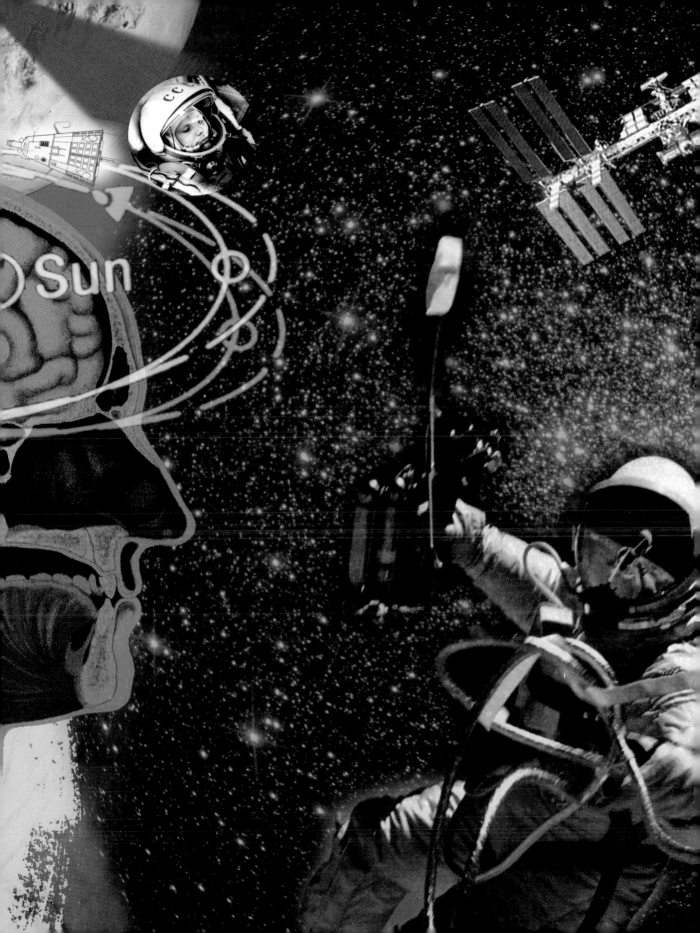

CLIMATE CHANGE IN THE RIFT VALLEY
AND HUMAN EVOLUTION

The Great Rift Valley; evocative words that immediately suggest origins. There are many reasons I love visiting Ethiopia. I love the people. I love the food. I love the high-altitude freshness of Addis. I love the mountains and valleys and high plains. I even loved visiting Erta Ale, the legendary shield volcano at the Afar Triple Junction known as the gateway to hell, although I probably won't do it again. But I also love an idea. It's impossible to visit this ancient country and not catch a glimpse in your peripheral vision of a chain of ghosts stretching back ten thousand generations, because it is

firmly embedded in popular culture that we came from here. Every one of us is related to someone who lived in Ethiopia hundreds of thousands of years ago. It is the Garden of Eden, the place where humanity began. What popular culture has yet to assimilate, however, is the fortuitous and precarious nature of the ascent of man. When I was growing up I remember talk of 'the missing link', that elusive fossil that would tie us definitively to our ape-like ancestors. When I started school, DNA sequencing was not yet invented, and Lucy hadn't been unearthed. Today, we have a significantly more complete view of how Australopithecines like Lucy are related to modern humans, and whilst the details are still debated and new evidence is continually updating the standard model of hominin evolution, it is now possible to tell the broad sweep of the story in some detail.

GATEWAY TO HELL?
The Erta Ale basaltic shield volcano is located in the Danakil depression in Ethiopia. It has an active lava lake around 100 metres in diameter. This lava lake is part of the summit caldera; the constant motion of the lava lake's surface resembles plate tectonics on a smaller scale.

CRANIAL CAPACITY

The internal volume of the primate skull increases from 275–500cc in chimpanzees to 1130–1260cc in modern humans. Neanderthals had a brain capacity in the range 1500–1800cc – the largest of any hominids. Recent research indicates that, in primates, whole brain size is a better measure of cognitive abilities.

CHIMPANZEE SKULL

AUSTRALOPITHECINE SKULL

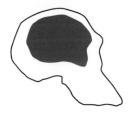

HUMAN SKULL

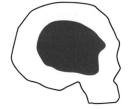

The members of our human evolutionary family are referred to as hominins. The split between hominins and the ancestor of the chimpanzee occurred at some point before 5 million years ago in Africa, and by 4 million years ago, Australopithecus afarensis – Lucy – was present. Their brain size was approximately 500cc, around the same as a chimpanzee and less than one-third of that of a modern human. Around 1.8 million years ago, there was a step change in both brain size and the number of hominin species in the East African Rift. Several species of our genus Homo appeared, including Homo habilis and Homo erectus. They lived for a time alongside other species, including several Australopithecines and a genus known as Paranthropus. There are anthropologists who prefer to classify Paranthropus as a different species of Australopithecus. I make this point not to be confusing, but to highlight an important fact; the study of hominin evolution is a difficult area, and it is not surprising that there are ongoing debates about the classification of 2-million-year-old fossils and DNA sequences. What is important for our story, however, and what nobody disputes, is that there seems to have been a jump in both brain size and the number of species of hominins in the Rift Valley region around 1.8 million years ago. By around 1.4 million years ago, only one of these species had survived – Homo erectus – with a brain size of 1000cc. The next milestone is the appearance of Homo heidelbergensis around 800,000 years ago. Homo heidelbergensis is generally accepted to be the ancestor of Homo sapiens and the Neanderthals who lived alongside us in Europe until around 45,000 years ago, and possibly later. Homo heidelbergensis represented another jump in brain size, up to around 1400cc, which is close to that of modern humans.

In the late 1960s and early 1970s, two hominin skulls were found near the Omo River in Ethiopia. Known as Omo 1 and Omo 2, argon dating of the volcanic sediments around the level they were found dates them at 195,000+/-5000 years old. These are the earliest fossilised remains to have been identified as Homo sapiens.

The interesting question is what caused these rapid increases in brain size, driving hominin intelligence from the chimpanzee-like capabilities of Australopithecus to modern humans in only a few million years. Again, this is a very active area of research, and there are differences of opinion amongst experts. This is the nature of science at the frontier of knowledge, and this is what makes science exciting and successful. The model we are focusing on is the most widely accepted theory of human evolution. It is known as the recent single origin hypothesis, or more colloquially the 'Out of Africa' model, and the dates and locations we have described so far might be referred to as 'text book'. There is broad consensus, therefore, about the 'When?' and the 'Where?'. But not 'Why?', and it is to 'Why?' that we now turn.

The figure on page 143 is reproduced from a paper published in 2013 by Shultz and Maslin. The lower figure shows the cranial capacity, or brain size, of skulls found in the Rift Valley, plotted against their age. The skulls are labelled according to their species. There is a trend towards larger brain size over the 4 million years since the emergence of Australopithecus, but the trend is not gradual. As we noted above, there is a large jump around 1.8 million years ago with the emergence of Homo erectus, and another jump just under 1 million years ago with Homo heidelbergensis. The final jump occurs when Homo sapiens emerges 200,000 years ago. The time period around 1.8 million years ago also corresponds to a leap in the number of hominin species present in the Rift Valley; there were at least five or six species living side by side, suggesting that something interesting occurred around this time which may have been responsible for, or was a contributing factor to, the observed increase in brain size, particularly in Homo erectus. A suggestion as to what this might have been can be seen in the top figure, which shows a measure

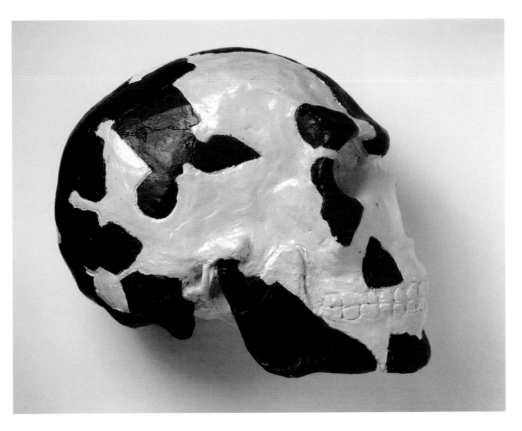

of the rate of appearance and disappearance of deep-water lakes in the Rift Valley. The large number of lakes appearing temporarily around 1.8 million years ago indicates that at this time the climate, and in particular the level of rainfall, was varying quickly and violently. Similar climate variation occurs around 1 million years ago and 200,000 years ago, and this appears to be correlated with increase in hominin brain size. The theory is that rapidly changing climatic conditions in the Rift Valley at these specific times played an important role in driving the increases in brain size. The selection pressures that may have led to these increases are unclear. Selection for adaptability was probably an important factor, but social factors such as the ability to live in large groups, and intra-species competition as a result of the larger number of species living side by side, particularly around 1.8 million years ago, must also have played a role. Having said that, it does appear that climate variation in the Rift Valley 1.8 million, 1 million and 200,000 years ago could have been a contributing factor to the development of our intelligence. This is known as the Pulse Climate Variability hypothesis.

We can now bring all these threads together to reveal a surprising and, for me, dizzying hypothesis which, if correct, sheds new light on the immensely contingent nature of the existence of our modern civilisation – or, in simpler language, why we are bloody lucky to be here!

The three dates – 1.8 million, 1 million and 200,000 years ago – correspond to the times when the Earth's orbit was at its most elliptical. As described above, the mechanism by which climate changes due to precession at these times is well understood. The Pulse Climate Variability hypothesis asserts that the unique geology and position of the Great Rift Valley amplified these changes, and that early hominins responded by increasing their brain size. If this is correct, our brains evolved as a response to changes in the Earth's orbit, driven by the precise

TRACES OF HUMAN PAST
Omo 1 and Omo 2 are the earliest fossilised remains of Homo sapiens so far recovered. The partial skulls will help scientists in their quest to uncover the secrets of our evolution.

BRAIN POWER
The human brain is the most complex physical structure we know of anywhere in the universe. There are around 85 billion neurons in the average human brain – that's comparable to the number of stars in an average galaxy.

arrangement of the orbits of the other planets around the Sun, and precession, driven primarily by the gravitational interaction between the Moon and Earth's axial tilt, both of which date back to a collision early in the history of the solar system, and all this is plainly blind luck. Without an inconceivably unlikely set of coincidences, and the way these conspired together to change the climate in one system of valleys in wonderful Ethiopia, we wouldn't exist.

If this is correct, then what a response! I held a brain for the cameras at St Paul's teaching hospital in Addis. It is the most complex single object in the known universe, a most intricate example of emergent complexity assembled over 4 billion years by natural selection operating within the constraints placed upon it by the laws of physics and the particular biochemistry of life on Earth. It contains around 85 billion individual neurons, which is of the same order as the number of stars in an average galaxy. But that doesn't begin to describe its complexity. Each neuron is thought to make between 10,000 and 100,000 connections to other neurons, making the brain a computer way beyond anything our current technology can simulate. When we do manage to simulate one, I have no doubt that sentience will emerge; consciousness is not magic, it is an emergent property consistent with the known laws of nature. But that doesn't lessen the wonder one iota. Out of this evolutionary marvel, we emerge. Thoughts, feelings, hopes and dreams exist on Earth because of electrical activity inside a 1.5-kilogram blob of stuff, which hasn't changed much since the earliest modern humans began the long journey out of Africa. If you could travel back in time and bring a newborn baby from 200,000 years ago into the twenty-first century, allowing it to grow up in our modern society with a modern education, it could achieve anything a modern child could. It could even become an astronaut. Which sets up one more question: if the hardware was present 200,000 years ago, then what changed to lift us from the Great Rift Valley into space?

CRANIOFACIAL DEVELOPMENT

Homo neanderthalensis has a unique combination of features on its skull that is distinct from fossil and extant 'anatomically modern' modern humans. Modern research involving morphological evidence, direct isotopic dates and fossil mitochondrial DNA from three Neanderthals indicates that the Neanderthals were a separate evolutionary lineage for at least 500,000 years. However, it is unknown when and how Neanderthal's unique craniofacial features emerged.

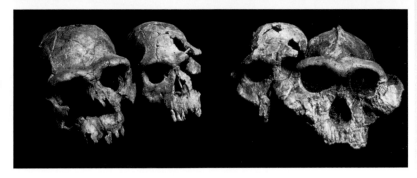

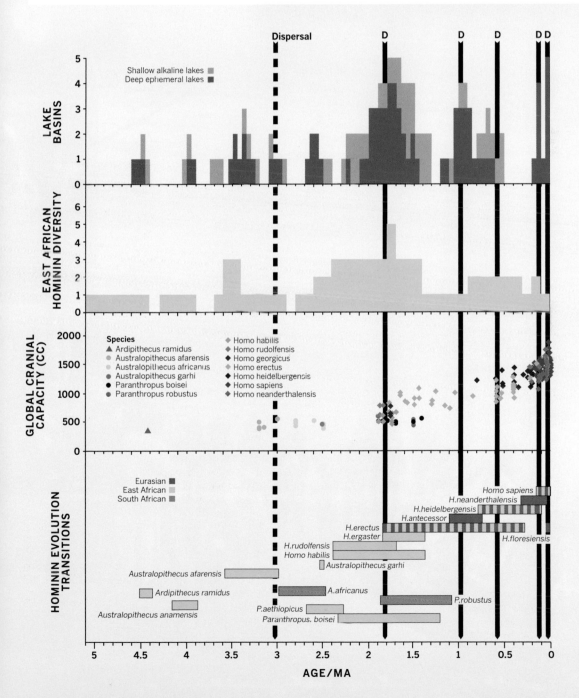

'AN UNPRECEDENTED DUEL WITH NATURE'

'The best thing we can do now is just to listen and hope', said Cliff Michelmore, broadcasting from the BBC's studios 24 minutes from the expected splashdown of Apollo 13. On 17 April 1970, I was too young to watch the live broadcast, but I've seen the recording many times since. Grainy pictures from the deck of the USS *Iwo Jima*, its flight deck crammed with nervous sailors off the coast of Samoa; Patrick Moore and Geoffery Pardoe grim-faced in the studios, and James Burke, famously, with fingers crossed behind his back. 'Apollo control, Houston, we've just had loss of signal from Honeysuckle'. Honeysuckle Creek Tracking Station in Canberra, Australia, was the last ground station to contact Apollo 13 before it entered the Earth's atmosphere on its way home. Signal loss during re-entry is routine high drama on all space missions; the ionisation of the atmosphere caused by the frictional heating of the spacecraft blocks radio signals, typically resulting in radio silence for four minutes. On Apollo 13, six minutes passed in silence. The brilliance of the BBC's quartet of commentators was in the silence they allowed on the airwaves. The only sound was the static of the NASA feed – a moment of genuine tension. No need for vacuous media babble; nobody could bring themselves to speak. 'We'll only know whether that heat shield was damaged by that explosion three days ago when they come out of radio blackout in just over two minutes' said Burke. Silence. As four minutes passed, Houston reports '10 seconds to end of radio blackout'. Silence. Houston: 'We've had a report that Orion 4 aircraft has acquisition of signal.' 'They're through' says Burke. 'Let's not anticipate, because the parachutes may have been damaged.' 'Shutes should be out', murmurs Burke; not broadcasting, just saying. 'There they are, there they are!' 'They've made it' remarks Moore. And then applause. 'I make it no more than 5 seconds late!' shouts Burke, 'No more than 5 seconds late!'

The safe return of Apollo 13 was arguably NASA's finest hour; 55 hours 54 minutes and 53 seconds into the mission, 320,000 kilometres from Earth, Lunar Module pilot Jack Swigert switched on a system of stirring fans in the hydrogen and oxygen tanks in the service module, a routine procedure. A piece of Teflon insulation inside the tank had been damaged, it was later discovered, by a series of unlikely events that happened on the ground during the preparation of the spacecraft for flight. The wire shorted, the tank exploded, and the side of the service module was blown off, critically damaging the spacecraft's power supply systems and venting the crew's oxygen supply out into space.

The Command Module, the only part of the spacecraft capable of surviving a re-entry through the Earth's atmosphere, was now running on batteries and with a rapidly diminishing oxygen supply that would not keep the astronauts alive long enough to return to Earth. The only option was to shut down the Command Module and retreat to the Lunar Module, effectively using it as a life raft. Lovell later spoke of how he didn't regret the mission at all. He was robbed of his Moon landing, which must have been doubly frustrating given he'd already flown to the Moon on the historic Apollo 8 mission. But his reaction, revealed in interviews in later life, offers great insight into the character of a test pilot. 'We were given the situation,' Lovell explained, 'to really exercise our skills, and our talents to take a situation which was almost certainly catastrophic, and come home safely. That's why I thought that 13, of all the flights – including [Apollo] 11 – that 13 exemplified a real test pilot's flight.' Both Lovell and Haise have said that the idea of not returning safely to Earth never really came up. 'There was nothing there that said irrefutably we don't have a chance'.

Haise was correct, of course, because they did return safely. But they only had enough food and water to sustain two people for a day and a half

THE RETURN OF APOLLO 13
Apollo 13 was launched on 11 April 1970, and was planned as the third manned Moon landing. Two days into the flight, 300,000 kilometres from Earth, an oxygen tank in the spacecraft exploded. With their normal supplies of oxygen and electricity destroyed, the astronauts used the Lunar Module as a 'life raft' to keep them alive.

and had to improvise a carbon dioxide filter to provide them with enough breathable air for the return journey. Locked in the Lunar Module with limited supplies of food and water and temperatures dropping towards freezing, life was far from comfortable. With the Command Module powered down to preserve the sparse battery supplies left after the loss of the fuel cells, the crew had to survive in a hostile environment with limited resources. Like so many outposts of human civilisation throughout history, shortage of water was a primary concern. Water was critical on the Lunar Module for two reasons; as well as being needed to keep the crew hydrated and to rehydrate the food, it also cooled the electrical systems on the spacecraft. Conserving water therefore became a critical part of the plan to return to Earth. Reducing their intake to just one-fifth of a normal human water ration, each of the crew suffered severe dehydration and together they lost 31.5 pounds in weight – nearly fifty per cent more than any other Apollo crew.

Despite the discomfort, setting a new mission trajectory and navigating their way along it remained the primary challenge. The standard way to make in-flight course corrections on Apollo was to use the Command Module's main engine, but the system was located close to the damaged site and mission controllers decided that lighting it was too great a risk. Instead, the decision was made to use the LM's descent engine to send them around the far side of the Moon and back to Earth in four and a half days. This is known as a free-return trajectory – a slingshot around the Moon at the correct angle to return directly to Earth. No one knew if an engine designed for a completely different purpose would perform this function successfully – but they knew that if it failed they would not return.

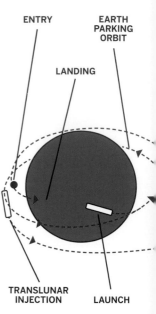

HOW APOLLO 13 GOT BACK

ENTRY   EARTH PARKING ORBIT

LANDING

TRANSLUNAR INJECTION   LAUNCH

Five hours after the initial explosion, the LM engine was fired for a 35-second burn, successfully putting the crew onto a free return trajectory. This solved one problem but raised another. Calculations of the trajectory estimated return to Earth 153 hours after launch, which would push the key reserves on the craft too low for comfort, so it was decided to speed up the spacecraft with another burn, cutting the total time of the voyage by ten crucial hours. Such were the slim margins on Apollo 13. The main navigation system in the Command Module was out of action, so Lovell had to calculate the correct navigational inputs, while back at base, mission control worked through the same calculations as a cross check. Lovell also got to use his sextant, which he played with on Apollo 8, to navigate by the stars for real.

The calculations are preserved as handwritten notes, in the Lunar Module System's Activation Checklist. This was the checklist Lovell and Haise would have used to fly down to the Moon's surface. Now useless, Lovell used the waste paper to write down instructions to put the ship on course for Earth. Two hours after they rounded the far side of the Moon, the LM engine fired, following Lovell's handwritten checklist, increasing the speed of the spacecraft by 860 feet per second and buying them ten precious hours.

The most dramatic rescue in the history of human spaceflight stands as a testament to the brilliance of the three test pilots Lovell, Haise and Swigert, and also to the brilliance of the engineers on the ground who simply knew their stuff. NASA's Apollo engineers were young by today's standards; the average age of the team in mission control for the splashdown of Apollo 11 was 28 years old. This is one of the reasons

NOTES FROM SPACE
Astronaut Jim Lovell's handwritten checklist which helped ensure the Apollo 13 crew's safe return to Earth.

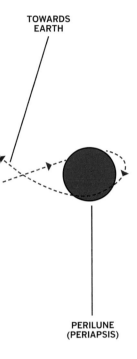

TOWARDS EARTH

PERILUNE (PERIAPSIS)

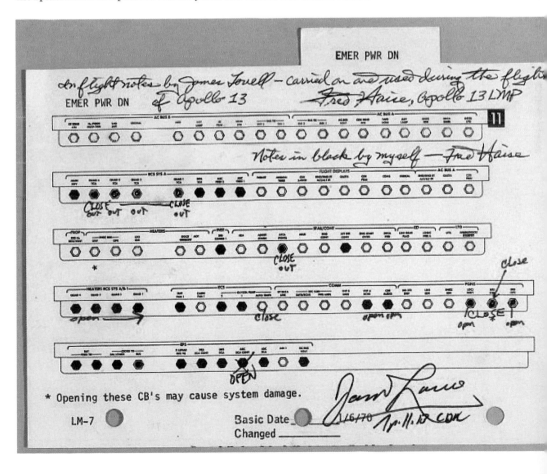

ACT 30

7:26   97:26

IMU COARSE ALIGN   298 360 /658   SUIT FAN/H2O SEP CHECK

CSM In Min DEADBAND ATT HOLD   1   CB(16) ECS: SUIT FAN 2 - Open
te LM Gimbal Angles   (Master Alarm, SUIT/FAN Warning
                                             SUIT FAN Comp Lts - On)

        IG   MG   2   CB(11) ECS: SUIT FAN 1 - Close
                                         H2O SEP SEL - PUSH SEP 1
0   180.00   360.00

                                     3   SUIT FAN - 1 (SUIT/FAN Warning,   355 57
0 +Rc (See TLC-1)   FAN Comp Lts-Off,ECS Caution,   298 00
                                         H2O SEP Comp Lts -Off In 2 min)
57 -CM 167.78 +CM 351.87 -CM   CB(16) ECS: SUIT FAN 2 - Close   -37 57
   (112.5)   (22.5)

3 LM 347.78 LM 08.13 LM   360 00
   (292.5)   (337.5)   302.43
                                          57.57
E COARSE ALIGN IMU   97:28
   LOAD ICDU ANGLES OG,IG,MG (.01°)
TT Lt - On, FDAI Torques)   1   GLYCOL PUMP CHECK
   *PROG Lt-On   *
   *V05 N09E 00211 COARSE *   1   CB(11) ECS: GLYCOL PUMP 1 - Open
   *   ALIGN ERROR,Go*   (Master Alarm, ECS Caution
   *   To 3   *   Lt - On Momentarily)
                                         CB(11) ECS: GLYCOL PUMP 1 - Close
                                         (GLYCOL Comp Lt-On)

              Basic Date _____ 2/6/70
              Changed _____

              Basic Date _____ 2/6/70
              Changed _____
                          ACT 31 -31

OE ZERO CDU (NO ATT Lt-Off)   2   GL
 CSM ATT HOLD No Longer Required   CB

7E
7 SET REFSMFLG
000E,1E, V01 N01E,77E Confirm   3   GL
13 Is Set (Set If 1st Digit Is
5, or 7)   CB

1E   GL

OE   4   Bi

O On LM MARK - ENTR
ime; Copy CSM & LM OG, IG, MG
:08:06

        IG   MG
9 CM 163 42 CM 346 67 CM   1   CSM Configure for VHF Simplex B
26 LM 345 92 LM 011 79 LM   VHF B XMTR - VOICE
                                         VHF B RCVR - ON
Gimbal Angles And Time To MSFN   VHF ANT - FWD
                                         AUDIO (Both): VHF B - T/R

                                    2   Both CDR & LMP Perform Voice Check
                                         On VHF Simplex B

This pub. was utilized
to transfer CSM guidance
data to LM guidance
system so the spacecraft
data of our attitude with
respect to the celestial
sphere would not be lost.
Note the time these calculations
were made GET 58 08 06
about two hours after the
explosion. Jim Lovell

                                         VHF B CHECKOUT

EPLOY | RCS C/O | VHF C/O LGC/CMC CLOCK SYNC | DAP SET ASC BAT CK
SS

OUT OF AFRICA

Evidence from fossils, ancient artefacts and genetic analyses combine to tell a compelling story of the migration of anatomically modern humans. Two possible routes have been identified for the human exodus out of Africa. A northern route would have taken our ancestors from their base in eastern sub-Saharan Africa across the Sahara desert, then through Sinai and into the Levant. An alternative southern route may have charted a path from Djibouti or Eritrea in the Horn of Africa across the Bab el-Mandeb strait and into Yemen and around the Arabian peninsula.

THE MATHS THAT SAVED APOLLO 13
The Lunar Module Systems Activation Checklist of Apollo 13 shows Lovell's handwritten numbers, which were part of the calculations made just two hours after a Service Module's oxygen tank explosion left them marooned in space. Lovell explains it briefly in the blue post-it note.

why the United States reaped such a colossal economic reward from its investment in Apollo. The generation of scientists and engineers who worked on and were inspired by Apollo went out into the wider economy and delivered a huge investment return; a series of studies, including one by Chase Econometrics, showed that for every dollar invested in Apollo, at least $6 or $7 was returned as increased GDP growth. This should, of course, be bloody obvious – new knowledge grows GDP – but every generation of politicians seems to require re-educating to understand the difference between spending and investment. And while I'm polemicising, let me say that the usual political argument – that public support is needed for such large investments – is drivel. Firstly, the investment in NASA wasn't that large, never exceeding 4.5 per cent of the Federal budget throughout the lifetime of Apollo. And secondly, it is a politician's job to lead from the front. Make the case that investment in knowledge, in pushing the boundaries of human capabilities and exploring all frontiers, both physical and intellectual, is the key to the future wealth, prosperity and security of civilisation. Aspire to be Kennedy, not a hand-wringing apologist for intellectual and technological decline.

The nine Apollo flights to the Moon remain the furthest modern humans have explored beyond the Rift Valley in our 200,000-year history. Homo sapiens first left Africa in large numbers 60,000 years ago, so on geological timescales we didn't hang around. Our ancestors followed waves of earlier hominins. Homo erectus were in South East Asia 1.6 million years ago, and half a million years later Neanderthals had colonised Europe and Homo floresiensis were in Southern Asia. The details of the migration 60,000 years ago are particularly well understood as a result of the combination of genetic, archaeological and linguistic studies. The precision comes in part from the tracking sequences of mitochondrial DNA, which is passed down from the mother and not shuffled by sex. This makes it relatively stable and easy to track – changes are caused by mutations alone. The most widely accepted interpretation of the data suggests that a small population of between 1000 and 2500 individuals left East Africa 60,000 years ago and moved north across the Red Sea and through Arabia. The group then split, moving into Southern Europe 43,000 years ago, and travelling through India and into Australia on roughly the same timescale. The crossing into North America, via eastern Russia, was probably later, around 15,000 years ago.

These early groups of humans were hunter-gatherers. It has been estimated that the basic social units would have reached a maximum of around 150 individuals. This is known as Dunbar's number, after the British anthropologist Robin Dunbar, who suggests that the largest social group amongst any given population of primates is related to the size of their brains (specifically the neocortex). Dunbar's number can be observed today in the size of the average person's social network, both in the real world and online; our hardware – the brain – has not changed appreciably since the first humans appeared in Africa 200,000 years ago. These social groups would have lived in loosely bound tribes, perhaps reaching a size of between one and two thousand individuals, operating within an area of around 100 kilometres. Populations would stabilise, perhaps in response to social factors, but also as a result of increased mortality rates caused by parasitic diseases and diminishing per-capita resource availability, before fragmenting and spreading. In this fashion, the rate of progression of our ancestors across the globe has been estimated to have been around 0.5 kilometres per year, or 15 kilometres per generation. Population density did not rise significantly beyond these levels until these proto-societies shifted from a hunter-gatherer lifestyle to agriculture around 12,000 years ago. This shift was the trigger for the development of civilisation: the most important single step, following the migration out of Africa, in the journey from apeman to spaceman.

HOMO ERECTUS/ERGASTER
There are differences in the literature concerning the appropriate classification of Homo erectus in Africa and in Asia. Homo erectus (sensu lato) is the term used to describe both the African and Asian populations. The population in Africa is sometimes referred to as Homo ergaster, and the Asian population as Homo erectus sensu stricto. What is widely accepted is that the African population evolved in the Rift Valley from Homo habilis around 1.9 million years ago, and subsequently spread into Asia.

FARMING: THE BEDROCK OF CIVILISATION

There are many competing theories as to the reason for the domestication of crops, but many note the correlation between the first evidence of agriculture and the beginning of the current inter-glacial period known as the Holocene, 12,000 years ago. In the fertile crescent around modern-day Jordan and Syria, people known as the Natufians were beginning to settle into larger communities, perhaps because of the relatively benign climate. The area would have been forested and rich in wild cereals, fruits and nuts, rather than the austere desert of today. One theory is that a brief 1000-year cold period known as the Younger Dryas, beginning around 10,800 BCE, triggered drier conditions in the region, forcing the Natufians to begin cultivating the previously abundant wild crops on which they had come to rely. Whatever the reason, it is generally agreed that the foundational crops of modern agriculture, including wheat, barley, peas and lentils, were all to be found in the Fertile Crescent by 9000 BCE, and by 8000 BCE the banks of the Nile were being cultivated. At approximately the same time, evidence of farming can be found in Asia's Indus Valley, in China and in Mesoamerica. This suggests that there was no single environmental or developmental cause for agriculture, because it appeared independently at many sites across the world. Rather, our large brains and relatively large social groups were ready to take up the challenge when the need arose.

Once agriculture was established, larger numbers of people could live together, taking advantage of the more stable food supply. The freedom from continual hunting and gathering would have introduced a new aspect to human life – free time – and it was used to great effect. Some of the earliest farmers settled in a place known as Beidha in modern-day Jordan around 7000 BCE. Living in round, stone-built houses, they grew barley and wheat and kept domesticated goats, engaged in ritual and ceremony and buried their dead. Importantly, each of these activities was carried out in specific areas of the settlements: the beginning of 'town planning'. By the 2nd century BCE a Semitic people known as the Nabataeans lived around Beidha. They employed new technologies to increase the reliability of farming and constructed walled agricultural terraces on the hillsides around the village to collect and store water. Animal husbandry was also expanding, with the domestication of cows, pigs, donkeys and horses. Even previously dangerous animals were coerced into living with humans; there is evidence that the Nabataeans kept dogs. As the great empires of Egypt, Greece and Rome prospered, the Nabataeans remained partially nomadic, driving their camel trains across the desert along the long-established trade routes between North Africa and India and the great cities of the Mediterranean. But then, around 150 BCE, they decided to try something different. A few kilometres south of Beidha, in a narrow gorge naturally formed in the soft sandstone rock, they built the city of Petra.

Today tourists stream through a magnificent passageway lined with buildings carved out of the desert rocks and known as the Siq, but 2000 years ago the great and good of Mesopotamia, Rome and Egypt would have walked this route into this jewel of late antiquity.

The grandeur of the buildings is still overwhelming; they stand not as great architecture for their time, but as simply great, with no caveat. The most famous is called Al Khazneh, which means 'Treasure Box', because of the carved urn above the entrance which, Bedouin legend has it, contains the treasure of a Pharaoh. Monumental architecture is a common feature in the rise of human civilisation. It is a statement of power and grandeur to impress and cow outsiders, but it also serves an internal purpose, cementing the position of the rulers in the hierarchy and therefore providing the stability and security on which civilisation rests.

LOST CITY
Petra was the capital of the Nabataean kingdom and was carved into a red sandstone gorge over 2000 years ago in what is now Jordan. The hillsides running down the valley from the carved tombs are scattered with rocks, but closer inspection reveals them to be bricks, the remains of houses, temples and palaces.
At its peak, Petra had a population of thirty thousand.
Today, it lies empty and abandoned, as it has for nearly 1500 years. Its only occupants are a handful of Bedouin tribespeople who have made their homes amongst the ruins.

Over time, a virtuous circle emerges; the buildings help the civilisation prosper, and the more prosperous the civilisation, the more impressive the buildings become.

Petra's wealth was derived from its location. Built within a natural gorge, the area is prone to flash floods, which provided precious water in a landscape that was arid by the time the Nabataeans began to build. The city also sits at the fulcrum of the ancient nomadic trade routes along which wood, spices, incense and dyes were transported from Africa and India and into the great Mediterranean civilisation beyond. The appetite of the Greeks and Romans for exotic goods was insatiable; black pepper alone fetched forty times its own weight in gold in a Roman market. Petra, because of its strategic location, controlled all that trade and taxed it. Today, 1500 years after the city was abandoned, it is still a magnificent site – an overused but entirely accurate statement. Talk to an archaeologist, however, and you quickly realise how much more impressive it would have been in its heyday. The hillsides running down the valley from the carved tombs are scattered with rocks, but closer inspection reveals them to be bricks, the remains of houses, temples and palaces. Everything from Al Khazneh to the houses would have been covered in white plaster and painted in bright colours which would have appeared resplendent against the monochrome desert sands.

To build on this scale required a huge labour force; Petra was home to at least thirty thousand people living in a few square kilometres of desert. Such a population density required technological innovation on a metropolitan scale, and the Nabataeans, perhaps more than any other civilisation in antiquity, were masters of fluid engineering. Virtually every drop of rainwater that fell on the surrounding hillsides was captured in grooves and stored in giant reservoirs and cisterns. They were better at plumbing than the Romans, who employed the Petran engineers in Rome. Petra had the world's first pressurised water system, which could deliver 12 million gallons of water a day into the city.

Outside the city, the irrigation system continued out into the surrounding fields, lining the hillsides in still-visible terraces; the Nabataeans didn't simply build a city, they terra-formed a landscape. I stood and imagined the ancient valley views with some awe; the mountain slopes would have been green with maize, barley, pulses and vineyards – a desert turned green and feeding this grandest of desert civilisations for six centuries. Whenever I see the ruins of Petra, Rome, Athens or Cairo, I wonder what Earth would be like today if the great civilisations of antiquity had not fallen. I blame the philosophers for not discovering the scientific method earlier and inventing the electric motor. How hard can it be?

Agriculture, then, was fundamentally important to the rise of civilisation because it enabled large numbers of people to live in one place, and gave them access to resources and time, which would have been unavailable to hunter-gatherers. With resources and time comes the division of labour, freeing up a small but important subset of individuals to engage in pursuits other than those necessary for immediate survival. Farmers, stonemasons, priests, soldiers, administrators and artisans emerge, together with a ruling class who begin to direct the construction of monumental architecture, partly for their own selfish ends. And cities like Petra become possible.

Petra was a relative latecomer in the emergence of the cities and civilisations of antiquity. The first great ancient civilisation, the Old Kingdom of Egypt, arose around 2600 BCE along the fertile and farmed banks of the Nile, and precisely the same pattern of agriculture, followed by social stratification, ritual and monumental architecture, can be seen. Present also in the Old Kingdom, and possibly developed there, was the one final vitally important innovation we will soon discuss: the written word.

TOWERING STRUCTURES
The Monastery (Ad Deir) at Petra dates from the 1st century BCE and is the ancient city's largest monument. Architecturally it is an example of the Nabataean Classical style. It may have been used as a church or monastery by later societies but most likely began as a temple.

THE KAZAK ADVENTURE: PART 1

It all seemed so simple when written down on a piece of paper. The BBC prepares something known as a call sheet, which tells a film crew everything they need to know about a trip. Call sheets are very neat; all the timings work beautifully, carefully documenting flights, ground transfers to locations and filming and rest periods, all of course in accordance with health and safety regulations and all that. Things never quite work out the way they're envisaged back in the office, of course, but filming the return of the Expedition 38 crew from the International Space Station to the Kazak Steppe in March 2014 was the wildest adventure I've experienced.

The call sheet said that we would fly into Astana on 8 March, arriving at 1am on the 9th into our hotel. After a leisurely breakfast at 9am, we'd drive to a city called Karaganda, which has a spectacular statue of Yuri Gagarin in the town square. There, we'd meet up with our drivers who, embedded with Roscosmos, the Russian space agency, would drive us out to the landing site the following morning, arriving in time for a 'hot meal' and a good rest on the Steppe, ready to film the landing on the morning of the 11th after, of course, a 'hot breakfast'. We'd then drive back to the airport, hop on a flight, and be home in time for lunch on the 12th. A doddle. Bollocks.

A HOME IN SPACE
Five times a year, astronauts make the journey to and from our permanent home in space – the International Space Station – which has been manned since 2 November 2000. The training mock-up is an exact replica of the real thing, which orbits 400 kilometres above our heads.

The Steppe of central Kazakhstan in March is a featureless frozen wilderness covering around 800,000 square kilometres of the country's interior. There are no towns and few roads; just tufts of stunted brown grass and snow fading into an ice-grey leaden sky. In March 2014 temperatures were unseasonably cold, falling below -20°C at night, and it was snowing. Our team had standard 4×4 vehicles, which got stuck in the snow by mid-afternoon the day before the landing, even though we'd set off three hours earlier than the 6am officially sanctioned health and safety call time because of the weather. This was problematic, because our *Apeman Spaceman* film was constructed carefully around this moment – the return of three human beings from space. Over vodka, cold meat and bread, we discussed our options.

We'd been helped along the snowy roads by a Russian team from the Siberian city of Tobolsk in two spectacular 6-wheel-drive vehicles, hand-built by a company called Petrovich. Tobolsk is best known for being the place dissidents were sent during the Soviet era. Tsar Nicholas II and his family enjoyed the Tobolskian hospitality for a year before being transported to Ekaterinburg to be shot. Mendeleev, the inventor of the Periodic Table, was born there, but so was Rasputin. It's a tough place, and they know how to build tough vehicles. Our guide from Roscosmos managed to radio the Petrovich team, and they agreed that if we could catch them up in the frozen wilderness, they could take two of us out to the landing site. The cameraman and I jumped aboard a pair of snowmobiles, and headed out into the rapidly dimming late-afternoon twilight in search of the men from Siberia. If we hadn't found them, then presumably you wouldn't be reading this, but we did.

It was a difficult decision to jump onto the snowmobiles. We didn't have a satellite phone because they are illegal in Kazakhstan, and nobody spoke English so we couldn't quite assess the level of difficulty associated with finding these two Siberian needles in a Kazak Steppe. And we didn't know who the Siberians actually were. It seemed that they were free-lancers, hired to take photographs and broadcast live television pictures back from the landing site for the Russian space agency. We also had to decide whether we could make the film with only two people. Much as I spend a lot of time dreaming about jettisoning directors, producers and executives, there is a reason why we usually take a crew of six. Sound is particularly important; you don't really miss the soundman until he's not there (our soundman on the series is called Andy, but we always called him soundman – there are too many other things to remember).

As it turned out, the Petrovich crew were a hospitable and professional bunch, although their willingness to spend many days out in the wilderness waiting for the Soyuz – they'd driven down from Siberia and were in no hurry to get home – played on our minds. Approaching midnight on the night before the landing, we received a message from Roscosmos that the landing might be postponed due to the poor weather, and the decision was made to camp out on the Steppe and wait. In the distance, we could make out a small group of farm buildings through the snow, and we headed towards them. In broken English, one of the crew told us that it is a Kazak tradition to welcome travellers into your home, at any time of the day or night, and offer them food. And so we found ourselves inside a farm house that appeared to have heated walls and resembled the inside of an oven, eating a feast of jam, bread, assorted sweets and horse, all washed down with vodka, which the Petrovich crew carried in large crates alongside their satellite broadcasting hardware. It was unforgettable. *Human Universe* was filmed as a love letter to the human race, and time and again when I've found myself immersed unexpectedly in a culture, I've been reminded about why it is appropriate to want to write one.

At 4am, soaked in vodka, the call came through. Commander Oleg Kotov, Sergey Ryazansky and Mike Hopkins had climbed aboard the

BATTLING WITH
THE ELEMENTS
Filming the return of the
Expedition 38 crew from the
International Space Station to
the Kazak Steppe was one of
the wildest adventures I have
ever experienced. That we got
to see it is a testament to the
determination of man!

Soyuz and were preparing to depart the International Space Station. I was elated, because I genuinely thought the landing would be called off, and I had no idea what that would have meant, other than waiting for the storms to clear on the Steppe.

At 6.02am Kazak time, the Soyuz TMA-10M, the 199th Soyuz to fly since 1967, undocked from the ISS. This is the point of no return, except in an emergency. Just 2 hours and 28 minutes later, it fired its engine for a pre-programmed burn of 4 minutes and 44 seconds. This reduced the spacecraft's velocity by 128 m/s relative to the Station, which in its orbit that day was travelling at 7358 m/s. That number is not arbitrary. It is given by a simple equation which can be derived easily from Newton's Law of Gravitation and his Second Law of Motion, $F=ma$. We leave it as an exercise for the reader to show that these two laws of nature can be re-arranged to show that the velocity v of any object in a circular orbit a distance r from the centre of the Earth, mass M_e, is given by

$$v = \sqrt{\frac{GM_e}{r}}$$

To derive this result, you need to know that the force required to maintain an object of mass m in a circular orbit is mv^2/r.

BACK FROM SPACE
A Soyuz spacecraft returning from the ISS is shown as it safely lands in a remote part of the Kazak Steppe.

SAFE LANDING
A search and recovery team helps to extract ISS crew members from the spacecraft. Re-entry is an extremely physical experience, and Earth's gravity a powerful returning force.

The Space Station orbits at an altitude of between 330 and 445 kilometres – let's choose the middle ground of 387 kilometres – this is a back-of-the-envelope calculation. 'Estimate is the name of the game', as my old physics teacher used to say at school. The radius of the Earth is 6,378 kilometres, and the mass of the Earth is 5.97219×10^{24} kg. Newton's gravitational constant is 6.67384×10^{-11} m^3 kg^{-1} s^{-2}. Do the calculation yourself; maths is good for you. With these numbers, v is approximately 7675 m/s, which is close enough – the difference is due to the precise altitude of the ISS that day. I love doing little calculations like this. They reveal the immense power of mathematical physics; this really is the orbital velocity of the International Space Station, and it is forced to be so by laws of nature first published by Isaac Newton in 1687. If you've never done a calculation like this before, you should feel elated. The biologist Edward O. Wilson called this feeling the Ionian Enchantment, a poetic term he introduced to describe the realisation, credited to Thales of Miletus in 600 BCE, that the natural world is orderly and simple, and can be described with great economy by a small set of laws. It is nothing short of wonderful that we can calculate the orbital velocity of the International Space Station together in a few lines of a popular book, and this points us neatly towards the story of the last great innovations in the ascent from apeman to spaceman: the written word.

CLOSE QUARTERS
ISS crew members, US astronaut Daniel Burbank and Russian cosmonauts Anton Shkaplerov and Anatoly Ivanishin are seen inside the Soyuz capsule on another mission in 2012, shortly after landing in Kazakhstan.

INTERMISSION: BEYOND MEMORY

I began my degree at the University of Manchester in 1992, which is when I started doing physics full time. I gained my PhD in 1998, spent the next 11 years working as a particle physicist at the DESY laboratory in Hamburg, Fermilab in Chicago and CERN in Geneva. In 2009 I began filming *Wonders of the Solar System*, which slowed down my research a bit. But I've been at it now for 22 years, which is almost half my life. In that time, I've learnt a lot about how to be a scientist, how to think about scientific problems, how to make measurements of nature, particularly the behaviour of subatomic particles, and how to interpret those measurements to generate new knowledge and make new discoveries. But given all that, there is no way that I would be able to calculate the orbital velocity of the International Space Station from scratch. Given Newton's laws, it's trivial. Without them, it would be virtually impossible. Newton's laws are far from obvious; they took Newton a scientific lifetime to produce, and he was a genius – one of the greatest scientific minds of all time. And even he didn't start from scratch. He relied heavily on the previous works of Galileo, Euclid and a hundred other philosophers, geometers and mathematicians whose names have been forgotten but whose works remain as cornerstones of our scientific culture. The reason we could run through that simple calculation together is that the thoughts and discoveries of these generations of philosophers, scientists and mathematicians were not lost; they were preserved forever in the written word.

Writing appears to have arisen independently in several different cultures, just as with the development of agriculture, and just as agriculture triggered the birth of civilisation 12,000 years ago, so the emergence of writing supported a rapid increase in the complexity of civilisation. The earliest known system of writing is generally accepted to be Cuneiform, the Sumerian system that emerged around 5000 years ago in the cities of Mesopotamia, although it is possible that Egyptian hieroglyphs may predate it. Literally meaning 'wedge-shaped', cuneiform comprises a thousand or more symbols created using a stylus made from reed that was pressed into a soft clay tablet. Following cuneiform and hieroglyphs, other forms of script emerged in Greece, China, India and, later, Central America.

Writing seems not to have arisen out of a deep human need to share and record intimate thoughts and lay down knowledge for future generations; that would be far too romantic. Rather, it appears to have served a more practical purpose, revealed in a set of around 150 Nabataean scrolls discovered by archaeologists in 1993. The scrolls date from around 550 CE, in the final period before Petra was abandoned. One of the most intact documents relates to a court case between two priests. It is alleged that one of the priests decided to run away from their shared house, taking a key to one of the upstairs rooms, two wooden beams that presumably held the roof up, six birds and a table. This is probably how writing began; the invention upon which modern human history rests arose, disappointingly, for admin purposes. This is seen not only in the relatively late Nabataean scrolls, but in many of the early texts. Cuneiform

HIEROGLYPHIC WRITING
Hieroglyphs ('sacred carving') are symbols, here inscribed in rock, which made up ancient Egyptian writing. This carving features the profiles of many different types of bird, as seen at the Temple of Karnak in Luxor, Egypt.

developed because of a need to keep track of trade and accounts in the increasingly complex economy of Mesopotamia. Egyptian hieroglyphs may be an exception, as there is a strong ritual component, but there is also evidence of their early use in commerce, administration, trade and law – the foundations of a modern society. Information about the natural world was also recorded; in hieroglyphs we see the cycle of the seasons chronicled, as well as important environmental events. There are also some beautiful early examples of the use of writing to express deeper human desires and feelings that resonate strongly today and show, yet again, that our ancestors had inner lives not too distant to our own.

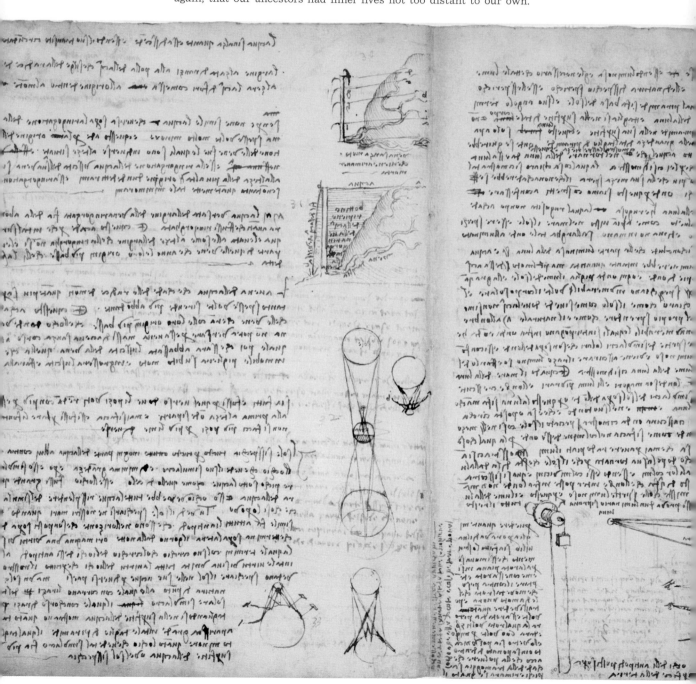

But the oldest surviving papyrus documents from the Old Kingdom are marvellously prosaic. From Dynasty 5, in the reign of Pharaoh Djedkare-Izezi between 2437 and 2393 BCE, can be found an early version of the parrot sketch.

'As Re, Hathor and all the gods desire that King Izezi should live forever, and ever, I am lodging a complaint through the commissioners concerning a case of collecting a transport-fare.'

And so the letters continue; whilst the tombs are covered in the names of pharaohs and stories of the Gods, the people of Egypt were using writing as we do today, and I find it wonderful, reassuring and moving in a funny sort of way to hear ancient voices complaining down the years. Perhaps we humans really will never change. From Dynasty 20, a millennium later during the reigns of Ramesses III and IV between 1182 and 1145 BCE, the complaints continue.

'The scribe Amennakht, your husband, took a coffin from me saying, "I shall give the calf in exchange for it", but he hasn't given it until this day. I mentioned this to Paakhet, who replied "Give me a bed in addition to it, and I will bring you the calf when it is mature". And I gave him the bed. Neither the coffin nor the bed is yet here to this day. If you are going to give the ox, send it on; but if there is no ox, return the bed and the coffin.'

Alongside the letters, the ritual, the complaints, the admin and the legal documents, there was also a sophisticated literary and storytelling tradition in Ancient Egypt, and a powerful appreciation of the value of the written word. Three thousand years ago on the banks of the Nile, during the reign of Queen Twosret, someone wrote a Eulogy for the writers;

These sage scribes ...
Their names endure for eternity,
Although they are gone, although they have completed their lifetimes, and
all their people are forgotten.
They did not make for themselves pyramids of bronze with stelae of iron ...
They made heirs for themselves
as the writings and Teachings that they begat ...
Departing life has made their names forgotten;
Writings alone make them remembered.

Taken from The Tale of Sinuhe and other Egyptian Poems
1940–1640 BC, Oxford World's Classics

Writing was the final pivotal moment in our ascent from early agrarian civilisations to the International Space Station, because it frees the acquisition of knowledge from the limits of human memory. The hardware restrictions set down in the Rift Valley 200,000 years ago no longer matter. Writing allows a practically unlimited amount of information to be passed from generation to generation, and to be shared across the world. Knowledge is no longer lost but is always added to; it becomes widespread, accessible and permanent. A little boy from Oldham, Lancashire, can inhabit the mind of Newton, assimilate his lifetime's work and derive new knowledge from it. Writing created a cultural ratchet, an exponentiation of the known that allowed humanity to innovate and invent way beyond the constraints of a single human brain. We now work together as a single mind spread across the planet and with a memory as long as history. It is this collective effort, enabled by the written word, that carried us, the human race, paragon of animals, from the Great Rift Valley to the stars. I deliberately borrow from Shakespeare; the most precious objects on Earth are not gems or jewels, but ink marks on paper. No single human brain could conceive of *Hamlet, Principia Mathematica* or *Codex Leicester*; they were created by and belong to the entire human race, and the library of wonders continues to grow.

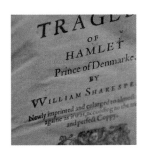

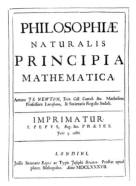

SHARED WISDOM
The written word has enabled great minds such as Leonardo da Vinci, William Shakespeare and Isaac Newton to pass on their knowledge, vision and findings to future generations, to be shared across the world.

THE KAZAK ADVENTURE: PART 2

The drive from the farm to the Soyuz landing site was agricultural. The Petrovich vehicles work as a pair, dragging each other out of snowdrifts when they get stuck. I wondered through the mildly paranoid haze that descends after 48 hours of wakefulness and 48 shots of vodka (which is not optional if Russian sensibilities are to be respected) what would happen to us if both vehicles got stuck. By dawn, we arrived at the GPS coordinates given to us by Roscosmos, and waited. We knew precise timings for re-entry, because those are given by physics alone once the de-orbit burn of 4 minutes and 44 seconds occurs. Recall that the Soyuz, along with the Space Station, was in a circular orbit travelling at 7358 m/s, and the engine burn slowed it down by precisely 128 m/s. This put the Soyuz into an elliptical orbit, which, when the breaking effects of the atmosphere are taken into account, put the craft on a collision course with Kazakhstan. It's quite simple, and it works. In my experience filming with Roscosmos, the words 'it's quite simple and it works' sum up Russia's successful half a century in space. They don't do things in as shiny, hi-tech a fashion as the United States; the Soyuz has been flying astronauts into space with minimal design changes since 1967. But today, the Soyuz is the only way to get to and from the ISS, and it is a reliable system. But to my inexperienced eyes, unused to the way the Russians do things, the return of the Expedition 38 crew after six months in space felt like a traction engine rally in Yorkshire arranged by Fred Dibnah. That's not meant as a criticism, because I'd trust Fred Dibnah to organise a traction engine rally, and I'd trust the Russians to get me back from space. But neither stands on ceremony.

At precisely 9.23am, the Soyuz emerged from the snow-filled skies above the Steppe, swinging from its parachutes, and touched down with a burst of soft landing jets. One of our Petrovich colleagues saw it with his binoculars, and we headed off towards the spaceship in the snow. In one of the most bizarre moments of my life, we arrived, and, without thinking, jumped out and stumbled through the drifts towards the spacecraft. I fumbled around with the microphone for a while (recall that soundman didn't make it), and then realised that there were no other vehicles around. A single helicopter had just landed; apart from that, there was only the wind driving gentle flurries across the Steppe.

Minutes later, the support vehicles arrived and Oleg Kotov, Sergey Ryazansky and Mike Hopkins were dragged from the hatch of their Soyuz, wrapped in sleeping bags and put into deckchairs. They looked happy, but knackered, and mildly discombobulated as a parade of Russian army generals in very big hats seized the opportunity for a photo. The Russians don't overdo things; they just do them. Five times a year men and women make this voyage back to Earth having spent half a year in space, living amongst the stars on the International Space Station. Since the first expedition began on 2 November 2000, the station has been continuously occupied, and I hope that there will never again come a time when every human being is confined to Earth.

I carried in my pocket a reminder of my time in Ethiopia, the small flint we used for filming in the Rift Valley. I imagined a human, my great, great-grandfather, sitting somewhere in the vicinity of what would one day become Addis Ababa, diligently chipping away at the obsidian in my hand, the whole of history away. I set it down in the snow next to the Soyuz, descended from it as I am from him.

SPACEMAN
When I was young I dreamt of being an astronaut – it was why I became interested in astronomy and physics. Floating in a most peculiar way in the ISS simulator tank is the closest I will ever get.

KAZAK ADVENTURE PART 2

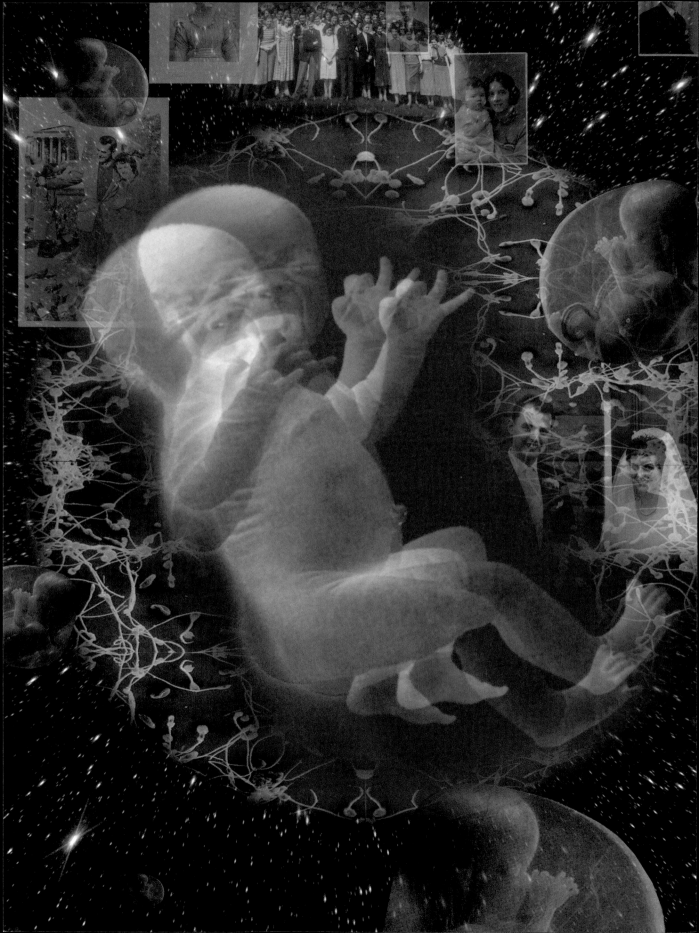

WHY ARE WE HERE?

But, after all, who knows, and who can say
Whence it all came, and how creation happened?
The gods themselves are later than creation,
so who knows truly whence it has arisen?

Ancient Brahmin Verse

A NEAT PIECE OF LOGIC

There is tension at the interface between science and language. Language is concerned with human experience. Everyone understands what is meant by questions such as 'Why are you late?' 'I'm late because my alarm clock didn't go off'. But this answer is incomplete, and could be followed by a series of further questions in an attempt to establish precisely why.

'Why didn't it go off?'

'Because it's broken.'

'Why is it broken?'

'Because a piece of solder melted on the circuit board.'

'Why did the solder melt?'

'Because it got hot.'

'Why did it get hot?'

'Because it's August and my room is hot.'

'Why is it hot in August?'

'Because of the details of the Earth's orbit around the Sun.'

'Why does the Earth orbit the Sun?'

'Because of the action of the gravitational force.'

'Why is there a gravitational force?'

'I don't know.'

All scientific 'Why?' questions end with 'I don't know' if you keep pushing far enough, because our scientific understanding of the universe is not complete. The most fundamental description we have for anything comes down to a set of theories describing the smallest known building blocks of the universe and the forces of nature that allow them to interact with each other. These theories are known as laws of physics, and when we ask about the origin of these laws, the answer is 'We don't know'. This is because in the Big Bang model, our understanding of physics before 10^{-43} seconds after the origin of the visible universe is virtually non-existent, and the origin of the laws lies at some point before that. 'The laws themselves are later than creation, and who knows truly whence it has arisen'. Our best theory of space and time, Einstein's General Theory of Relativity, no longer applies at the earliest times; the conditions were so extreme in those first moments, known as the Planck epoch, that some kind of quantum theory of gravity, which we do not possess, will be needed to describe it.

The universe is now 13.798 +/- 0.037 billion years old, according to our current best measurements and theoretical understanding, and has been gently expanding and cooling ever since the Big Bang. The universe appears to be gently increasing its expansion rate, and approximately 68 per cent of the energy in the universe is associated with this sedate acceleration. The energy has a name – dark energy – but its nature remains one of the great unsolved challenges for twenty-first-century theoretical physics. Of the 32 per cent that remains, approximately 27 per cent is in a form of matter known as dark matter. The nature of this is also unknown, but it probably comes in the form of as yet undiscovered subatomic particles. The remaining 5 per cent makes up the stars, planets and galaxies we see in the night sky, and of course human beings. The part of the universe we can see is around 93 billion light years across and has reached a relatively chilly temperature of 2.72548 +/- 0.00057 Kelvin due to its expansion.

The question of the origin of the universe is an old one in philosophy, and often framed in terms of the 'First Cause' argument. Leibniz is associated with a 'proof' of the existence of God in this context, which goes something like this:

Everything that exists must have either an external cause or must be eternal. If there are eternal things, then they must necessarily exist,

EXPLORING THE BIG BANG
In March 2014 this telescope, the BICEP2, detected a pattern in the cosmic microwave background which supports the inflation theory attributed to the Big Bang, the origins of our universe which we are still exploring.

because they don't have a cause. Since the universe exists and is not eternal, it must have an external cause, and to avoid infinite regress that cause must be an eternal and necessary thing, which we'll call God.

This is quite a neat piece of logic, obviously, because Leibniz wasn't an idiot. I don't consider such questions to fall necessarily within the domain of science. Rather science is concerned with answering more modest questions, and this is the reason for its power and success. The goal of science is to explain the observed features of the natural world.

יְהוָֹה:

Et vidit Deus lucem quod esset bona

Mundus Intellectualis

SYLVA SYLVARVM
or
A NATVRALL HISTORY
In ten Centuries.
Written by the right Hon:ble Francis
Lo: Verulam Viscount S:t Alban.
Published after ye Autho:rs Death
by W: RAWLEY D:r of Diui:
nity. &c

Tho: Cecill sculp:

Anno

LONDON
Printed for W: Lee and are to be sould at
the Great Turks head, next to the Mytre
Taurne in Fleetstreet

1627

By 'explain', I mean 'build theories that make predictions that are in accord with observation'. This is a humble idea; there is no *a priori* aim to discover the reason for the existence of our universe or to build theories of everything. Science proceeds in tiny steps, attempting to find explanations for the blue sky, the green leaves of plants or the stretched, red-shifted light from distant galaxies. Sometimes, those tiny steps build up to something rather grand, like a measurement of the age of the observable universe, but that's not what anyone set out to do. This is why science is more successful than any other form of human thought when applied to questions within its domain, which is the explanation of the natural world. It starts small and works its way slowly and methodically forwards, deepening our understanding in careful increments.

Our chapter title 'Why are we here?' might therefore appear to be unanswerable by science; it's too grand a question. But that may no longer be the case, because the careful steps are taking science into this territory and the scientific language is now in place to at least address the question 'What happened before the Big Bang?' This is clearly a prerequisite for being able to make any meaningful attempt to address the reasons for our existence, although it is surely not sufficient. Immediately, I have to explain a semantic distinction before a thousand philosophers throw their togas aside and prepare to engage in a naked yet civilised and eloquent battle of ideas. I am defining the term Big Bang as the astronomer Fred Hoyle originally introduced it into physics in 1949. It is to be understood as the beginning of the hot, dense state in which our observable universe once existed. Conventional cosmological theory, as described in Chapter 1, traces the evolution of the universe backwards in time, with conditions getting hotter and hotter and denser and denser until the point where we are unsure of the correct rules of physics. Currently this is earlier than approximately 10^{-10} seconds, which is associated with the current power of the Large Hadron Collider. If the universe existed in some other form before the hot, dense state came into existence 13.798 billion years ago, then that's what I'm referring to as the time before the Big Bang. Science might accidentally wander into Leibniz's territory if, for example, this time before the Big Bang were discovered to be infinite, or that the state before the Big Bang was logically necessary and describable by current or yet-to-be discovered laws of physics. Such a theory would also have to explain precisely all the properties of the universe we see today. From a scientific perspective of course, we don't care about Leibniz; it is not the role of science to prove or disprove the existence of God. Rather we are only interested in taking our careful steps backwards in time as far as the evidence and theoretical understanding allow. The exciting thing is that developments in cosmology since the 1980s now point quite firmly towards the existence of a state before the Big Bang as defined above, and that is primarily what this chapter is about.

This chapter is also about you. I suspect most of us have mused about the question 'Why are we here?' For some, the question and answer may be absolutely central to their lives. For others, myself included, it's something I used to think about on a hillside desolate beside a punctured bicycle whilst wearing a secondhand overcoat I bought from Affleck's Palace, but my existentialism faded with my hair.

Having said that, a little existentialism, like the Manchester rain, never did anyone any harm, so let's place ourselves at the centre of things for a while and explore the immense contingency of our personal existence as a warm-up for the much deeper problem of the origin of the universe itself. It's a pretty deep chapter this, so put on *Unknown Pleasures*, grab a bottle of cheap cider and let's get going.

市市　（株）アットハウス　代表取締役社長　加藤優次

都台東区浅草橋二ノ五ノ六　テージー株式会社　玉越　進

札幌市北区屯田六条十一丁目三ノ一〇　井家律子

東京都世田谷区砧二ノ五ノ三　裕和産業（株）　藤田照雄

株式会社ミズモリ　代表取締役　毎日刀志

川崎市多摩区

東京都品川区東大井　久保佳子

東京都世田谷区　恩田伊都子

NEW DAWN FADES

It was me, waiting for me,
Hoping for something more,
Me, seeing me this time,
Hoping for something else.
Ian Curtis, New Dawn Fades, Unknown Pleasures

If, in a moment of solipsism, you decide to work out the odds of your own existence, you might come to the conclusion that you are astonishingly special. You began as a particular egg inside your mother, fertilised by a particular sperm from your father. There were 180 million sperm around that day, each with a different genetic code, only one of which became 'you' in combination with one of your mother's million or so genetically unique eggs. So without going any further, you might feel lucky. If you chose to carry on, you might factor in the odds of your parents having sex on that particular day, because sperm are constantly manufactured. Then there are the odds of them meeting at all, and the odds of them being THEM. And whilst we're picking up increasing armfuls of odds at the 1-in-a-100-million level, recall from Chapter 1 that there exists an unbroken line of your ancestors stretching back over 3.8 billion years to LUCA – the Last Universal Common Ancestor. If any one of those living things had died before it reproduced, you wouldn't exist. That's pretty lucky, but also completely devoid of any meaning at all. Yes, the odds of YOU existing are almost, but not quite, zero. But given the existence of the human race and a mechanism for procreation, someone has to be born. So whilst the probability of any given individual existing is tiny, it is inevitable that new babies will be born every day. Seen in this light, you are not special and your existence in the grand scheme of things is entirely understandable. Time for Joy Division and cider.

UNKNOWN PLEASURES
Ian Curtis from Joy Division muses on our hope for something more; the reality is that we can always strive to be more, but the laws of nature remind us that we are not special and our existence in the grand scheme of things is understandable!

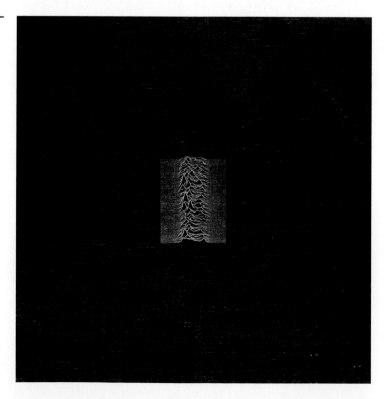

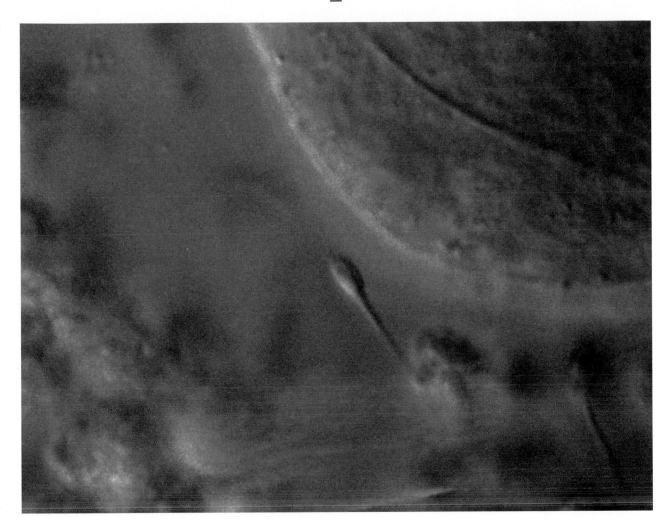

This demolition of your individual self-importance relied on the fact that a mechanism exists for the inevitable production of large numbers of human beings, given the important precondition that humans already exist. We've explored the road to human existence at length in the book already, and argued that complex multicellular life and intelligence at or beyond the level of humans may be rare in our universe. It is also clear that there are fundamental properties of the universe itself that are necessary for the existence of any form of life. The universe must live long enough and have the right properties for stars to form, and those stars must be capable of producing the chemical elements out of which living things are made, carbon being the most important. What do we mean by 'properties'? We are back to the nature of the laws of physics once again, because they describe the behaviour of matter and forces at the most fundamental level. The laws restrict the possible physical structures that are allowed to appear in the universe, and stars, planets and human beings are all examples of such possible physical structures. Questions now naturally arise; more modest perhaps than our grand 'Why are we here?' puzzle, but more amenable to scientific enquiry. How do the laws of nature allow for human beings to exist, and by how much could those laws vary before life could no longer exist in the universe?

Let us begin in the spirit of taking small steps with a brief summary of the known fundamental laws of nature.

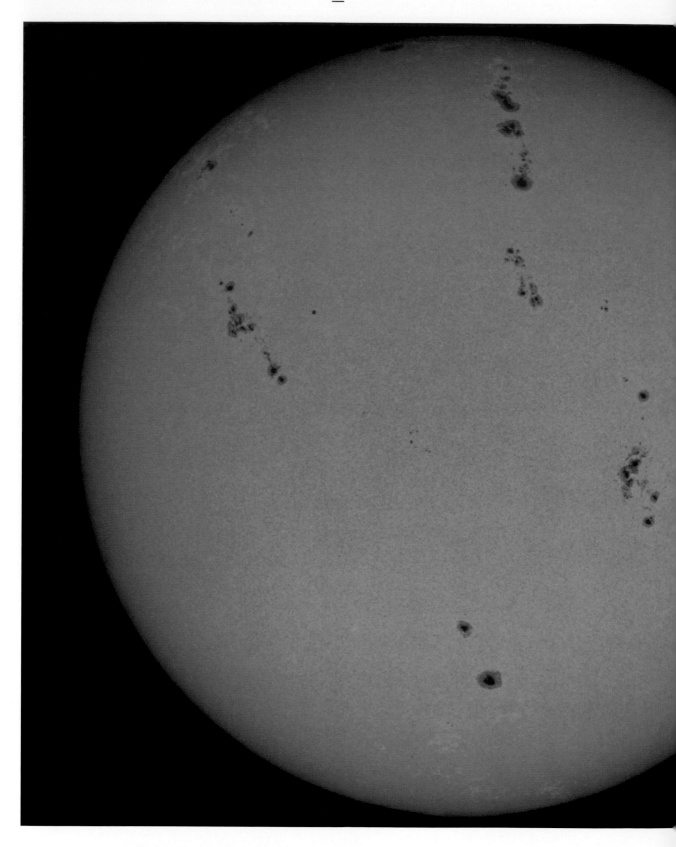

WHY ARE WE HERE?

THE RULES OF THE GAME

*What really interests me is whether God
had any choice in the creation of the world.*
Albert Einstein

Attempting to describe the laws that govern the existence of everything from galaxies to human beings in a single paragraph of a book of a TV series might seem overly ambitious. It is at one level; otherwise everyone would complete physics, chemistry and biology degree courses in an afternoon. What we can do, however, is to outline the known fundamental laws in a concise and accurate way, so let us do that.

There are twelve known particles of matter, listed on page 182. They are arranged into three families, or generations. You are made out of particles in the first generation alone. Up quarks and down quarks bind together to make protons and neutrons, which in turn bind together to form your atomic nuclei. Your atoms are composed of electrons bound to those nuclei. Molecules, such as water and DNA, are built up out of collections of atoms bound together. That's all there is to you; three fundamental particles arranged into patterns. Particles called gauge bosons carry the forces of nature. There are four known fundamental forces; the strong and weak nuclear forces, electromagnetism and gravity. Gravity is missing from the top figure on page 182, and we'll get to that in a moment. The other three forces are represented in the fourth column. To see how this all works, let's focus on the familiar electromagnetic force. Imagine an electron bound to the atomic nucleus of one of your atoms. How does that binding happen? The most fundamental description we have is that the electron can emit a photon, which you can think of as a particle of light. That photon can be absorbed by one of the quarks inside the nucleus, and this emission and absorption acts to assert a force between the electron and the quark. There is a vast number of ways in which the electrons and the quarks inside the nucleus can emit and absorb photons, and these all combine to keep the electron firmly glued to the nucleus. A similar picture can be applied to the quarks themselves. They also interact via the strong nuclear force by emitting and absorbing force-carrying particles called gluons. The strong nuclear force is the strongest known force (the clue is in the name) and binds the quarks together very tightly indeed. This is why the nucleus is significantly smaller and denser than the atom. Only quarks and gluons feel the strong nuclear force. Finally, there is the weak nuclear force. This is mediated by the exchange of the W and Z bosons. All known particles of matter feel the weak nuclear force but it is extremely weak relative to the other two, which is why its action is unfamiliar, but not unimportant. The Sun would not shine without the weak nuclear force, which allows protons to convert into neutrons, or more precisely up quarks into down quarks, which has the same result. This is the first step in the nuclear burning of hydrogen into helium, the source of the Sun's energy. During the conversion of a proton into a neutron, an anti-electron neutrino is produced along with an electron. The neutrino is the remaining particle in the first generation we haven't discussed yet. Because neutrinos only interact via the weak nuclear force, we are oblivious to them in everyday life. This is fortunate, because there are approximately sixty billion per square centimetre per second passing through your head from the nuclear reactions in the Sun. If the weak force were a little stronger, you'd get a hell of a headache. Actually, you wouldn't because you wouldn't exist, and this foreshadows the subject of the fine-tuning of the laws of nature we will undertake later in this chapter. The one remaining type of particle is the Higgs Boson, on its own in the fifth column. Empty space

THE POWER OF THE SUN
Without the weak nuclear force the Sun would not shine as it is an essential element in the Sun's energy production. We should be grateful it is still weak, otherwise life on Earth would be very uncomfortable.

ATLAS DETECTOR
ATLAS is one of six detector experiments being conducted at CERN, Geneva, at the Large Hadron Collider.

STANDARD MODEL

The Standard Model of particle physics is a theory that explains the interactions between sub-atomic particles in the form of the strong, weak and electromagnetic forces. The original theory has been tested experimentally since it was first postulated and has proven extremely robust. In 2013 the Higgs Boson that had been predicted by the theory was discovered using the Large Hadron Collider at CERN.

ELEMENTARY PARTICLES IN THE STANDARD MODEL

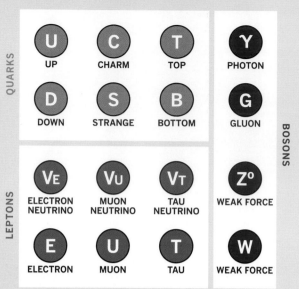

INSIDE THE ATOM

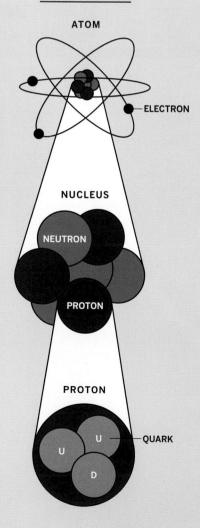

FUNDAMENTAL FORCES

		STRENGTH	RANGE (M)	PARTICLE
STRONG		1	10^{-15} (diameter of a medium-sized nucleus)	GLUONS
ELECTRO-MAGNETIC		$\frac{1}{137}$	INFINITE	PHOTON MASS = 0 SPIN = 0
WEAK		10^{-6}	10^{-8} (0.1% of the diameter of a proton)	INTERMEDIATE VECTOR BOSONS W^+ W^- Z^0 mass > 80 GeV spin = 1
GRAVITY		6×10^{-39}	INFINITE	Graviton ? mass = 0 spin = 2

isn't empty, but is jammed full of Higgs particles. All the known particles apart from the photon and the gluons, which are massless, interact with the Higgs particles, zigzagging through space and acquiring mass in the process. This is the counter-intuitive picture that was confirmed by the discovery of the Higgs Boson at CERN's Large Hadron Collider in 2012.

Two further generations of matter particles have been discovered. They are identical to the first generation except that the particles are more massive because they interact with Higgs particles more strongly. The muon, for example, is a more massive version of the familiar electron. The reason for their existence is unknown.

This is all there is in terms of the description of the fundamental ingredients of the universe. There are almost certainly other particles out there somewhere – the dark matter that dominates over normal matter in the universe by a factor of 5 to 1 is probably in the form of a new type of particle which we may discover at the Large Hadron Collider or a future particle accelerator. The evidence for dark matter is very strong and comes from astronomical observations of galaxy rotation speeds, galaxy formation models and the cosmic microwave background radiation that we met in Chapter 1 and will meet again later in this chapter. But because we don't know what form the dark matter takes, we are not able to incorporate it into our list.

The mathematical framework used to describe all the known particles and forces other than gravity is known as quantum field theory. It is a series of rules that allows the probability of any particular process occurring to be calculated. The whole thing can be described in one single equation, known as the Standard Model Lagrangian. Here it is:

$$L = -\frac{1}{4} W_{\mu v} W^{\mu v} - \frac{1}{4} B_{\mu v} B^{\mu v} - \frac{1}{4} G_{\mu v} G^{\mu v}$$

$$+ \overline{\psi}_j \gamma^\mu (i\delta_\mu - g\tau_j \cdot W_\mu - g' Y_j B_\mu - g_s T_j \cdot G_\mu) \psi_j$$

$$+ |D_\mu \phi|^2 + \mu^2 |\phi|^2 - \lambda |\phi|^4$$

$$- (y_j \overline{\psi}_{jL} \phi \psi_{jR} + y'_j \overline{\psi}_{jL} \phi_o \psi_{jR} + \text{conjugate})$$

It takes a lot of work to use this piece of mathematics to make predictions, but the predictions are spectacularly accurate and agree with every experimental measurement ever made in laboratories on Earth. This equation even predicted the existence of the Higgs particle; that's how good it is. It probably looks like a set of squiggles unless you are a professional physicist, but in fact it isn't too difficult to interpret, so let's dig just a little deeper. The 12 matter particles are all hidden away in the symbol ψ_j. The Standard Model is a quantum field theory because particles are represented by objects known as quantum fields. There is an electron field, an up quark field, a Higgs field and so on. The particles themselves can be thought of as localised vibrations in these fields, which span the whole of space. Fields will be important for us later, when we'll want to think about a certain type of field that may have appeared in the very early universe, known as a scalar field. The Higgs field is an example of a scalar field. The mathematical terms between the two ψ_js on the second line describe the forces and how they cause the particles to interact. The forces are also represented by quantum fields. The term $-g_s T_j \cdot G_\mu$ for example, describes the gluon field that allows the quarks in the ψ_j terms to bind together into protons and neutrons. The term g_s is known as the strong coupling constant. It is a fundamental property of our universe that encodes the strength of the strong nuclear force. Each of the forces has one of these coupling constants. We will want to discuss these coupling constants later, because they define what our universe is

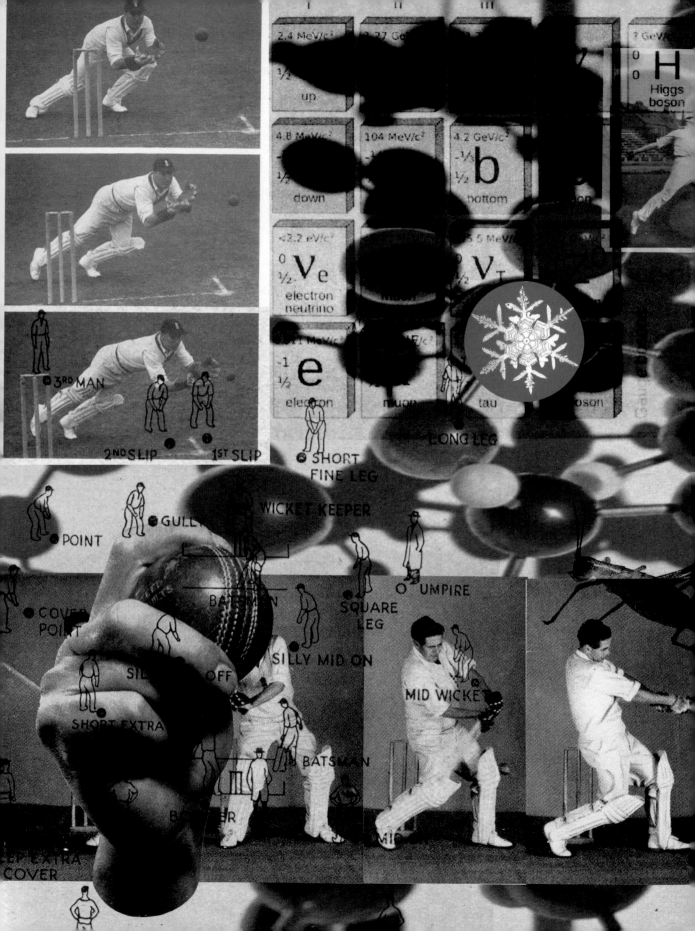

like and what is allowed to exist within it. The last two lines deal with the Higgs Boson. The strength of the interaction between a matter particle and the Higgs field is contained in the y_j terms, which are known as Yukawa couplings. These must be inserted to produce the observed masses of the particles of matter. That's pretty much it.

Here ends our crash course on particle physics. The central point is that there exists a remarkably economical description of everything other than gravity, and it is contained within the Standard Model.

We considered the gravitational force in some detail in Chapter 1. It is described by Einstein's Theory of General Relativity, which is what physicists call a classical theory. There are no force-carrying particles in Einstein's theory; instead the force is described in terms of the curvature of spacetime by matter and energy and the response of particles to that curvature. A quantum theory of gravity, which we have already noted will be necessary to describe the first fleeting moments in the history of the universe, would involve the exchange of particles known as gravitons, but as yet nobody has worked out how to construct such a description. This is why Einstein's theory remains the only fundamental non-quantum theory we have.

For completeness, let's refresh our memory of Einstein's Theory of General Relativity:

$$G_{\mu\nu} = 8\pi G T_{\mu\nu}$$

General Relativity, like the Standard Model, contains a coupling constant encoding the measured strength of gravity: G, Newton's gravitational constant. The amount of dark energy is inserted by hand, in accord with observations, as was the case for the strengths of the forces and the masses of the particles in the Standard Model.

General Relativity and the Standard Model are the rules of the game. They contain all our knowledge of the way that nature behaves at the most fundamental level. They also contain almost all the properties of our universe that we think of as fundamental. The speed of light, the strengths of the forces, the masses of the particles (encoded as the strength of their interaction with the Higgs Bosons via the Yukawa couplings) and the amount of dark energy are all in these equations. In principle, any known physical process can be described by them. This is the current state of the art, but it doesn't mean that we know how everything works and can all retire, by a long shot or well-timed cover drive.

Most games are skin-deep, but cricket goes to the bone.
John Arlott and Fred Trueman

I timed a cover drive properly once when I was 14 years old playing at Hollinwood Cricket Club near Oldham. Front foot, head in line with the ball, sweet sound of the middle, four runs. I know what I have to do, but I never did it quite as well again. Cricket is an art built on simple rules, first codified by the members of the Marylebone Cricket Club on 30 May 1788; a significant date in world history according to historians with good taste. Those original laws still form the basis of the game today. There are 42 of them, and they define the framework within which each game evolves. Yet despite the rigid framework, no two games are ever alike. The temperature and humidity of the air, a light scatter of dew on the grass, the height of grass on the wicket, and hundreds of other factors will subtly shift and change throughout the game. More importantly, the players and umpires are each complex biological systems whose behaviour is far from predictable, with the exception of Geoffrey Boycott. The presence of so many variables makes the number of possible permutations effectively

A GENIUS AT WORK
Einstein's manuscript for his General Theory of Relativity is a historic piece of work-in-progress.

DARK MATTER
This makes up 26.8 per cent of the total energy of the observable universe and is not described within the Standard Model. It is likely that dark matter will take the form of a new type of particle, or family of particles. There are extensions to the Standard Model, the simplest of which is known as the Minimal Supersymmetric Standard Model, which are capable of describing dark matter, and we have no reason to suspect that an entirely new framework beyond quantum field theory will be needed if and when the nature of dark matter is discovered.

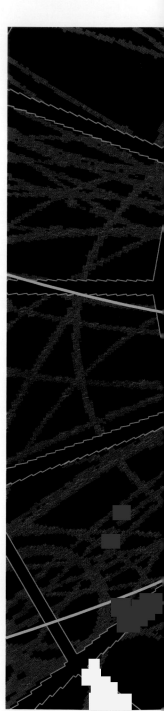

PRODUCING QUARK-GLUON PLASMA
This computer simulation reveals the type of particle collision that occurs within the Large Hadron Collider which is expected to produce quark-gluon plasma.

infinite, which is why cricket is the most interesting of human pursuits excluding science, sex and wine tasting.

Knowledge of the laws is therefore insufficient to characterise the infinite magic of the game. This is also true for the universe. The laws of nature define the framework within which things happen, but do not ensure that everything that can happen will happen in a finite universe – that rather obscure 'finite' caveat will be important for us later on. Virtually all of science beyond particle physics and theoretical

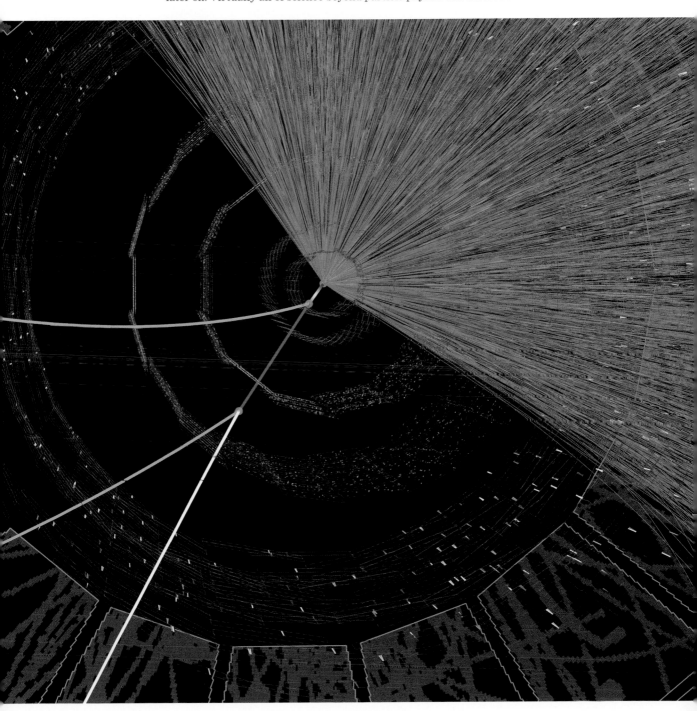

WHY ARE WE HERE?

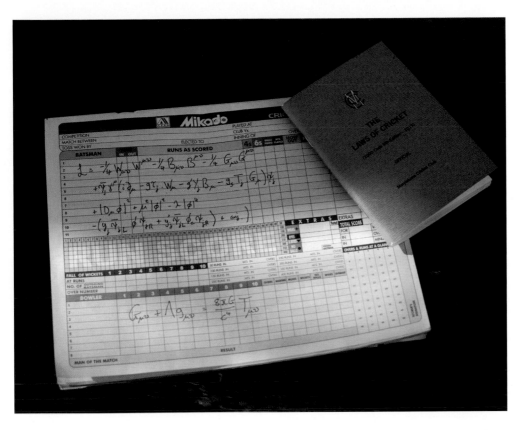

THE NATURE OF CRICKET
Just as in cricket, the laws of
nature have been set down
by watching the game of the
universe unfold, which is
what makes it, and the game
of cricket, so unique, and
ultimately so unpredictable.

cosmology is concerned with the complex outcomes allowed by the laws rather than the laws themselves, and in a certain sense our solipsistic initial question 'Why are we here?' is also a question about outcomes rather than laws. The answer to the question 'Why did England beat Australia in the great Ashes series of 2005?' is not to be found in the MCC rule book, and similarly the natural world that emerges from the Standard Model and General Relativity cannot be understood simply by discovering the laws themselves.

It's worth noting that the laws of nature were not written by the MCC, or even the committee of Yorkshire County Cricket Club. We had to work them out by watching the game of the universe unfold, which makes their discovery even more wonderful. Imagine how many matches would have to be viewed in order to deduce the laws of cricket, including but not restricted to the Duckworth Lewis method? The great achievement of twenty-first-century science is that we've managed to work out the laws of nature by doing just this; observing many millions of complex outcomes and working out what the underlying laws are.

The Standard Model, then, cannot be used to describe complex emergent systems such as living things. No biologist would attempt to understand the way that ATP is produced inside cells using the Standard Model Lagrangian and no telecommunications engineer would use it to design an optical fibre. They wouldn't want to even if they could; you wouldn't gain any insight into how a car engine works by starting off with a description of its constituent subatomic particles and their interactions. So whilst it is important that we have a detailed model of nature at the level of the known fundamental building blocks, we must also understand how the complexity we observe around us emerges from these simple laws if we are to make progress with our difficult 'Why?' question.

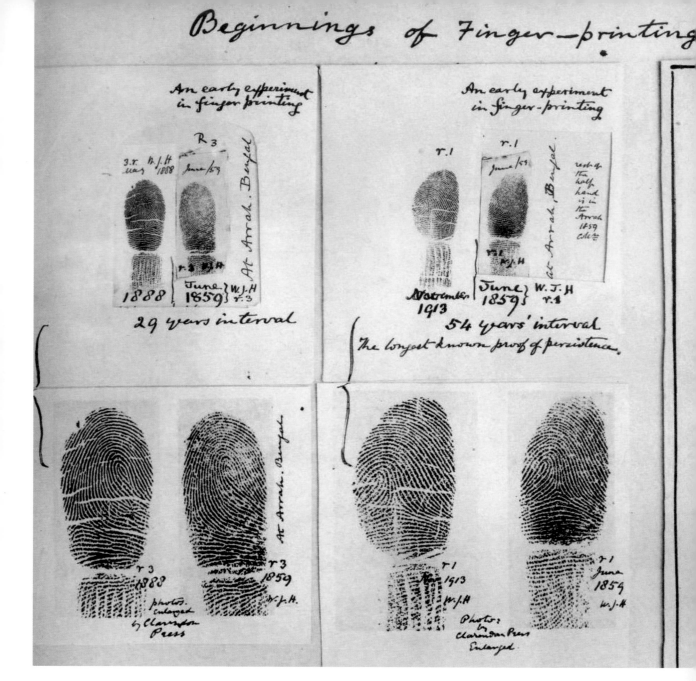

Beginnings of Finger-printing

NATURE'S FINGERPRINT

When you have eliminated the impossible, whatever
remains, however improbable, must be the truth.
Sherlock Holmes

On Monday 27 March 1905 at 8.30am, William Jones arrived at
Chapman's Oil and Colour Shop on Deptford High Street ready for a
day's work. Jones normally arrived a few minutes after the shop manager
Thomas Farrow had raised the shutters. On this particular Monday,
however, the shutters were down. Farrow lived with his wife Anne
above the shop, but no matter how hard Jones knocked on their door,

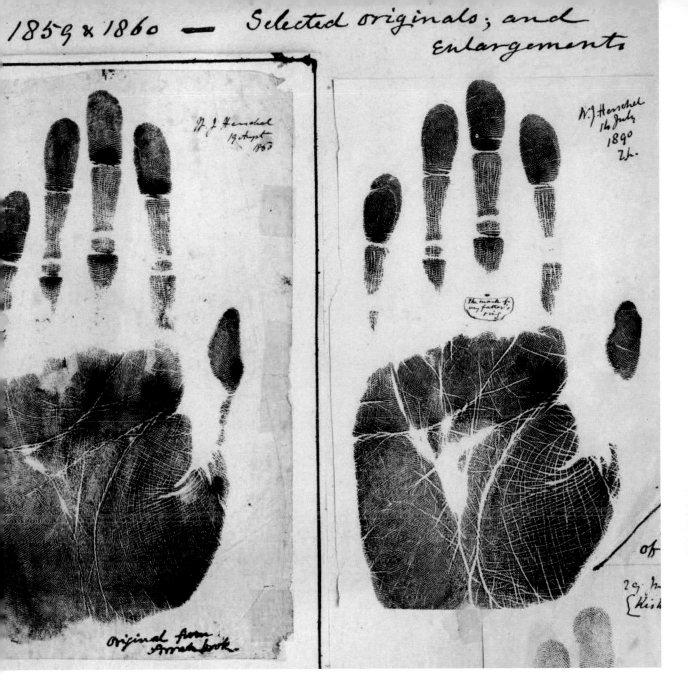

1859 & 1860 — Selected originals; and enlargements

H. J. Herschel 19 August 1860

H. J. Herschel 16 July 1890 Zh.

the mark of my father's proof

Original from [Arrest] book.

there was no response. This was a most unusual start to the day, and his concern increased when a glimpse through a window revealed chairs strewn across the floor of the normally tidy shop. Jones and another local resident forced the door, to be confronted by Farrow lying dead in a pool of blood. Anne had been similarly bludgeoned in her bed, although she clung to life for four more days without regaining consciousness.

Such scenes were not uncommon in Edwardian London. The reason that this crime is of note is because it was the first in the world to use a new technology to catch and convict the killers. On an inner surface of the empty cash box, the police noticed a fingerprint. They already had a suspect; a local man named Alfred Stratton, who was arrested three days later along with his brother Albert. The Strattons' fingerprints were taken, and a positive match was made between the cash-box print and

COMPLEX CLUES OF THE UNIVERSE
The uncovering of the uniqueness of fingerprints changed the face of police work in the early twentieth century. Although fingerprints appear intricate and complex, the process by which they were formed is far simpler.

Alfred Stratton's right thumb. Although never used before in a murder case, expert witnesses convinced the jury that the complex patterns of the cash-box fingerprint could only belong to Alfred Stratton. The jury took just two hours to find the Stratton brothers guilty of murder, and the pair were sentenced to death by hanging, with justice swiftly dispatched on 23 May.

Take a look at your fingerprints now; there is seemingly endless complexity in the swirls and ridges. Since every human being carries different fingerprints on the hands and the soles of their feet (which aren't fingerprints, but there isn't a word for them), the size of database required to characterise every human being's fingerprints would be colossal. One of the most important properties of nature, however, is that the blueprints for the construction of the natural world are far simpler than the natural world itself. In modern language, there is a tremendous amount of data compression going on. The instructions to create fingerprints are far simpler than the fingerprints themselves, and more than that, the same instructions, run over and over again from slightly different starting points in the embryonic stage of our development, always lead to different fingerprints. This behaviour shouldn't come as a

SHIFTING SANDS
The formation of sand dunes and patterns within deserts may appear arbitrary but is in fact the product of simple laws which govern their movement.

surprise. The sweep of desert dunes or the patterns in summer clouds are all described by a handful of simple laws governing how sand grains or water droplets behave when agitated by shifting air currents, buffeted by chaotic thermals and winds and re-ordered by the action of the forces of nature. And yet from a simple recipe, complexity emerges.

The quest to understand how the boundless variety of the natural world emerges from underlying simplicity has been a central theme in philosophical and scientific thought. Plato attempted to cast the world available to our senses as the distorted and imperfect shadow of an underlying reality of perfect forms, accessible through reason alone. The modern expression of Plato's ethereal dualism was captured eloquently by Galileo, 500 years ago: 'The book of nature is written in the language of mathematics'. The challenge is not only to discern the underlying mathematical behaviour of the world, but also to work back upwards along the chain of complexity to explain how those forms that Plato would have defined as imperfect arise from the assumed lower-level perfection. A rather beautiful early example of this quest is provided by Galileo's illustrious contemporary, Johannes Kepler.

A STUDY IN SKIN
Each fingerprint reminds us that although they originate from simple starting points, their development will always lead to different results.

A BRIEF HISTORY OF THE SNOWFLAKE

As I write it has begun to snow, and more thickly than a
moment ago. I have been busily examining the little flakes.
Johannes Kepler

Johannes Kepler is rightly best known for his laws of Planetary Motion that paved the way for Newton to write *Principia*. Hidden within his illustrious CV, however, is a publication that had a rather more whimsical earthbound ambition. Two years after publishing the first part of *Astronomia Nova* in 1609, Kepler published a short 24-page paper entitled *De nive sexangula – On the Six-Cornered Snowflake*. It is a beautiful example of a curious scientific mind at work. In the dark December of 1610, Kepler was walking across the Charles Bridge in Prague when a snowflake fell on the lapel of his coat. In the freezing night he stopped and wondered why this ephemeral sliver of ice possessed a six-sided structure, in common with all other snowflakes, notwithstanding their seemingly infinite variation (see next page). Others had noticed this symmetry before, but Kepler realised that the symmetry of a snowflake must be a reflection of the deeper natural processes that underlie its formation.

'Since it always happens when it begins to snow, that the first particles of snow adopt the shape of small six-cornered stars, there must be a particular cause,' wrote Kepler, 'for if it happened by chance, why would they always fall with six corners and not with five, or seven?' Kepler hypothesised that this symmetry must be due to the nature of the fundamental building blocks of snowflakes. This stacking of frozen 'globules', as he referred to it, must be the most efficient way of building a snowflake from the 'smallest natural unit of a liquid like water'.

To my mind, this is a leap of genius and a tremendously modern way of thinking about physics. The study of symmetry in nature lies at the very heart of the Standard Model, and abstract symmetries known as gauge symmetries are now known to be the origin of the forces of nature. This is why the force-carrying particles in the Standard Model are known as gauge bosons. Kepler was searching for the atomic structure of snow before we knew atoms existed, motivated by the observation of a symmetry in nature – the six-sided shape of all snowflakes. The inspiration for this idea, which is way ahead of its time, came from a peculiar source. In the years leading up to the publication of *De nive sexangula*, Kepler had been in communication with Thomas Harriot, an English mathematician and explorer. Amongst multiple claims to fame, Harriot was the navigator on one of Sir Walter Raleigh's voyages to the New World, and had been asked to solve a seemingly simple mathematical problem. Raleigh wanted to know how best to stack cannonballs to make the most efficient use of the limited space on the ship's deck. Harriot was driven to exploring the mathematical principles of sphere packing, which in turn led him to develop an embryonic model of atomic theory and inspire Kepler's consideration of the structure of snowflakes. Kepler imagined replacing cannonballs with globules of ice, and supposed that the most efficient arrangement creating the greatest density of globules was the six-sided hexagonal form he observed in the snowflake on his shoulder. Kepler also observed hexagonal structures across the natural world, from beehives to pomegranates and snowflakes, and presumed that there must be some deeper reason for its ubiquity.

'Hexagonal packing', as Kepler referred to it, must be 'the tightest possible, so that in no other arrangement could more pellets be stuffed into the same container'. This became known as the Kepler Conjecture. It took almost 400 years to prove Kepler's conjecture, and this required the help of a 1990s supercomputer. Despite the time lag, Kepler's work

THE SYMMETRY OF SNOWFLAKES
A snowy walk in Prague led Johannes Kepler to formulate what became known as the Kepler Conjecture, based on the symmetrical, hexagonal structure of the snowflakes that settled around him.

had a more immediate impact, inspiring the beginnings of modern crystallography that led eventually to the discovery of the structure of DNA. What a lovely example of serendipity coupled with curiosity and a sprinkling of genius; from cannonballs to snowflakes to the code of life.

As for Kepler's original thought on that frozen bridge, he never found the connection between the underlying structure of his ice globules and the hexagonal symmetry of snowflakes. Even though he realised that the regular patterns must reveal something about the shape of the building blocks of snowflakes and the details of the packing, he couldn't explain the ornate complexity or the flatness of the structure. Instead he acknowledged his failure with the good grace of a true scientist: 'I have knocked on the doors of chemistry' he writes at the end of his paper, 'and

Philos. Trans. Vol. XLIX. TAB. XXI. p.647.

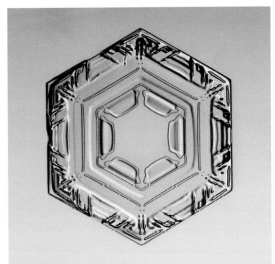

seeing how much remains to be said on this subject before we know the cause, I would rather hear what you think, my most ingenious man, than wear myself out with further discussion.'

Three and a half centuries later, Japanese physicist Ukichiro Nakayara made the first artificial snowflakes in a laboratory. Writing in 1954, he describes a process that begins not with the snowflake itself but with smaller substructures called snow crystals, which are in turn built up from collections of ice crystals – the globules Kepler was searching for. The hexagonal packing that Kepler suspected to be the origin of the snowflakes' symmetry begins with the formation of these ice crystals, when water molecules link together in a hexagonal structure via hydrogen bonds. Hydrogen bonding occurs because of the structure of the water molecules themselves, with a greedy oxygen atom hungry for electrons grabbing them off two hydrogen atoms, forming covalent bonds that lock the H_2O molecules together, leaving a residual positive electrical charge in the vicinity of the two protons and a negative charge in the vicinity of the oxygen. This slight separation of charge in the water molecules allows them to bind together into larger structures through the mutual attraction and repulsion of the electrical charges, just as an electron is bound into its position around an atomic nucleus. The entire configuration, including the structure of the oxygen nucleus and the single protons that comprise the hydrogen nuclei, can be predicted in principle by the Standard Model of particle physics. Yet the details of any particular snowflake are beyond computation, because the seemingly infinite variety reflects the precise history of the snowflake itself. Once ice crystals form as agglomerations of water molecules held together by hydrogen bonds, they cluster around dust particles in the air, building on their underlying hexagonal symmetry to form larger snow crystals. As the crystals begin the long journey down to Earth they join in ever-larger, more complex combinations, shaped by endless variations of air temperature, wind patterns and humidity into myriad unique forms. The symmetry is all that remains of the simplicity, and it takes a careful and patient eye to see the endless variation for what it is; a reflection of the complex history of the snowflake convoluted with the underlying simplicity of the laws of nature.

The most vivid example of emergent complexity, and the closest to our hearts, is life. As we discussed in Chapter 2, the origin of life on Earth has a sense of inevitability about it, because its basic processes are chemical reactions that will proceed given the right conditions. Those conditions were present in the oceans of Earth 3.8 billion years ago, possibly earlier, and they led to the emergence of single-celled organisms. The fateful encounter which produced the eukaryotic cell around 2 billion years ago looks rather more like blind chance, but it happened here and laid the foundations for the Cambrian explosion 530 million years ago. There is a bit of hand-waving going on here, though, and to make a more persuasive case that all the complexity of Darwin's endless forms most beautiful can at least in principle emerge from simple underlying laws, one more example is in order.

Perhaps the most beautiful manifestation of the artful complexity of nature can be found in the spots, stripes and patterns on the coats and skin of living things; emergent pattern writ large across venomous striped surgeonfish, emperor angelfish, zebra swallowtail butterflies and the big cats of Africa and Asia. Everyone agrees that these patterns evolved as a result of natural selection of one form or another, and the raw material for the variation was provided by random mutations in the genetic code. But a very challenging scientific question of fundamental importance in modern biology is precisely how patterns such as these appear.

NEW PERSPECTIVES
Johannes Kepler got the scientific world talking about and observing snowflakes in a whole new light. English scientist Robert Hooke published his sketches and observations in *Micrographia: or some physiological descriptions of minute bodies made by magnifying glasses, with observations and enquiries thereupon* in 1665.

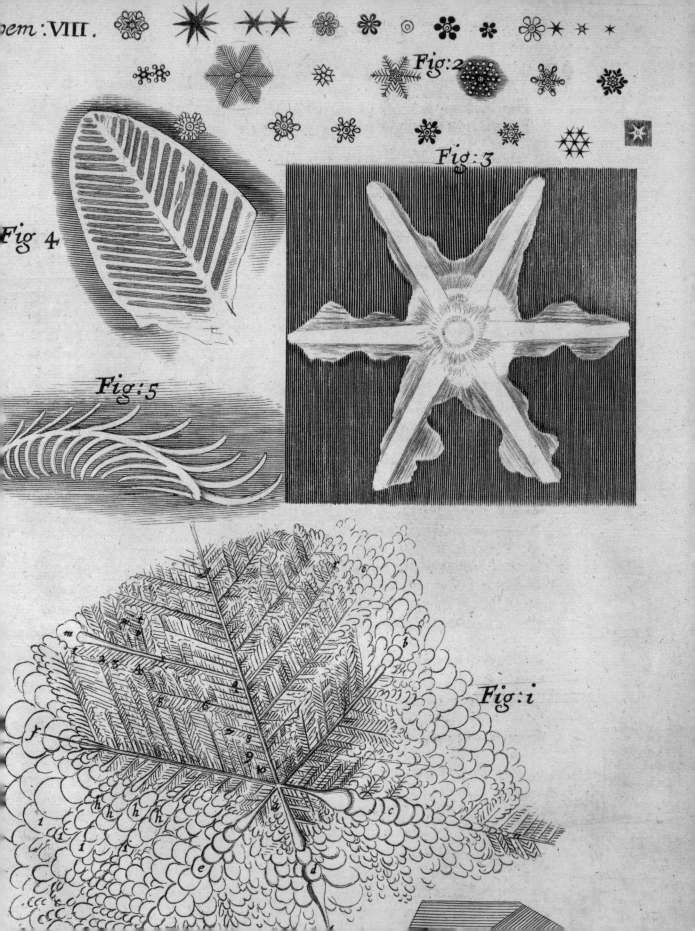

Fig: 2

Fig: 3

Fig 4

Fig: 5

Fig: i

ART IN NATURE
The natural world illustrates its complexity even through the simplest observation of appearance. Patterns reveal themselves through spots and stripes on animal hides and skins and in the composition of plants and their fruits, as in this Romanesco broccoli.

HOW THE LEOPARD GOT ITS SPOTS

*...Zebra moved away to some little thorn-bushes where the sunlight fell all
stripy and the Giraffe moved off to some tallish trees where the shadows fell
all blotchy.
'Now watch,' said the zebra and the giraffe. 'This is the way it's done. One...
two...three! And where's your breakfast!' ... All they could see were stripy
shadows and blotched shadows in the forest, but never a sign of Zebra and
Giraffe.
'That's a trick worth learning. Take a lesson from it, Leopard!'
...Then the Ethiopian put his five fingers close together and pressed them
all over the leopard, and wherever the five fingers
touched, they left five black marks, all close together...
Rudyard Kipling*

Rudyard Kipling's *Just So* story, 'How The Leopard Got His Spots', tells the story of an Ethiopian man and a leopard. They went hunting together, but one day the man noticed that the leopard wasn't very successful. The reason, he deduced, was that the leopard had a plain sandy coat, whereas all the other animals had camouflage. 'That's a trick worth learning, leopard' he said, taking his fingers and thumb and pressing them into the leopard's coat to give it the distinctive five-pointed pattern. If you don't believe in evolution by natural selection, this is the most plausible theory open to you. If you do, then what remains is to identify the mechanism by which the pattern is formed. The answer might appear to be solely a matter of genetics, but genes are not the whole story. It would take a terrific amount of information to instruct every single cell to colour itself according to its position on the leopard's skin, and this is indeed not what is done. Nature is frugal and deploys a much more efficient mechanism for producing camouflage patterns. As with so many things in this book, I get to say yet again that this is an active area of research, and therefore exciting. The reason for the attention is that camouflage patterns on the skin self-organise during the development of the embryo, and embryonic development is of course fundamental to an understanding of biology. In the case of the leopard, it is thought, though not proven, that the camouflage is an example of a Turing pattern, named after the great Bletchley Park code-breaker and mathematician Alan Turing.

In 1952, Turing became interested in morphogenesis – the process by which an animal develops its shape and patterning. He was particularly interested in the mathematics behind regularly repeating patterns in nature such as the Fibonacci numbers and golden ratio in the leaf arrangements of plants and the scales of pineapples, and the appearance of camouflage patterns such as the tiger's stripes and the leopard's spots. Turing's influential and ground-breaking paper, 'The Chemical Basis of Morphogenesis', published in March 1952, begins with a simple statement. 'It is suggested that a system of chemical substances, called morphogens, reacting together and diffusing through a tissue, is adequate to account for the main phenomena of morphogenesis.' These systems are known as reaction diffusion systems, and they can produce patterns from a featureless initial mixture if the two reactants diffuse at different speeds. There is a nice analogy that describes how such a system can work. Imagine a dry field full of grasshoppers. They are strange grasshoppers, because when they get warm they sweat, generating a large amount of moisture. Now imagine that the field is set alight in several different places. The flames will spread at some fixed speed, and if there were no grasshoppers the whole field would be charred. As the flames approach the grasshoppers, however, they will start to sweat, dampening the grass behind them and inhibiting the flames as they hop away ahead of the approaching flames. Depending on the different parameters, including the different speeds of the flames and the grasshoppers, and the amount of sweat necessary to quell the advancing flames, a Turing pattern can be formed, with areas of charred grass and green areas where the inhibiting grasshoppers prevented the fire from taking hold.

It is thought that the leopard gets its spots in this way during embryonic development: an activator chemical (fire) spreads through the skin and stimulates the production of the dark pigmented spots (charred grass) but is inhibited by another chemical (sweating grasshoppers) spreading with a higher diffusion rate. The precise pattern produced depends on the 'constants of nature' of the system, such as the speeds at which the chemicals diffuse, and on what a mathematician would call the boundary conditions: the size and geometry of the grassy field in our analogy. In embryonic development, it is the size and shape of the embryo when the reaction-diffusion begins that determines the type of

pattern produced. A long and thin domain produces stripes. A domain that is too small or too large produces uniform colour. In between can be found the distinctive coat patterns of cows, giraffe, cheetah and, of course, the leopard. Computer simulations of Turing patterns have been remarkably successful, not only in describing the generic features, particularly of mammalian coats, but also some of the interesting details seen in nature. For example, the mathematical models predict that it is possible for spotted animals to have stripped tails, as cheetahs do, but not for striped animals to have spotted tails; and indeed, no such examples exist.

Kepler's snowflakes and the leopard's spots are two picturesque examples of emergent complexity: the appearance of intricate, ordered patterns from the action of simple underlying laws. Nature contains systems far more complex than these, of course: you being a case in point. But to return to the question at the beginning of our solipsistic meander, the reason that you exist, given the laws of nature, is that you

CHEMICAL WAVES
The chemical waves in this solution demonstrate the theory that just a tiny alteration in conditions or contents can cause an altered image, such as a dust particle on the surface or the level of moisture in the air.

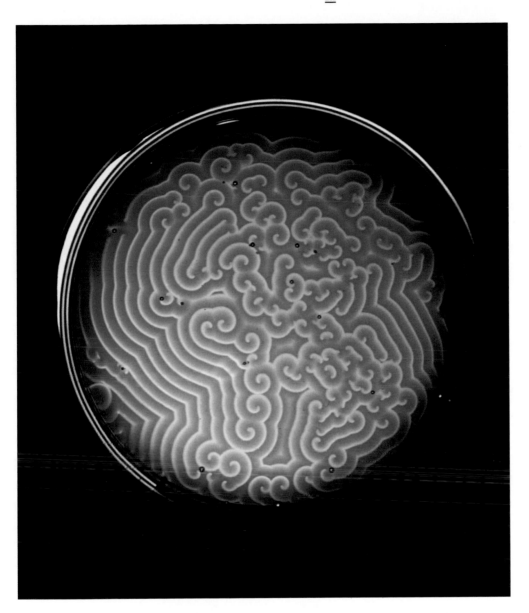

are allowed to. Just as all snowflakes and all leopards' coats are unique in detail because of their individual formation histories, so you are unique because no two human beings share a common history. But we wouldn't read any deep meaning into the existence of one particular snowflake in a snowstorm, and the same is true for you. Our focus should therefore shift from trying to explain the appearance of humans, or our planet, or even our galaxy, to a rather deeper question: the origin of the whole framework – of spacetime and the laws that govern it and the allowed structures within it. What properties of the laws themselves are essential for galaxies, planets and human beings to exist? After all, as we've noted, the laws might be mathematically elegant and economical, but they do contain a whole host of seemingly randomly chosen numbers, discovered by experimental observation and with no known rhyme or reason to them – the constants of nature such as the strengths of the forces, the masses of the particles and the amount of dark energy in the universe. How dependent is our existence on these fundamental numbers?

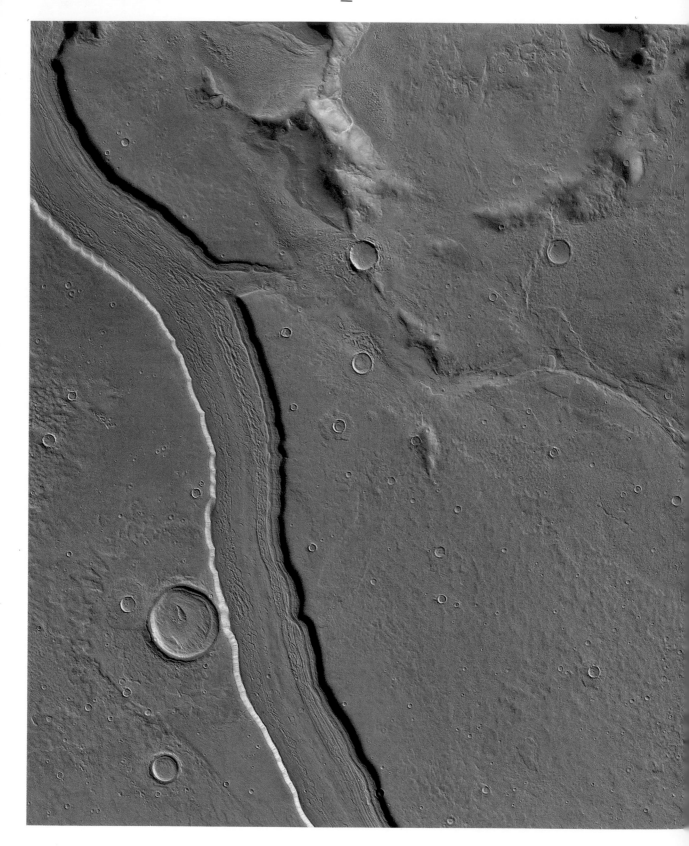

WHY ARE WE HERE?

Ongoing research hopes
to reveal that nature on all
planets within the galaxies
plays a major part in shaping
their landscapes. This image,
taken by the ESA Mars Express
Orbiter on 14 May 2012,
reveals a surface texture and
a river-like channel that have
been sculpted by flowing
water sometime in the planet's
ancient past.

A UNIVERSE MADE FOR US?

Our universe appears to be made for us. We live on a perfect planet, orbiting around a perfect star. This is of course content-free whimsy. The argument is backwards. We have to be a perfect fit for the planet because we evolved on it. But there are interesting questions when we look deeper into the laws of nature and ask what properties they must have to support a life in the universe. Take the existence of stars, for example. Stars like the Sun burn hydrogen into helium in their cores. This process involves all four forces of nature working together. Gravity kicks it all off by causing clouds of dust and gas to collapse. As the clouds collapse, they get denser and hotter until the conditions are just right for nuclear fusion to occur. Fusion starts by turning protons into neutrons through the action of the weak nuclear force. The strong nuclear force binds the protons and neutrons together into a helium nucleus, which in itself exists on account of the delicate balance between the strong nuclear force holding it together and the electromagnetic force trying to blow it apart because of the electrically charged protons. When stars run out of hydrogen fuel, they perform another series of equally precarious nuclear reactions to build carbon, oxygen, and the other heavy elements essential for the existence of life. What happens if the strengths of the forces, those fundamental constants of nature we met earlier in the chapter, are varied a bit?

There are many examples of apparent fine-tuning in nature. If protons were 0.2 per cent more massive, then they would be unstable and decay into neutrons. That would certainly put an end to life in the universe because there would be no atoms. The proton mass is ultimately set by the details of the strong and electromagnetic forces, and the masses of the constituent quarks, which are set by the Yukawa couplings to the Higgs field in the Standard Model. There really isn't much freedom at all.

The mother of all fine-tunes, however, is the value of our old friend dark energy, the thing that is causing our universe to gently accelerate in its expansion. Although dark energy contributes 68 per cent of the energy density of the universe, the amount of dark energy in a given volume of space is actually small. Very small: 10^{-27}kg per cubic metre to be precise. The point is that every cubic metre of our universe has this amount of dark energy in it, and that adds up! Explaining why dark energy has this small, but non-zero, value is one of the great problems in cosmology, not least because if a particle physicist sits down with quantum field theory and decides to calculate how big it should be, it turns out that it would be more naturally of the order of 10^{97}kg per cubic metre. That's a lot bigger than 10^{-27}kg per cubic metre. Over a million times bigger, in fact. That's embarrassing for the particle physicists, of course, but from the perspective of fine-tuning it's even worse. If the value of dark energy were only 50 times larger than it is in our universe, rather than somewhere else in this immensely large theoretical range, then it would have become dominant in the universe around one billion years after the Big Bang during the time that the first galaxies were forming. Because dark energy acts to accelerate the universe's expansion and dilute matter and dark matter, gravity would have lost the battle in such a universe and no galaxies, or stars, or planets or life would exist. What could possibly account for this incredible piece of luck? It can't really be luck – the odds are too long by a Geoffrey Boycott innings. One possibility is that there is some as yet unknown physical law or symmetry that guarantees that the amount of dark energy will be very close to, but not quite, zero. This is certainly possible, and there are physicists who believe that this may be the case. The other possibility, which was raised by one of the fathers of

the Standard Model, Steven Weinberg, is that the value of dark energy is anthropically selected. Anthropic arguments appear at one level to be a statement of the obvious: the properties of the universe must be such that human beings can exist because human beings do exist. This is, of course, true, but it is fairly devoid of content from a physical perspective *unless* there is some way in which all possible values of dark energy, and indeed all the other constants of nature, are realised somewhere. If, for example, there exists a vast, possibly infinite swathe of different domains in the universe, or indeed an infinity of other universes, each with a different amount of dark energy selected by some mechanism from the span of allowed values, then we would indeed have a valid anthropic explanation

DARK MATTER DETECTOR
The LUX Dark Matter Detector.

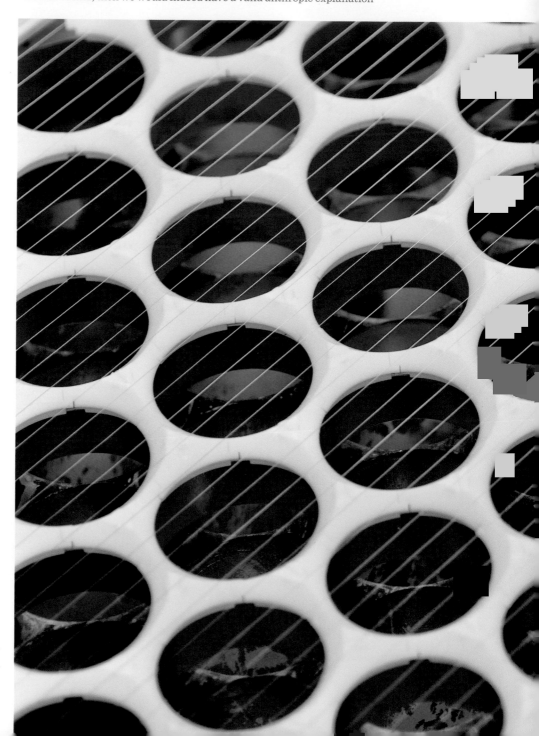

for our 'special' human universe. It must exist, because they all do, and of course we appear in the one that permits our existence.

But surely it makes no sense to take refuge in a vast infinity of universes to explain our existence? Absolutely correct, if that's why the idea is introduced – it's no better than a God-of-the-gaps explanation. If, however, there were some other reason, based on observations and theoretical understanding, that suggested an infinity of universes, then such an anthropic explanation for our perfect, human universe would be admissible. Remarkably – and that remarkably overused word is appropriate for once – this outlandish suggestion is a widely held view amongst many cosmologists.

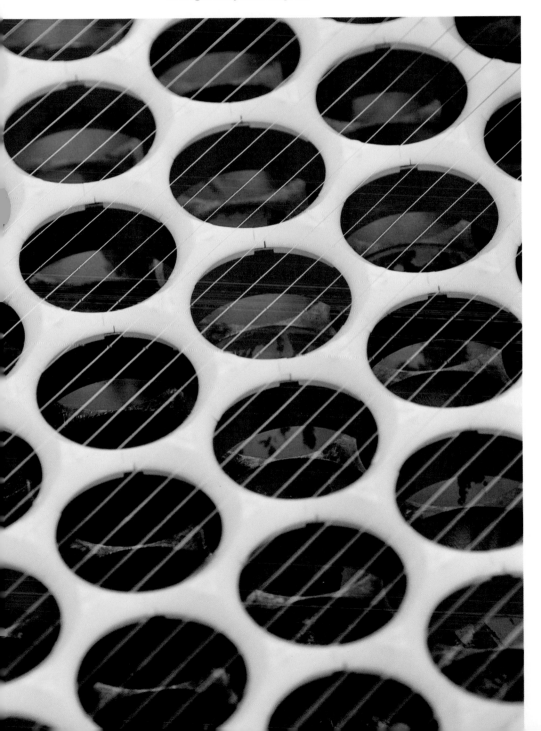

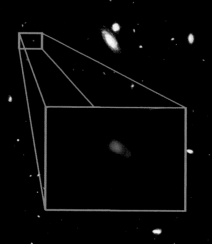

A DAY WITHOUT YESTERDAY?

It suddenly struck me that that tiny pea, pretty and blue, was the Earth.
I put up my thumb and shut one eye and my thumb blotted out the planet
Earth. I didn't feel like a giant. I felt very, very small.
Neil Armstrong

If we look at our universe on the largest distance scales, by which I mean at distance scales far larger than the size of single galaxies, it has a number of properties that any theory of its origin has to explain. The most precise picture of the young universe we have is the photograph of the Cosmic Microwave Background Radiation (CMB) taken by the Planck satellite.

This is the afterglow of the Big Bang, a photograph of the universe as it was 380,000 years after the initial hot, dense phase when the expansion had cooled things down sufficiently for atoms to form. The most obvious feature of the CMB is that it is extremely uniform, glowing at a temperature of 2.72548 degrees above absolute zero, with small fluctuations at the level of 1 part in 100,000. Those very tiny temperature differences are represented by the colours in the photograph. This uniformity is extremely difficult to explain in the standard Big Bang model for a simple reason. Our observable universe today is 90 billion light years across. This means that if we look out to the CMB from opposite sides of the Earth, we are looking at two glowing parts of the ancient sky that are now separated by 90 billion light years. The universe, however, is only 13.8 billion years old, which means that light, the fastest thing there is, has only had time to travel 13.8 billion light years. Two 'opposite' parts of the CMB could therefore never have been in contact with each other in the standard Big Bang model, and there is absolutely no reason why they should be *almost* precisely the same temperature. I've italicised 'almost' in the previous sentence because, as we noted, there are very slight variations in the CMB at the level of 1 part in 100,000, and these are very important. The universe was never completely smooth and uniform everywhere, and these variations in density are encoded into the CMB as differences in temperature. The regions of slightly greater density ultimately seeded the formation of the galaxies, and so without them we wouldn't exist. What caused these small variations in the otherwise ultra-smooth early universe?

Another fundamental property of the universe that is difficult to explain is its curvature – or lack of it – which can also be measured from the CMB. Space appears to be absolutely flat; a veritable ice rink. Recall from Chapter 1 that the shape of space is related to the density and distribution of matter and energy in the universe through Einstein's equations. In the standard Big Bang theory, the universe doesn't have to be flat. In fact, it requires a great deal of fine-tuning to keep it flat over 13.8 billion years of cosmic evolution. Instead, the radius of curvature is measured to be much greater than the radius of the observable universe – more than sixty orders of magnitude larger. That's a big problem!

In the early 1980s, the need to explain these and other properties of the observable universe led a group of Russian and American physicists to propose a radical idea. The modern version, the best-known proponents of which are Alan Guth, Andrei Linde and Alexei Starobinsky, is known as the Theory of Inflation. We'll describe a particular version of inflation below, driven by something called a scalar field, which was first described by Andrei Linde.

Spacetime existed before the Big Bang, and for at least some of that time was described by Einstein's Theory of General Relativity and a quantum field theory like the Standard Model. The central idea in quantum theory is that anything that can happen does happen.

THE COSMIC MICROWAVE BACKGROUND RADIATION

The Cosmic Microwave Background Radiation, photographed by the European Space Agencies Planck Satellite. The photograph is of the entire celestial sphere, which is why it has this distinctive oval shape; you might think of it as a map of the surface of the Earth, which can be represented on a flat piece of paper in the same way. The colours correspond to very slight variations in the density of the universe 380,000 years after the Big Bang.

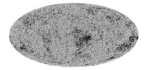

Everything that is not explicitly ruled out by the laws of nature will happen, given enough time. One of the types of things permitted to exist in quantum field theory are scalar fields. We've met an example of a scalar field earlier in the chapter in the guise of the Higgs field, which we know to exist because we've measured it at the Large Hadron Collider. Scalar fields have the property that they can cause space to expand exponentially fast. We touched on such a scenario in Chapter 1 without being explicit about the mechanism – it is the de Sitter's matter-less solution to Einstein's field equations first discovered in 1917. Given general relativity and quantum field theory, therefore, it must be the case that scalar fields will fluctuate into existence in such a way that an exponential expansion of spacetime is triggered. In this exponential phase, spacetime expands faster than the speed of light. This might sound problematic if you know some relativity, but it isn't. The universal speed limit exists for particles moving through spacetime, but does not apply for the expansion of spacetime itself. In a tiny fraction of a second – around 10^{-35} seconds in fact – an exponential expansion of this type can inflate a piece of spacetime as tiny as the Planck length to a quite mind-boggling size: trillions of times larger than the observable universe. Any pre-existing curvature is completely washed out, leading to a flat observable universe. It's like looking at a square centimetre-sized piece of the surface of a balloon of a light year in radius; you won't see any curvature, no matter how hard you try.

Likewise any variations in density will be washed out, leading to the smooth and uniform appearance of the CMB. Perhaps the greatest triumph of inflationary models such as these, however, is that they don't predict a completely uniform, homogeneous and isotropic universe. Quantum theory doesn't allow for absolute uniformity. Empty space is never empty, but a fizzing, shifting soup of all possible quantum fields. Like the surface of a stormy ocean, waves in the fields are constantly rising and falling, and the exponential expansion can freeze these undulations into the universe. Remarkably, when calculations using the known laws of quantum theory are carried out, the sort of density fluctuations that result from such a mechanism are precisely of the form seen in the CMB. These quantum fluctuations are the seeds of the galaxies and therefore the seeds of our existence, frozen into the oldest light in the cosmos and photographed by a satellite built by the people of Earth 13.8 billion years later.

Inflation in this guise explains the observable properties of our universe, and in particular all the details of the CMB, which has been measured to high accuracy. This is why it is currently widely accepted as an essential ingredient by many cosmologists. As if this wasn't enough to get excited about, however, there is much more.

One obvious question that arises is this: if inflation gets going, how does it stop? The answer is that inflation stops completely naturally, but with a fascinating twist that drives right to the heart of our 'Why are we here?' question. The scalar field driving inflation fluctuates up and down in accord with the laws of quantum theory, just like the waves on the surface of an ocean. If the energy stored in the field is high enough, inflation begins. One might expect that such a rapid expansion would dilute the energy extremely rapidly, causing inflation to stop. But scalar fields have the interesting property that their energy density can stay relatively constant as space expands. You can think of the expanding space as doing work on the field, pumping energy into it and keeping its level high. And in turn, the high level of the field's energy continues to drive the expansion. This might sound like the ultimate free lunch, and in a sense it is, almost, although gradually the energy will become diluted and decay away. The time this takes depends on the size of the initial fluctuation in the field and the details of the field itself, but in general

INFLATION IN ACTION
The sport of zorbing brilliantly illustrates the theory of inflation; putting in action the analogy of a very large ball rolling down a slope!

the higher the initial energy, the longer the field takes to fall in value as the expansion continues. An analogy often used to picture this scenario is to imagine a ball rolling down the side of a valley. The height of the ball up the valley side represents the energy density of the scalar field. When the ball is high up, the energy in the field is high, driving the inflationary expansion. As the ball rolls slowly down the valley the energy reduces and inflation turns off. At the valley floor, the ball oscillates back and

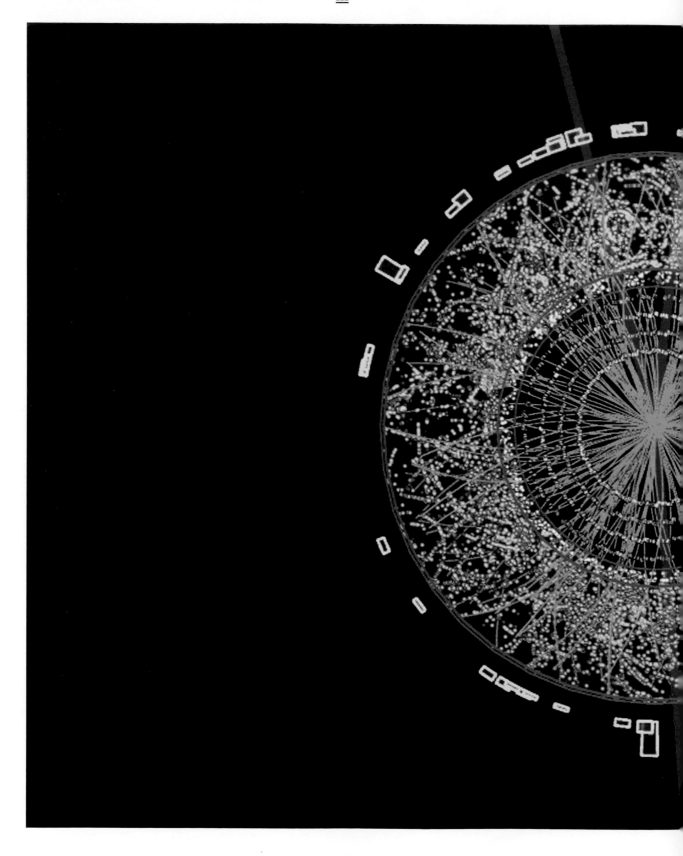

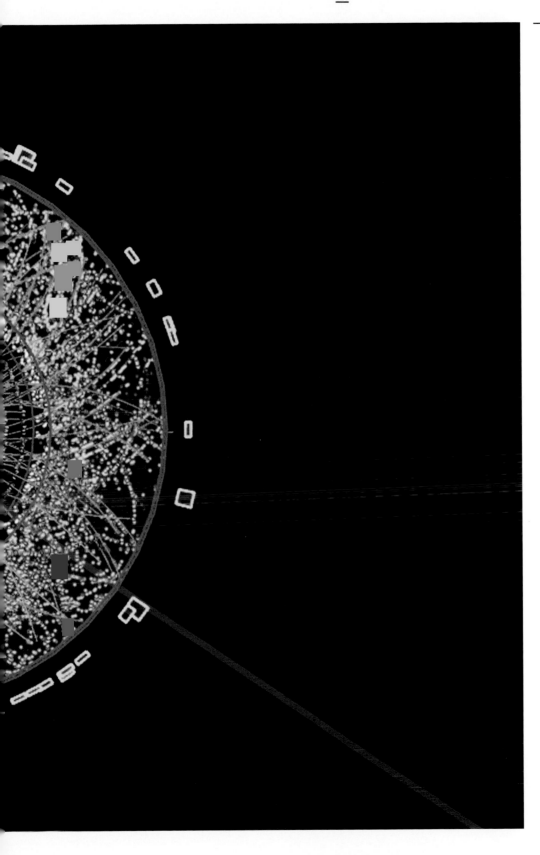

PARTICLES COLLIDE
This graphic shows one of many particle collision events that have been recorded by scientists at CERN in their quest to discover the Higgs Boson.

BICEP2 B-MODE SIGNAL

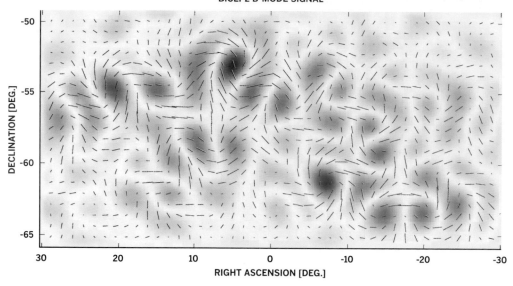

EVIDENCE FOR INFLATION
The results from the BICEP2 project in 2014 reveal the pattern detected in the cosmic microwave background which is a crucial piece of evidence to support the inflation theory in the study of the Big Bang.

forth until it comes to rest. The scalar field likewise oscillates and in so doing dumps its energy into the universe in the form of particles. In so doing it creates a hot dense soup, which we identify as the 'Big Bang'. In other words, inflation ends naturally and the standard Big Bang follows. The decay of the scalar field that drove inflation is the cause of the Big Bang!

Let us step back for a moment and recap with broad brush-strokes, because we seem to be wandering onto Leibniz's territory, and that's an astonishing place for physics to have arrived at. Our claim is that there exists a quantum field that causes the universe to expand exponentially fast for some period of time, and in doing so produces all the features of the universe we observe today, including the existence of galaxies and the matter out of which they are made. This is a triumph, and is now part of cosmology textbooks. Before the Big Bang, there was inflation. Fine, our philosopher friends would say, but what happened before inflation? Here, we must leave the textbooks and become a little more speculative, but not too speculative. We are still going to be working within the domain of mainstream physics.

There is an extension of what we might term standard inflationary theory. It is known as eternal inflation. Put simply, there seems to be no reason why inflation should stop everywhere at the same time. There should always be regions of the universe where the scalar field fluctuates to such high values that the exponential expansion continues, and these regions will always come to dominate the universe, however rare they may be, because they are exponentially expanding. Where inflation stops, Big Bangs herald the beginning of more sedately expanding regions like ours. But elsewhere, there is an ever-growing exponentially expanding universe, constantly spawning an infinity of Big Bangs. This theory, known as eternal inflation, leads to an infinite, immortal multiverse, growing fractal-like without end. This is truly mind-numbing, but we must emphasise that it is an entirely natural extension of standard inflationary cosmology.

Eternal inflation opens up even more exciting possibilities. As we discussed above, one of the great mysteries in physics today is the origin of the constants of nature such as the strength of gravity, the masses of the particles and the value of dark energy. These values appear to be fine-tuned for the existence of life, and understanding where they come from is a prerequisite for understanding our existence. In eternal inflationary models, each mini-universe can have different values of these constants and different effective laws of physics. The word 'effective' is important. The idea is that there is some overarching framework, out of which our laws and the constants of nature are selected randomly. If this is correct, then each of the infinite number of mini-universes that branch off the fractal inflationary multiverse can have different effective laws of physics, and all possible combinations will be realised somewhere. No matter how fine-tuned our laws appear for the existence of life, it is inevitable that such mini-universes as ours will exist, and there will be an infinite number of each possible set of combinations. There is no fine-tuning problem. Given the multiverse, we are inevitable. This is reminiscent of our rejection of your own personal uniqueness whilst listening to Joy Division at the beginning of the chapter. Yes, in isolation, the odds of you existing are almost vanishingly small. But given a mechanism for producing human beings, babies are born all the time and their existence is not surprising. Here, we have a mechanism for producing universes – and with an even greater statistical sledgehammer, the mechanism doesn't simply produce a few billion of them, it produces a potentially infinite number.

This is a quite stunning theoretical model, and I understand that it sounds like wild speculation. It isn't, though. Inflation is probably correct

ROSETTA PROBE
Our quest to understand the origins of our universe goes on and sees scientists breaking the boundaries of space travel in order to do so. On 6 August 2014 the European Space Agency's Rosetta spacecraft entered the orbit of the Churyumov-Gerasimenko comet, hoping to map and study the comet's surface and core to give us some more clues into how the solar system was formed some 4.6 billion years ago.

MULTIVERSE
We live in an infinite, eternal, fractal multiverse comprised of an infinite number of universes like ours, alongside an infinite number of universes with different physical laws. What does it mean if we exist because it is inevitable? What does it mean if the existence of our universe is inevitable? Perhaps we can only ask: what does it mean to us?

INFLATION
Andrei Linde, 'Inflationary Cosmology after Planck 2013', arXiv:1402.0526v2 [hep-th].

in some form, in the sense that before what we call the Big Bang, there was an exponential expansion of spacetime. Scalar fields, which are known to exist, have the correct properties to drive such an expansion, although there are other theoretical models of inflation, as well. Theoretical physicists studying inflationary models have discovered that almost all of them are eternal, in the sense that they stop inflating in patches rather than all at once. This means that the potential for creating universes, in the guise of inflation, is always expanding faster than it is decaying away, and it will therefore never stop. We live in an infinite, eternal, fractal multiverse comprised of an infinite number of universes like ours, alongside an infinite number of universes with different physical laws. We exist because it is inevitable. Almost.

There is one very important caveat to this picture. Recent research suggests that eternal inflationary models may be eternal in the future, but not in the past. They never stop, but they may have to start. I can't give you a definitive answer to this ultimate question, because nobody yet knows. I can quote from Andrei Linde's recent review of inflationary cosmology, published in March 2014.

'In other words, there was a beginning for each part of the universe, and there will be an end for inflation at any particular point. But there will be no end for the evolution of the universe *as a whole* in the eternal inflation scenario, and at present we do not know whether there was a single beginning of the evolution of the universe as a whole at some moment t=0, which was traditionally associated with the Big bang.'

And so we reach the end. Defining the Big Bang as the initial hot, dense phase of our observable universe that gave rise to the CMB 380,000 years later, we understand what happened before. There was a period of inflationary expansion, which could have been driven by a scalar field in accord with the known laws of physics. That inflationary expansion is probably still going on somewhere, spawning an incalculable number of universes as we speak, and it will continue doing this forever. We live in an eternal universe, in which everything that can happen does happen. And we are one of the things that can happen. Did the whole universe have a beginning, an essential, external cause in the spirit of Leibniz's God? We still don't know. Possibly there was a 'mother of all Big Bangs', and if so, we will certainly need a quantum theory of gravity to say anything more.

What does this mean? The wonderful thing for me is that nobody knows, because the philosophical and indeed theological consequences of eternal inflation have not been widely debated and discussed. My hope is that in trying to summarise the issues, regrettably briefly and necessarily superficially in the television series and in a little more depth here, these ideas will be accessible to a wider audience and stimulate discussion. This is desirable and necessary, because ideas are the lifeblood of civilisation, and societies assimilate ideas and become comfortable with their implications through understanding and debate. If eternal inflation is the correct description of our universe, it will be the artists, philosophers, theologians, novelists and musicians, alongside the physicists, who explore its meaning. What does it mean if the existence of our universe is inevitable? What does it mean if we are not special in any way? What does it mean if our observable universe, with all its myriad galaxies and possibilities, is a vanishingly small leaf on an every-expanding fractal tree of universes? What does it mean if you are, because you have to be? I can't tell you. I can only ask – what does it mean to you?

For small creatures such as we, the vastness is bearable only through love.
Carl Sagan

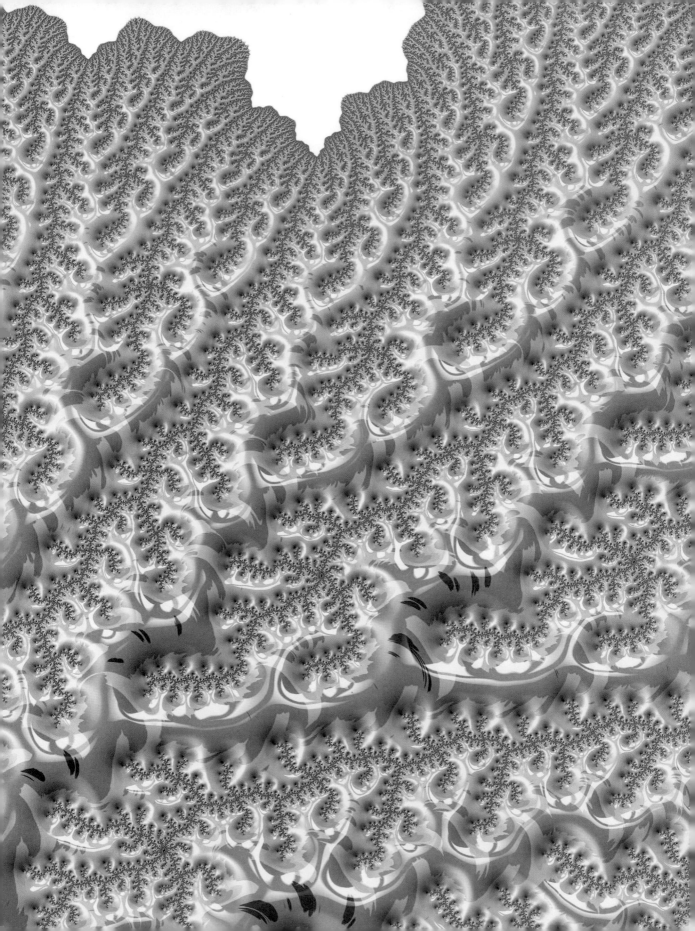

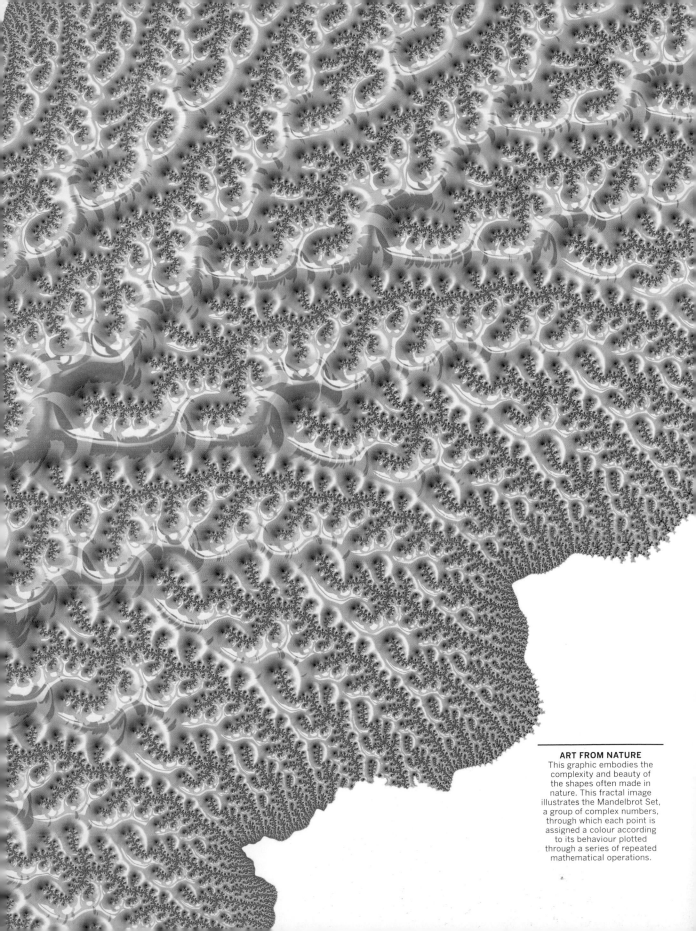

ART FROM NATURE
This graphic embodies the complexity and beauty of the shapes often made in nature. This fractal image illustrates the Mandelbrot Set, a group of complex numbers, through which each point is assigned a colour according to its behaviour plotted through a series of repeated mathematical operations.

WHAT IS OUR FUTURE?

I can hardly wait
To see you come of age
But I guess we'll both just have to be patient
'Cause it's a long way to go
A hard row to hoe
Yes it's a long way to go
But in the meantime
Before you cross the street
Take my hand
Life is what happens to you
While you're busy making other plans

John Lennon

MAKING THE DARKNESS VISIBLE

Yet from those flames, no light; but rather darkness visible.
John Milton. Paradise Lost *1, 63.*

They must have descended into the darkness for a reason. Their burning dry-grass torches would have filled the caverns with acrid smoke, sucking the oxygen from the wet air. They would have moved carefully, fearfully perhaps, enveloped in a dim, flickering sphere of red, fading into a profound silent dark, the like of which I don't experience. A child held her hand against the rock, and blew a red-pigmented mixture across it with a straw. She smiled – 'my hand'. Her companions reached into the pigment and, in careful movements, inked a line of dots beside the handprint. The precision of a young imagination. A retreat to the lightness of the cave mouth. 'Perhaps we'll come back someday,' she thought.

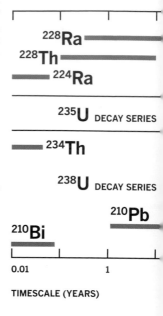

Over 40,800 years later, I held my hand next to hers, because the experts on the Upper Paleolithic told me that the handprints are always those of children, and most likely always female. El Castillo in Northern Spain contains some of the oldest cave-art in the world. It is not known precisely how old, because the pigments themselves cannot be dated. The art is covered in calcite, which dripped and crystalised across the handprints and dots as the whole of recorded history played out above. Calcite contains uranium-234 atoms, which decay with a half-life of 245,000 years into thorium-230, which in turn decays with a half-life of 75,000 years. Thorium is not soluble in water, so there was none when the limestone formed. By measuring the concentrations of the uranium isotopes 234 and 238, and the thorium-230, a precise date for the formation of the calcite can be measured. This gives a minimum date for the art, since of course it must have been created before it was covered. The limestone covering the red dots formed 40,800 years ago. The oldest handprint was covered 37,300 years ago.

These dates are significant, because before 41,000 years ago there is no evidence of modern humans in Europe. Homo sapiens arrived tantalisingly close to the minimum age of the art in the darkness of El Castillo, leading some anthropologists to suggest that the art is not human. Rather, it may have been created by our close cousins, the Neanderthals, who dominated Europe at the time. I find this possibility profoundly interesting, and moving. It is interesting because the creators of this art had all the attributes that we might lazily refer to as 'uniquely human'. The retreat into the deep caves was undoubtedly a sophisticated

REACHING OUT FROM AN ANCIENT LIFE
Two tiny handprints give a tantalising glimpse into an ancient way of living in the Altamira caves in northwestern Spain.

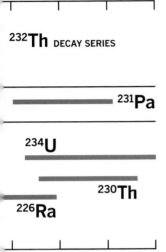

URANIUM SERIES DATING

Dating ranges of different nuclides within the three U-series decay chains to show their utility.

^{232}**Th** DECAY SERIES

^{231}**Pa**

^{234}**U**

^{230}**Th**

^{226}**Ra**

10^4 10^6

response to the world. This is not mere decoration, because cave-art like this is not found near the cave entrances where these 'people' lived. Its creation is highly ritualised. The darkness is integral. One of the most beautiful pieces in El Castillo is a bison, half-carved out of a column of rock and shaded with pigments to emphasise the arch of its back. When illuminated by torchlight, the rock casts a flickering, animal shadow onto the cave wall. The interaction of light and dark was important to the rituals carried out here before history, perhaps before humans. The cave resonates with ideas, curiosities and fears. It represents a border; the transition from existence to living. If this is a human place, it is a record of the first stumbling steps towards humanity. But if it is Neanderthal, it is a record of an ending, an ascent cut short. 'Perhaps we'll come back someday,' thought the little girl in my imagination. Not long afterwards, her species became extinct, out-competed by their incoming cousins. Perhaps. It is possible that the date coincides with the migration of Homo sapiens into Europe because the art is indeed human. Some anthropologists believe that the art may have been a response to the native Neanderthal population; a sort of prehistoric shock and awe, asserting cultural dominance and engendering a sense of community and superiority in the nascent human population. Things never change. If this is the case, the Neanderthals inadvertently played a role in our ascent. The roles may have been reversed, however. Perhaps our ancestors found a young, emerging and more sophisticated culture when they crossed the Mediterranean. A species distantly related to us whose desire to explore the darkness we assimilated. Perhaps our intellectual climb was, in part, a response to them. Intellectual superiority does not guarantee survival; witness the fall of classical civilisation.

This possibility is illustrative of a fact that we modern humans often subconsciously rest in the shadows. Things can end, for ever. Species become extinct, and that doesn't only apply to animals with feathers and no feelings. The Neanderthals became extinct, and they may have begun to imagine a future before they lost it. The red handprints of El Castillo are overwhelming in this context. Go there. Hold your hand up to hers, hear the giggles, picture the smiles, imagine the beginnings of hope, and listen to the silence.

At least 40,800 years later, we can use our knowledge of nuclear physics to move backwards through time to piece together her story. Science is a time machine, and it goes both ways. We are able to predict our future with increasing certainty. Our ability to act in response to these predictions will ultimately determine our fate. Science and reason make the darkness visible. I worry that lack of investment in science and a retreat from reason may prevent us from seeing further, or delay our reaction to what we see, making a meaningful response impossible. There are no simple fixes. Our civilisation is complex, our global political system is inadequate, our internal differences of opinion are deep-seated. I'd bet you think you're absolutely right about some things and virtually everyone else is an idiot. Climate Change? Europe? God? America? The Monarchy? Same-sex Marriage? Abortion? Big Business? Nationalism? The United Nations? The Bank Bailout? Tax Rates? Genetically Modified Crops? Eating Meat? Football? X Factor or Strictly? The way forward is to understand and accept that there are many opinions, but only one human civilisation, only one Nature, and only one science. The collective goal of ensuring that there is never less than one human civilisation must surely override our personal prejudices. At least we have come far enough in 40,800 years to be able to state the obvious, and this is a necessary first step.

'We've woken up at the wheel of the bus and realised we don't know how to drive it'

SUDDEN IMPACT

On 15 February 2013 at 9.13am a 12,000-tonne asteroid entered Earth's upper atmosphere travelling at 60 times the speed of sound. It came from the direction of the Sun, so there was never any chance of seeing its approach. The rock broke up at an altitude of 29 kilometres, depositing over twenty times the energy of the Hiroshima bomb into the sky above the Russian town of Chelyabinsk. Thousands of buildings were damaged by the shockwave and 1500 people were injured, mainly by flying glass as windows smashed in multiple cities across the region. Sound waves from the explosion rattled around the globe twice, and were detected by a nuclear weapons monitoring station in the Antarctic. The Russian parliament's foreign affairs committee chief Alexei Pushkov took to Twitter: 'Instead of fighting on Earth, people should be creating a joint system of asteroid defence.' Naive idealism? Over-reaction? Hollywood? Not really. Sixteen hours later, a 40,000-tonne asteroid named 367943 Duende streaked by at an altitude of 27,200 kilometres, well within the orbits of many of our satellites, although it missed them all. This one had a name, because it was discovered by astronomers in Spain in 2012. There is a 1 in 3000 chance that Duende will strike the Earth before 2069; if it does, it could destroy a city, which isn't too bad.

Before Chelyabinsk, the last recorded large impact was the Tunguska event over Siberia in 1908. The shockwave created by the airburst flattened 2000km² of forest in an energy release close to that of the United State's most powerful hydrogen bomb test at Bikini Atoll in March 1954. Events on this scale are thought to occur on average once every 300 years, and could easily wipe out a densely populated region. The best-known impact in popular culture was the Chicxulub event in Mexico's Yucatan Peninsula 66,038,000 ± 11,000 years ago, which wiped out the non-avian dinosaurs. Precision is important when available. If they'd had a space programme, Carl Sagan once quipped, or perhaps lamented, the dinosaurs would still be around, although in that case we wouldn't. The Chicxulub asteroid was probably around 9.5 kilometres in diameter, and the energy release of such an object exceeds that of the world's combined nuclear arsenal by a factor of a thousand. Or, if you like scary statistics, that's 8 billion Hiroshima bombs. Such events are estimated to occur on average every 100 million years, give or take, and are quite capable of

CAPTURING THE CRASH
These images show the meteor hurtling through the dark early morning sky at 9.20am just before it crashes into the mountains above Chelyabinsk.

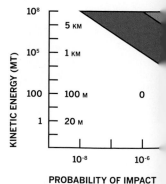

TORINO SCALE

The Chicxulub impact, believed by many to be a significant factor in the extinction of the dinosaurs, has been estimated at 10^8 megatons, or Torino Scale 10. The impact which created the Barringer Crater and the Tunguska event in 1908 are both estimated to be in the 3–10 megaton range, corresponding to Torino Scale 8. The 2013 Chelyabinsk meteor had a total kinetic energy prior to impact of about 0.4 megatons, corresponding to Torino Scale 0. In all cases their impact probability was of course 1, as they actually hit Earth. As of May 2014, there are no known objects rated at a Torino Scale level greater than zero.

destroying human civilisation and possibly causing our extinction. At the other end of the scale, rocks of around a millimetre in diameter hit the Earth at a rate of two a minute.

Alexei Pushkov was right. It is absolute idiocy not to pay attention to the danger of impacts from space, and fortunately our space agencies have begun to do so. NASA's Near Earth Object Program created the Sentry system in 2002, which maintains an automated risk table continually updated by new observations from astronomers around the world. I am writing these words on 3 September 2014, and there are currently no high-risk objects in the table, although there are 13 asteroids with the potential to impact Earth that have been observed within the last 60 days. The risk posed by an asteroid is quantified on the Torino Scale.

Every known near-Earth asteroid is assigned a value on the Torino Scale between 1 and 10, calculated by combining the collision probability with the energy of the collision in megatons of TNT (see table for 1–10 of the Torino Scale). Asteroid 99942 Apophis reached level 4 on the Torino Scale in December 2004. Initial observations and calculations suggested this 350-metre-wide asteroid had a 1 in 37 chance of a potential collision with the Earth on 13 April 2029 and a further chance of hitting us seven years later if it missed first time around. This would not have been a civilisation-threatening event, but it could have laid waste to a small country. Subsequent observations have effectively ruled out the risk from 99942 Apophis, but statistically speaking such an impact is expected to occur every 80,000 years or so. Although the Sentry table is currently benign, there are at least two very good reasons why we shouldn't relax and forget about impact risks. Firstly, we haven't detected all of the threatening objects by any means, as the Chelyabinsk event so effectively reminded us. And secondly, we don't currently know precisely what to do if we do observe an asteroid with our name on it, which could happen tomorrow. In 2015 a new early warning system called ATLAS (Asteroid Terrestrial Impact Last Alert Sytem) will come on line. Eight small telescopes will scan the sky for any sign of faint objects that may pose a threat to the Earth. ATLAS will give up to three weeks' warning of an impact, which is enough time to evacuate a large region, but probably not an entire country. The cost of our global insurance policy? One third of the annual wages of Manchester United striker Wayne Rooney. Such comparisons always sound childish of course; I'm well aware of how

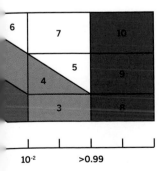

6	7	10
4	5	9
3		8

10^{-2} >0.99

FRAGMENTS FROM SPACE
A fragment from the meteor which caused so much damage as it hurtled through the skies to collide with Earth's surface.

MARS-500 PROJECT
The Mars-500 experiment was conducted between 2007 and 2011 at the Russian Institute of Biomedical Problems (IBMP) in Moscow, Russia. The final stage, held from June 2010 to November 2011, placed six crew members in an isolation facility to simulate a 520-day mission to Mars. The aim was to study the psychological and medical aspects of long-duration human spaceflights. Photographed during the 30-day 'Mars landing' period in February 2011, the photo shows Diego Urbana (Italy, ESA) carrying out a simulated 'Marswalk' using tools designed for Soviet lunar missions in the 1960s and 1970s.

capitalism functions, and I know that Wayne Rooney generates income for the Manchester United corporation in excess of his wages. But the aim of this chapter is to argue that there is a flaw in the majestic edifice of human civilisation; our myopic and cavalier disregard for our long-term safety. In my view, the reason for the short-sighted approach is that nothing catastrophically bad has happened to humanity in recorded history that we haven't inflicted upon ourselves, unless of course you believe in Noah's Ark, and even that was presumably down to us because one assumes that God is usually quite a patient sort. One of the central themes of this book has been to argue that the human race is worth saving because we are a rare and infinitely beautiful natural phenomenon. One of the other themes is that we are commonly and paradoxically ingenious and stupid in equal measure. I do not personally think that there is anyone out there to save us, and so it follows that we will have to save ourselves; at least, that would seem to me to be a good working assumption. This is why I don't feel naïve, idealistic or like a particularly radical member of the Student Union in a Che Guevara T-Shirt when I ask the question 'Is it reasonable to spend less on asteroid defence than on a footballer's annual salary?' When I look in the mirror and think about that, my face assumes an interesting shape – you should try it.

NASA is working hard in the face of apathy to do something to close the gap between the capabilities of the dinosaurs and us. Twenty metres beneath the surface of the Atlantic ocean, 8 kilometres off the coast of Key Largo, Florida, is the *Aquarius Reef Base*. Originally constructed as an underwater research habitat to study coral reefs, it is used by NASA to train astronauts for future long-duration space missions. The base allows for saturation diving, which greatly increases the length of time a researcher can spend exploring the reefs. On a normal scuba dive, a diver can spend a maximum of 80 minutes at a depth of 20 metres without having to go through decompression. The diver can remain at this pressure for several weeks, however, as long as they decompress when they return to the surface – a process that takes almost a day. Since the air pressure inside *Aquarius* is the same as the pressure outside in the water, researchers living inside the base can spend many hours a day exploring the sea bed using standard scuba equipment, but with the important caveat that they cannot return to the surface a few metres above their heads. If anything goes wrong, they must return to *Aquarius* and deal with the problem inside the base. For all practical purposes therefore, they are isolated; it's not possible to panic or simply loose patience and return to civilisation above. This is why NASA uses the *Aquarius* base to train astronauts to work in a hostile environment and test their psychological suitability for long-duration space missions.

Filming inside *Aquarius* was a personal highlight of *Human Universe*. We didn't want to have to decompress of course, so we had a strict time limit of 100 minutes inside the base spread over two dives. The ex-US Navy diver in charge of our dive was wonderfully clear as far as timings were concerned. 'If I say leave, you don't smile and take one more shot – you leave! Otherwise you stay, for a long time. Your choice. I know you media types.' *Aquarius* has the look and feel of a spacecraft from a science fiction film. There are six bunk beds piled three-high at one end, and a galley area complete with microwave and sink at the other. In between, there are control panels, some books on marine life, and a laptop computer station. Above the table, there is a single round window looking out across the reef. Through an air-lock-style exit, there is a dive platform with access to the scuba tanks and the open sea. NASA's Extreme Environment Mission Operations (NEEMO) team had just completed a nine-day mission when we arrived. Led by Akihiko Hoshide of the Japanese Aerospace Exploration agency, the mission was part of the long-term goal of landing astronauts on an asteroid, and developing the capability to deflect one, should the need arise. There are strong scientific and commercial reasons for exploring asteroids; they are pristine objects that will allow us to better understand the formation of our solar system over 4.5 billion years ago, and rich in precious metals precisely because they are pristine. On Earth, heavy metals such as palladium, rhodium and gold migrated into the Earth's core, leaving the accessible crust depleted. Asteroids are too small to have separated in this way, leaving the primordial abundances of these valuable metals untouched and accessible.

Whether for commercial, scientific or practical reasons, learning how to land on asteroids, exploit their resources and manipulate their orbits is clearly an eminently sensible thing to do. And make no mistake, we will have to move one at some point.

SEEING THE FUTURE

In the year 35,000 CE the red dwarf Ross 248 will approach the solar system at a minimum distance of 3.024 light years, making it the closest star to the Sun. 9000 years later it will have passed us by, ceding the title of nearest neighbour to Proxima Centauri once again. Coincidently, in 40,176 years, *Voyager 2* will pass Ross 248 at a distance of 1.76 light years. We know this because we can predict the future.

We've encountered Newton's laws several times in this book. In Chapter 3 we used them to calculate the velocity of the International Space Station in a circular orbit around the Earth. At a distance r from the centre of the Earth, the velocity v is

$$v = \sqrt{\frac{GM_e}{r}}$$

Let's look at this equation in a different way by rewriting it as

$$\frac{dx}{dt} = \sqrt{\frac{GM_e}{r}}$$

Here, we've used the notation of calculus. That may strike fear into your heart if you haven't done any mathematics since school, but don't worry. All we need to know is the meaning of the symbol

$$\frac{dx}{dt}$$

In words, this denotes the rate of change of the position of the space station with respect to time, otherwise known as its velocity v. You have an intuitive feel for this even if you've never done any mathematics. If you get into your car and drive it away from your house in a straight line at a velocity of 30 kilometres per hour, then in one hour you will be at a position 30 kilometres away from your house in the direction in which you drove the car. The equation is telling us what the position of the Space Station *will be* at some point later in time, given knowledge of where it is and how it is moving in the present. It predicts the future. This sort of equation is known as a *differential equation*. In Chapter 4 we wrote down the 'rules of the game' – Einstein's General Theory of Relativity and the Standard Model of particle physics. The notation is a little more complicated, but in the Standard Model you'll notice the symbols D_μ and δ_μ, which are more complicated versions of

$$\frac{dx}{dt}$$

In Einstein's equations, there are also these so-called derivatives hidden away in the compact mathematical notation. The known fundamental laws of physics all function in this way. Given knowledge of how some system or collection of natural objects is behaving *now*, we can compute what they will be doing at some time in the future. The system in question may be a solar system, a collection of atoms and molecules, or the weather. There are practical limitations, of course, and the weather forecast is a good example. Earth's climate system is very complicated, with many hundreds of thousands of variables. Ocean currents in the Pacific might affect future rainfall in Oldham, and so long-term forecasting of local weather conditions comes with increased uncertainty.

People do of course make statements, often based on human experience rather than science, which are more likely to be right than wrong. Red sky at night, Shepherd's delight. Red sky in the morning, Shepherd's warning.

OUR NEIGHBOURHOOD
A 3-D diagram of the stars nearest to our solar system.

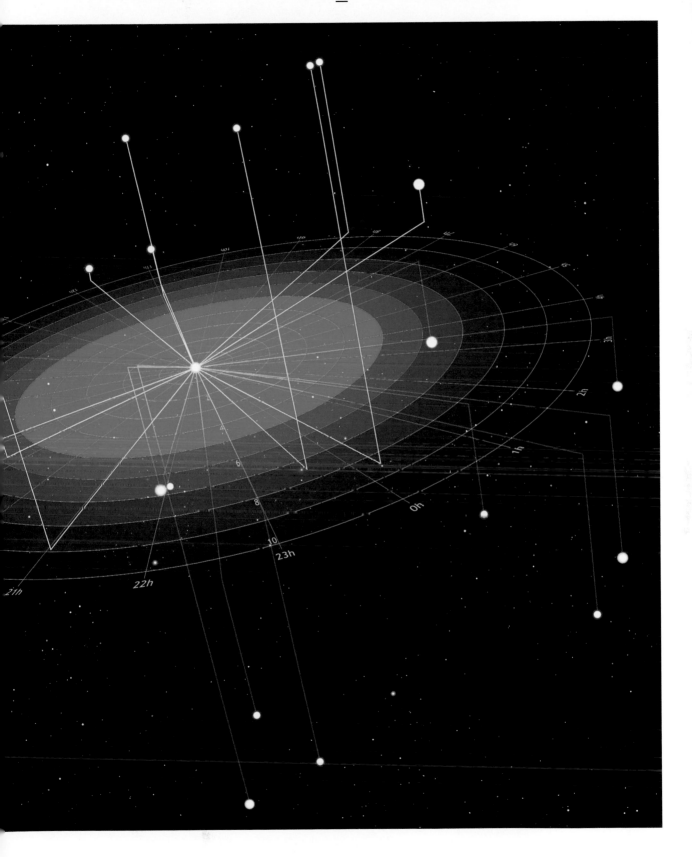

RED SKY AT NIGHT
The laws of physics can be used to describe weather patterns and the motion of the stars.

This is often true in countries like the UK whose weather is dominated by westerly winds, because a red sunset is usually a sign of high pressure to the west, which is associated with fine weather. But if you're doing well in a statistically significant sense using 'folklore' or 'ancient wisdom', it's because the patterns and regularities you are using to make your predictions emerge from underlying physical laws, which are described by differential equations. The laws of physics in essence reflect the underlying simplicity of nature and the regularity with which it behaves. They are not magic. We can describe the natural world using mathematics *because* it is regular and behaves consistently. It is my opinion that we *must* observe a universe that behaves in a regular and consistent way because such behaviour is necessary for complex structures like brains to evolve. A universe of anarchy, with sub-atomic particles interacting without some sort of framework or rules, would surely not support life, or indeed any structures at all. This is known as a selection effect. We observe a universe whose behaviour can be described by a limited set of

differential equations because we wouldn't exist if it were not so. This is my opinion, and there are scientists and philosophers who might disagree. It could be the case that there is no simple underlying framework to the universe, and our success to date has deceived us. Or perhaps the ultimate laws are and will forever remain beyond human understanding. We might simply not be smart enough to figure them out. There are also systems that cannot be described using differential equations. The patterns generated in Conway's Game of Life are an example, where algorithmic rules are used to generate complex patterns and even computing devices such as Turing machines. But what can be said with certainty is that, as far as we can tell, the natural world does behave in a way that is amenable to a description based on the differential equations of physics, and these allow us to predict the future, given knowledge of the present. This is why our asteroid defence system will work if we make enough high-precision observations of the sky. Sort of.

Ahhh, caveats. There are always caveats.

213.4kg

$$\Delta v = v_e \ln \frac{m_0}{m_1} \qquad E_k = \frac{1}{2}mv^2$$

SCIENCE VS. MAGIC

Chaos: When the present determines the future, but the approximate present does not approximately determine the future.
Edward Lorenz

We should be confident in science. It works. But it has limitations, some of which are fundamental. We've encountered Newton's laws of motion and gravitation time and again in this book. They are very simple – the archetypal physical laws – and are used every day by engineers, navigators and asteroid watchers. One of the simplest imaginable real-life systems to which Newton's law of gravitation can be applied is a single planet orbiting around a single star. For this case, Newton's laws allow for a precise prediction of the future position of the planet. The orbit is predictable and periodic, which is to say the planet returns to precisely the same position around the star every orbit. It's clockwork – the way the solar system is often pictured. If a third object – a moon, say – is introduced, it was proved in the late nineteenth century by Heinrich Burns and, later, Henri Poincaré, that no general solution to Newton's equations can be found. There are a handful of special cases, which are still being discovered, for which there are repeating solutions, but in general, the orbits of three bodies acting under gravity never repeat; their motion around each other traces out a tremendous ever-changing mess! This isn't a failure of mathematics. Natural systems really do behave in this way. The solar system is a case in point. The planets orbit like clockwork on timescales of millions of years, but we are currently unable to predict the Earth's orbit for more than 60 million years into the future. Beyond

THE POWER OF THE SUN
The Sun is a powerful marker of the seasons across ancient civilisations such as the Mayans in Chichen Itza, Mexico.

NATURE'S TIMEPIECE
The alignment of the Sun through carefully positioned stones served as an effective guide to the seasons for our ancient ancestors.

that, the sensitivity of the predictions to uncertainties in our current knowledge of the Earth's orbit, and the gravitational influence of other bodies in the solar system, become too great. This isn't only a reflection of our lack of knowledge. It also reflects an important fundamental point, which is that solar systems such as ours *are* unstable over long timescales. Their behaviour is chaotic; the apparent clockwork can break down into a whirling unpredictable swarm. Recent simulations suggest that Mercury *could* be wrenched out of its orbit and collide with the Sun, and that even the Earth *may* have a close encounter with Venus or Mars on time periods of 3–5 billion years. The words *could* and *may* are italicised for a reason. These predictions are statistical in nature – it is estimated that there is a 1 per cent chance that Mercury will be thrown into a much more elliptical orbit during the next 5 billion years. The uncertainty is down to the extreme sensitivity of the predictions to what physicists call the initial conditions – the current knowledge of precisely where everything in the solar system is at this instant, and how everything is moving at this instant. Other errors are caused by our precise knowledge of the mass and shape of all the objects in the solar system, not to mention the slight perturbations from incoming comets and the ever-shifting asteroids. The area of physics and mathematics concerned with such systems is called chaos theory, and as the pioneer of the field Edward Norton Lorenz put it, nature's complexity usually leads to a situation in which approximate knowledge of the present, which is in practice all we ever have, does not approximately determine the future.

For the asteroid hunters, this is an intensely problematic truth. It is not possible to observe an asteroid once, and then pop its position and velocity into a computer to work out whether it will ever hit us. Instead, a gravitational keyhole system is used. A keyhole is a small volume of

STONEHENGE
One of the earliest examples of stone markers used to determine the date of the summer solstice, Stonehenge dates back to 3000 BCE.

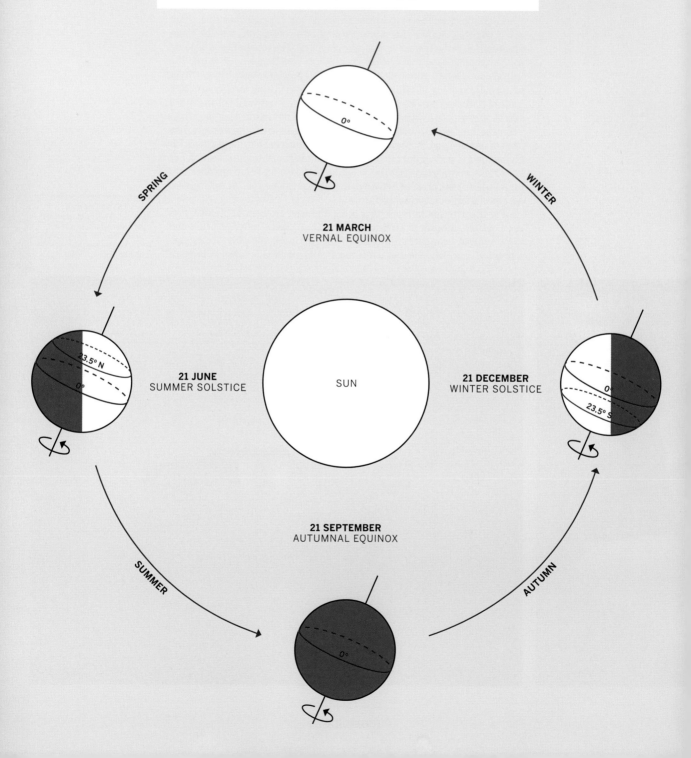

EQUINOXES AND SOLSTICES

When the Sun is crossing the celestial equator, day and night are of nearly equal length at all latitudes, which is why these dates are called the equinoxes ('equal nights'). In March, as the Sun is moving northwards along the ecliptic, this is called the vernal equinox, and in September as the Sun is moving southwards we refer to it as the autumnal equinox. The times when the Sun is at its furthest from the celestial equator are called the summer and winter solstices. The world 'solstice' comes from the Latin meaning 'Sun stands still' because the apparent movement of the Sun's path north or south stops before changing direction.

21 MARCH
VERNAL EQUINOX

SPRING

WINTER

21 JUNE
SUMMER SOLSTICE

23.5° N

0°

SUN

21 DECEMBER
WINTER SOLSTICE

0°

23.5° S

SUMMER

AUTUMN

21 SEPTEMBER
AUTUMNAL EQUINOX

0°

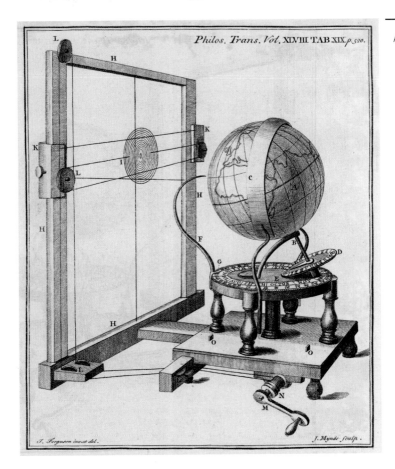

Philos. Trans. Vol. XLVIII TAB. XIX p. 520.

J. Ferguson invt del.

J. Mynde sculp.

PREDICTING ECLIPSES
An eighteenth-century solar
eclipse predictor, based
on observations of the
natural world.

space close to the asteroid's current orbit. If an asteroid passes through the keyhole, perhaps because of a gravitational nudge from some other object in the solar system, then it is highly likely that it will impact the Earth on its next pass. 99942 Apophis was assigned such a keyhole in 2004 when it was classified at 4 on the Torino Scale. Fortunately, it didn't pass through, and this is why it is currently classified as harmless. The keyhole system reflects the fundamental unpredictability of complex physical systems over long timescales. This is why we have to keep observing and retain a keen understanding of the fundamental limits of our calculational prowess. Science isn't magic. This realisation is of course important in a practical sense if one is interested in saving the planet from asteroid impact. But it is also very important to embed caution and humility into our/my polemical celebration of the power of science. Scientific predictions are *not* perfect. Scientific theories are *never* correct. Scientific results are always preliminary. Whole fields of study can be rendered obsolete by new discoveries. But, I insist, science is the best we can do because it is not simply another arbitrary system of thought based on dreamt-up human axioms. It is the systematic study of nature, based on observations of the natural world and our understanding of those observations. Scientific predictions are not matters of opinion. At any given time, science provides the best possible estimate of what the future might bring, given our current understanding. The predictions may be wrong, they may be inaccurate, the errors may be fundamental in origin, but there is simply no other rational choice than to act according to the best available science, imperfect though, by necessity, its predictions will always be.

THE WONDER OF IT ALL

As of September 2014, in a population of 7.24 billion, 545 people have been to space, 24 people have broken free of the Earth's gravitational pull and 12 have landed on another world.

In 2013 Charlie and Dorothy Duke, a retired, church-going couple from New Braunfels, Texas, reached their 50th wedding anniversary. With two grown sons and nine grandchildren, Charlie and Dottie must have celebrated a life well lived, captured in photographs adorning the walls and mantelpieces of the family home. There is one Duke family photograph, however, that holds a unique place in history. I myself have a copy of it on my wall at home, signed by Charlie, and it's one of my favourite things. The photograph, taken in 1972, is an image of Charlie, Dottie and their two young sons Charles and Thomas when they were just six and four years old. The picture itself is of no particular note – a simple portrait of a family in 70s clothes, sitting on a bench in a garden. It's not dissimilar to the one below, which is me and my grandad photographed at around the same time. I was in Oldham, the Dukes were in Florida.

The reason I have a copy of the Dukes' photograph is not what it is – we are not related – but where it is. Charlie and Dorothy Duke are the only grandparents on Earth who can point their grandchildren's eyes towards the Moon and tell them there is a photo of Grandma, Grandpa, Dad and Uncle resting on the surface.

Charlie Duke was the Pilot of *Orion*, the Apollo 16 Lunar Module. At the age of thirty-six he remains the youngest human ever to have walked on the Moon. Together with Commander John Young, my childhood hero, the two astronauts spent three days in late April 1972 exploring the Descartes Highlands, covering almost 27 kilometres in the Lunar Rover.

The primary scientific aim of the mission was to explore the geology of the lunar highlands. It was thought that the unique rock formations around the landing site were formed by ancient lunar volcanism, but Young and Duke's exploration demonstrated that this explanation was incorrect. Instead, the landscape had been forged by impact events, scattering material outwards from the craters and littering the surface with glass. After three days on the lunar surface and setting a lunar land-speed record of 17km/h, Charlie Duke removed his family portrait from his spacesuit pocket, placed it on the lunar surface and snapped it with his Hasselblad. Inscribed on the back are the words 'This is the family of Astronaut Duke from Planet Earth. Landed on the Moon, April 1972.'

OLDHAM
A photo of my grandfather and me, taken at the same time as Charlie Duke left his own family photo on the Moon.

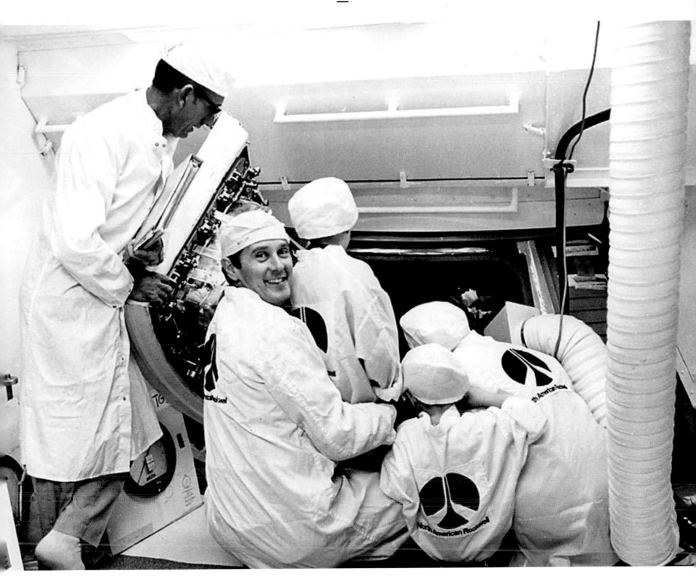

I remember being four years old in Oldham when Apollo 16 was on the Moon. Forty-two years later I talked to Duke for hours in a diner in Texas, with absolutely no regard at all for the film crew trying to make *Human Universe*. 'When I stepped onto the Moon it occurred to me that nobody had ever been here before. You looked out onto the most pristine desert – the most incredible beautiful place I've ever seen. No life, nothing like Earth, the rolling grey lunar surface with the blackness of space above.'

How ambitious was Apollo, I asked? 'They gave us eight and a half years to do it and we did it in eight years and two months. Nobody even knew how to do it,' replied the test pilot, who was used to doing things that nobody can do. 'Yeah sure. 15 minutes in space and we're going to land on the Moon in eight and a half years? But the remarkable part is that we did it, and I had a part in it.' Would it be possible now? 'No. We don't have the manpower to do it. Four hundred thousand people and unlimited budget and you can do a lot, and that's what we had!' What do you say to people who criticise manned exploration? There is surely more to human exploration than just science. 'It's the wonder of it all,' replied the astronaut. 'And that's what we bring – what manned flight brings to

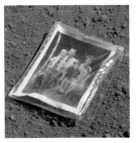

FIRST FAMILY ON THE MOON
Charlie Duke (pictured above) made sure his family shared in his adventure by leaving a photo of them on the lunar surface.

the human spirit, the human being – the wonder of it all. The beauty of the universe, the orderliness of the universe, and you see it with your own eyes and it just captures your imagination. Let's see it, let's do it and let's discover it – that's been the human spirit all along.'

I think Apollo is the greatest human achievement. People argue with me of course. Gil Scott-Heron wrote a song called 'Whitey's on the Moon'. 'A rat done bit my sister Nell, with Whitey on the moon. Her face and arms began to swell, and Whitey's on the moon. I can't pay no doctor bill, but Whitey's on the moon. Ten years from now I'll be payin' still, while Whitey's on the moon.' The economics of Apollo are interesting. As Charlie said, the budget was whatever it had to be to get to the Moon by 1970. At the peak of spending in 1966, NASA received 4.41 per cent of the Federal budget, equivalent to around $40 billion today. That's a lot of money – almost half of the United Kingdom's annual debt interest bill. That's meant to be sarcastic, of course. The total cost of Apollo was in the region of $200 billion at today's prices, which is around a quarter of the cost of the UK's bank bailout programme initiated in October 2008. That's unfair, a City-type might splutter over a glass of Dom Ruinart, because that money was an investment in financial stability and has been repaid, give or take the odd £100 billion, which is neither here nor there. My reply would be yes, but Apollo was probably the most savvy investment in modern history. In 1989, the then US President George Bush said Apollo provided 'the best return on investment since Leonardo da Vinci bought himself a sketchpad'. Many academic studies have been carried out, and the most commonly quoted figure is that for every $1 spent on Apollo, $7 was returned to the economy over the period of a decade. Why? Because Project Apollo was conceived and executed in a tremendously smart way, distributing high-technology jobs and R&D projects across the country. It was also unarguably inspirational, propelling thousands of kids into science and engineering. The average age in Mission Control, Houston, on 20 July 1969 when Neil Armstrong landed on the Moon was 26. The old man in charge, Gene Kranz, was 36, and the old man flying the lunar module was 35. What happened to all those brilliant engineers? They went out into the economy of course, took the technology and expertise developed for the Moon landings and invented the modern world. The kids they inspired became known as Apollo's Children; the generation of optimists steeped in possibility who powered the United States economy through the last third of the twentieth century. The world loves this America, the one that flies to the Moon not because it's easy but because it's hard. I think America has lost its way, which might seem rich from a citizen of a small island that spends more on the wages of Premier League footballers annually than it does on research into the physical sciences and engineering, including its contributions to CERN, the European Space Agency and all UK-based scientific facilities. We've lost our way too, and so has the world. The World Bank defines R&D as 'current and capital expenditures (both public and private) on creative work undertaken systematically to increase knowledge, including knowledge of humanity, culture, and society, and the use of knowledge for new applications'. The United States spent 2.79 per cent of its GDP on increasing knowledge in 2012 – the UK spent 1.72 per cent. It has been estimated that the return on R&D spending in today's world economy is approximately 40:1. Imagine what we could do if we took these figures seriously.

My grandad, sitting behind me in that 1972 family Christmas photograph, was born in 1900. He was three years old when, on 17 December 1903 at Kill Devil Hills in North Carolina, Orville Wright took the controls of the Wright Flyer and lifted off the ground for twelve seconds. He was 68 when he saw Neil Armstrong walk on the Moon. Orville Wright himself died in the year that Neil Armstrong began studying aeronautical engineering at Purdue University, Indiana. I still find it hard to believe that I have spoken to someone who was born before

WALKING ON THE MOON
Charlie Duke is shown collecting lunar samples at Station no. 1 during the first Apollo 16 extravehicular activity at the Descartes landing site. This photograph was taken by Astronaut John W. Young, commander. The parked Lunar Roving Vehicle can be seen in the left background.

MAN ON MARS?
We've had the man on the Moon. Now man's mission is to travel 225 million kilometres to the inhospitable planet of Mars.

powered flight, and to someone who walked on the Moon. It is important to notice that this sentence can't be followed. Someone who walked on the Moon, comma, and someone who .... What? Where will the next generation of Apollo's Children come from? Perhaps a new superpower will take America's place as the great exploring nation. China and India, those re-emergent cradles of civilisation, have ambitions in space. As Jacob Bronowski wrote in the *Ascent of Man*, 'Humanity has a right to change its colour.' But I share his regret that the retreat of Western civilisation may leave Shakespeare and Newton as historical fossils, in the way that Homer and Euclid are. If that is the case, it will be our choice.

Two more astronauts followed Duke and Young onto the lunar surface. They left at 10.55pm GMT on 14 December 1972. Commander Gene Cernan, as he prepared to step on to the ladder of the Lunar Module, quietly spoke the final words from the Moon.

... I'm on the surface; and, as I take man's last step from the surface, back home for some time to come – but we believe not too long into the future – I'd like to just say what I believe history will record. That America's challenge of today has forged man's destiny of tomorrow. And, as we leave the Moon at Taurus-Littrow, we leave as we came and, God willing, as we shall return, with peace and hope for all mankind. Godspeed the crew of Apollo 17.
Gene Cernan, Taurus-Littrow Valley, 14 December, 1972.

SATURN V
The Apollo 11 Saturn V space vehicle lifted off with astronauts Neil A. Armstrong, Michael Collins and Edwin E. Buzz Aldrin Jr. at 9.32am on 16 July 1969 from Kennedy Space Center's Launch Complex 39A.

DREAMERS, PART 1

Apollo was about many things. It was about winning a race against the Soviets. It was about national pride. It was born out of fear as well as optimism. It was about laying the foundations of American dominance in the late twentieth century. It was about economic stimulus. It was about dreams. It succeeded on all fronts. Was it really about dreams? 'Well, space is there, and we're going to climb it, and the Moon and the planets are there, and new hopes for knowledge and peace are there. And, therefore, as we set sail we ask God's blessing on the most hazardous and dangerous and greatest adventure on which man has ever embarked.' I think so. Kennedy was a politician, but I believe he meant it.

So what of the dreamers now? Is the twenty-first century the era of pragmatism? The era in which we believe, because we have to, that the interests of shareholders are aligned with the interests of humanity? Innovation funds the shops on New Bond Street, but is that all? A common governmental lament is that new knowledge is not converted efficiently enough into economic growth. Is that what knowledge is for? Who pays for progress? Who *should* pay for progress?

Human Universe is a piece of documentary television, and this book is based on the series. Television is about stories; examples that illustrate a point. *Human Universe* is also at heart optimistic, because I am optimistic. I think we as a civilisation could do better, as I'm sure you've gathered, but it would be ridiculous to suggest that we are not doing some things right. In the final episode, we found two stories that demonstrate that long-term thinking is not dead; one almost Apollo-like in state-funded grandeur, and the other more modest but equally important. The first was a project I'd visited once before, back in 2009, known as the National Ignition Facility at the Lawrence Livermore National Laboratory in California. The aim is to make a star on Earth.

Nuclear fusion is the power source of the stars. The Sun releases energy in its core by turning hydrogen into helium. Two protons approach each other at high speed, because the core is hot. The core became hot initially through the collapse of the gas cloud which formed the Sun. Protons are positively charged, and therefore repel each other through the action of the electromagnetic force, but if they get close enough, the more powerful nuclear forces take over. The weak nuclear force acts to turn the proton into a neutron, with the emission of a positron and an electron neutrino. The proton and neutron then bind together under the action of the strong nuclear force to form a deuterium nucleus, which is an isotope of hydrogen (because it contains a single proton) with a neutron attached. Very quickly, another proton fuses with the deuteron to form helium-3, and finally two helium-3 nuclei stick together to form helium-4, with the emission of the two 'spare' protons. The important result in this convoluted process is that four protons end up getting converted into a single helium-4 nucleus, made of two protons and two neutrons, and the helium-4 nucleus is less massive than four free protons. This missing mass is released as energy, in accord with Einstein's equation $E=mc^2$, and this is why the Sun shines. The energy released in fusion reactions is colossal by terrestrial standards. If all the protons in a cubic centimetre of the solar core were to fuse into deuterium, enough energy would be produced to power the average town for a year. Or to put it another way, one kilogram of fusion fuel produces as much energy as 10 million kilograms of fossil fuel, which is approximately a hundred thousand barrels of oil, with no CO_2 emissions; the waste product is helium, which can be used to fill party balloons.

Energy is the foundation of civilisation. Access to energy underpins everything, from public health to prosperity. Access to clean water is

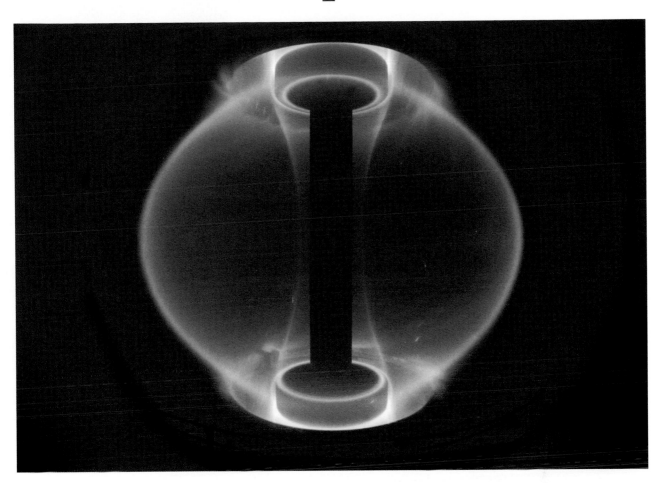

NUCLEAR FUSION RESEARCH
Spherical ball of plasma inside the START device at Culham, Oxfordshire, England.

surely more fundamental, you might say, but this requires energy. Even in the most arid regions, desalination plants or deep wells can deliver water in abundance *if* sufficient energy is available. It isn't, of course. Profligate energy use has a bad name today, but consider this. In every country in which the per capita energy use is greater than half the European average, adult life expectancy is greater than 70 years, literacy rates are greater than 90 per cent, infant mortality rates are low and more than one in five of the population is in higher education. The reason energy use has a bad name is not because it is bad in itself. It is good, it is the foundation of modern civilisation, and modern civilisation is a good thing. I don't want to live on a subsistence farm, sleep in stifling heat, run the risk of dying of malaria and have no access to clean water or cutting-edge medical care. I am lucky. I live in a city, I buy all the food I want from nice shops, I have a fulfilling job in a university and I get to do research at places like CERN, which is interesting. I want everyone in the world to have choices, like I have, and that means I want everyone in the world to have access to energy, like I have. In 2011, 1.3 billion people lacked access to electricity. Yes. Energy use is good. The problem with energy is how we produce it.

The world produces more than 80 per cent of its energy by burning fossil fuels. This is expected to fall to 76 per cent by 2035 as nuclear and renewables grow in importance. Burning things is humanity's oldest technology. The energy sector is responsible for two-thirds of global greenhouse gas emissions. The most recent scientific modelling suggests that global average temperatures will rise by around 2–2.5°C above the average of the years 1986 to 2005 by 2100. The rise could be less – as low

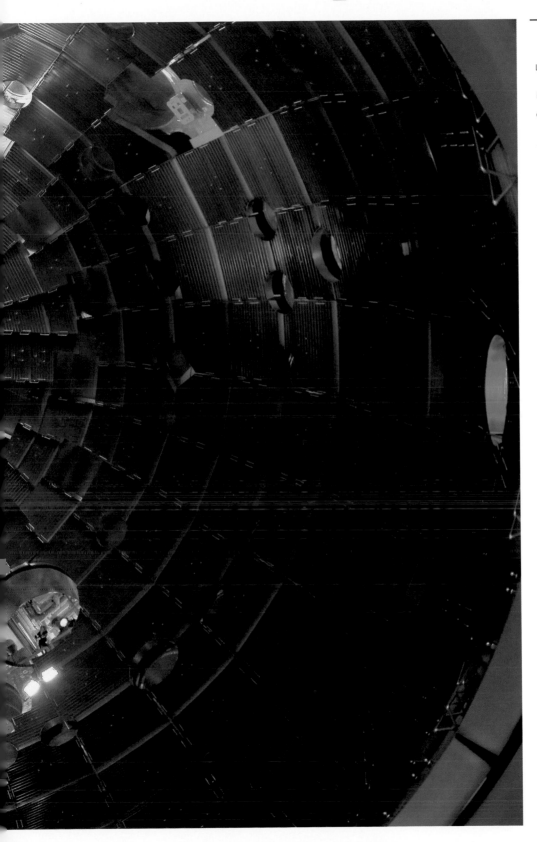

CONTAINING THE SUN
The inside of the target chamber at the National Ignition Facility (NIF), at the Lawrence Livermore National Laboratory, California, USA. This site is attempting to initiate and control hydrogen fusion as a sustainable energy source for future use. The beams from 192 lasers are focused here onto a 2-millimetre-wide capsule of deuterium–tritium (DT) gas. The total energy focused is 1.8 megajoules.

as 1 to 1.5°C, or it could be 4°C or more. Some of the uncertainty depends on our actions, and so there are assumptions about future behaviour built into the predictions. But over 90 per cent of computer models agree that global temperatures will have increased by 2100 as a result of greenhouse gas emissions from fossil fuel burning.

GLOBAL WARMING
The most recent summary is contained in the IPCC Climate Change 2014 Summary for Policy Makers: http://ipcc-wg2.gov/.

Nuclear fusion, then, is a good idea. If it can be made to work in an economically viable way, it will provide limitless, clean energy for everyone. It is not the *only* way of achieving this goal. One can make a case for solar power, and indeed an increased contribution from other renewables and nuclear fission. But it is a possible way to solve the world's energy problems for good, in principle, and is therefore worth exploring.

The challenge is technical rather than fundamental, in the sense that we know fusion works because the Sun does it. Fusion is difficult to achieve on Earth primarily because of the colossally high temperatures and pressures required. There are two approaches being followed, and each is Apollo-like. In Europe, a worldwide collaboration involving Russia, USA, the European Union, Japan, China, Korea and India is in the process of constructing ITER. This machine is in effect a magnetic bottle, which can store a plasma at temperatures in excess of 150 million °C – ten times that of the solar core. ITER will use deuterium and tritium, which is another isotope of hydrogen comprising one proton and two neutrons, to make helium-4. This bypasses the slow initial weak interaction in the Sun that makes deuterium out of hydrogen, making ITER a lot more efficient than our star. Deuterium is extracted from seawater, and tritium is made inside the reactor itself by irradiating a lithium blanket with the spare neutrons produced during the fusion reaction. An 800 MW fusion power station of this type would consume around 300 grams of tritium fuel per day. ITER is not particularly telegenic at the moment because it is under construction and will not be commissioned until 2019. This is why we chose to focus on the US National Ignition Facility, which is already up and running.

NIF is pure science fiction; in fact, it was used as a set for *Star Trek: Into Darkness*. It is the world's largest laser system by an order of magnitude. The laser delivers 500,000 gigawatts of power onto a target smaller than a peppercorn in a series of increasingly powerful hammer blows, tuned to arrive with a precision of better than a tenth of a billionth of a second. That is 1000 times the peak energy-generating capacity of the United States. This, as you can imagine, creates a bit of a bang. The peppercorn-sized target contains deuterium-tritium fuel, just like ITER. The laser pulses raise the temperature of the pellet's gold container, and the X-ray radiation produced drives a rapid collapse of the fuel, initiating fusion. The devil is in the detail; the precise timing and duration of the laser pulses, and the shape of the gold container, all contribute to the chances of success and the efficiency of the process. Despite the tremendous engineering difficulty, in September 2013 more energy was released from a deuterium-tritium fuel pellet than the pellet absorbed, although this was only 1 per cent of the total energy input to the lasers. Nevertheless, this demonstrates that so-called inertial fusion works in principle. The inertial fusion power station of tomorrow would use far more efficient laser systems – NIFs are now more than a decade out of date – and the fuel pellet technology being developed by NIF. The technology has been demonstrated to work, at least on a vast, government-funded research scale, and this is how difficult things like space exploration have to begin. Commercial companies will rarely take such enormous risks, and this means that we, the taxpayers, must pay for the creation of this type of knowledge. As with Apollo, we will be repaid, but the investment horizon is beyond that of the average accountant.

It therefore appears that there is no technical reason why such power stations could not be constructed. There is much research to be done,

HUMAN ENERGY
A NASA satellite image shows energy produced by man – white is light, yellow is oil/gas flares and red is agricultural burning.

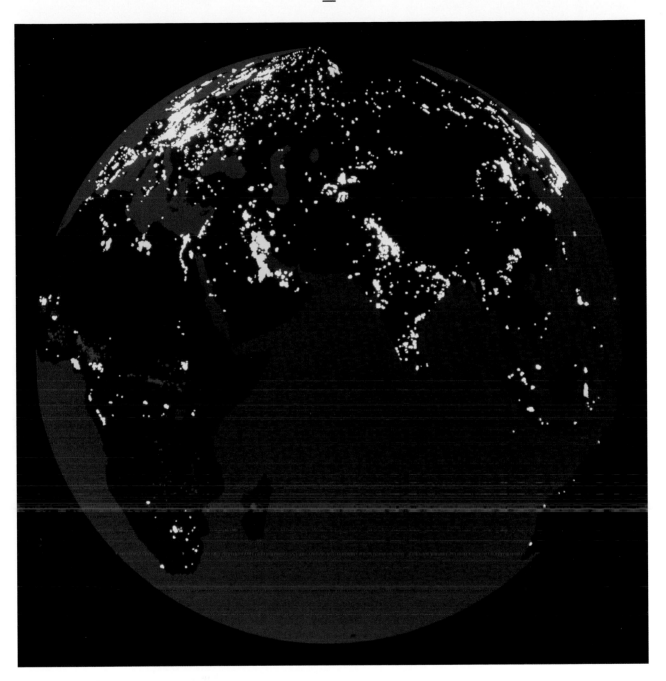

but the barriers are likely to be budgetary rather than fundamental; the United States spends more on pet grooming than it does on fusion research. There is a serious point behind that cheap shot. I think one of the primary barriers to progress is education. I am a believer in the innate rationality of human beings; given the right education, the right information and the right tuition in how to think about problems, I believe that people will make rational choices. I believe that if I said to someone: 'Here's the deal. You can have limitless clean energy for your lifetime, for your children and grandchildren's lifetimes and beyond, in exchange for grooming your own cat', then most people would reach for a comb. I have to believe that, otherwise this book is a futile gesture.

DREAMERS, PART 2

The second of our stories couldn't be more different. It involves no high technology and very little cash, but it may have a tremendous impact. Securing the future isn't all about money; it's also about action.

The Svalbard Global Seed Vault is modest and beautiful from the outside. In common with all publicly funded construction projects in Norway, the simple door on an Arctic hillside is a work of art, created by Dyveke Sanne. In the summer, it reflects the eternal Sun. In winter, fibreoptic cables shine in the perpetual night. The doorway leads into a converted coal mine, deep in the permafrost. There are three caverns, each maintained at a temperature of -18°C by a cooling system. The temperature was chosen very precisely; it is the temperature at which seeds metabolise slowly, but do not die. At -18°C, the most hardy seeds remain viable for over 20,000 years. Only one of the caverns is in use; the other two are for the future. Inside, there are over 800,000 populations of seeds from almost every country in the world. All the seeds are agricultural crop varieties – the raw material for and the foundation of global food production. Seeds from America and Europe nestle next to those from Asia and Africa. Syrian seeds, rescued from the recent

recent troubles in Aleppo, the home of a local seed bank, sit beside those from North Korea, South Korea, China, Canada, Nigeria, Kenya, and so on around the world. The vault contains virtually the whole history of human agriculture, stretching back to its origins in the Fertile Crescent all those years ago. Each seed population reflects some choices that were made, some environmental challenge or perhaps simply the taste of a farmer or his village. There are varieties manipulated by multinationals, or carefully cultivated and cherished by isolated tribes. The boxes are food for the imagination, time capsules, the stuff of dreams. They are also of fundamental importance.

Why protect agricultural seeds? The answer is that biodiversity is a very good thing. Life on Earth forms a tangled web, a great genetic database distributed across hundreds of thousands of extant species of animals, plants, insects and countless single-celled organisms. The more species there are, the more data there is in the database, and the more chance the whole biosphere has of responding to challenges, be they from disease, natural or human-induced climate change, loss of natural habitat or whatever. This is obvious. If there are genes somewhere in the great database of life that allow wheat to grow with less water, and the climate becomes more arid, then those genes will be valuable to us. If we lose particular genes, then we lose them for good. Today, fewer

'DOOMSDAY' SEED VAULT
A global initiative, the seed vault is located halfway between mainland Norway and the North Pole, deep inside a mountain on a remote island in the Svalbard archipelago. The purpose of the depository is to store duplicates of all seed samples from crop collections around the world.

than 150 species of crop are used in modern agriculture, and 12 of these deliver the majority of the world's non-meat food supply. There is diversity in the form of different varieties, of course; there are estimated to be more than 100,000 varieties of rice. But the overwhelming majority of crop species used throughout human history are no longer cultivated. They are stored, however, in seed vaults, ready for use if needed. The Svalbard Global Seed Vault is a back-up; our insurance policy, ensuring that even if countries lose their seed vaults through natural disasters, war or simple neglect, then irreplaceable parts of the great genetic database of life will not be lost with them.

The Norwegian government owns the seed vault, but the depositors own the seeds. A charitable trust, the Global Crop Diversity Trust, meets most of the operating costs through an endowment fund. Cary Fowler was the executive director of the Trust during the establishment of the seed vault. He was a pleasure to speak to when we filmed in Svalbard – a dreamer, yes, but a dreamer who gets things done.

'Those of us in my field, we live in a world of wounds,' said Fowler. 'We see the injuries, we see the loss of diversity, the extinction, and at a certain point, enough is enough, and you try to figure out what can we do that's not just stop-gap? That really is long term and that puts an end to the problem of crop diversity. Because we know that we are going to need this crop diversity in the future, it's the biological foundation of agriculture. We'll need it as long as we have agriculture.' Which is as long as civilisation exists, I added. Fowler nodded. 'After that, we won't be bothered, will we!'

The Svalbard Global Seed Vault is built, effectively, for eternity, or at least for tens of thousands of years. It is supported by practically all the governments of the world, and is a genuine investment in our future based on sound science and an understanding of the potential challenges and risks that we may face as a single, global civilisation. It's not big, flashy or expensive, but it's important and, perhaps as importantly, somebody actually did it. I find that inspiring.

So where does all this leave us? All I can do is give you my view. I want to be honest. We didn't set out to make a love letter to the human race when we started filming *Human Universe*. We set out to make a cosmology series, documenting our ascent into insignificance. Things changed gradually as we chatted, debated, experienced, photographed and argued our way around the world, and we realised that, for all our irrational, unscientific, superstitious, tribal, nationalistic, myopic ignorance, we are the most meaningful thing the universe has to offer as far as we know, and when all is said and done, that's a significant thing to be. It is surely true that there is no absolute *meaning* or *value* to our existence when set against the limitless stars. We are allowed to exist by the laws of nature and in that sense we have no more value than the stars themselves. And yet there is self-evidently meaning in the universe because my own existence, the existence of those I love, and the existence of the entire human race means something to me. I think this because I have had the remarkable luxury of spending my time in education. I teach, I am taught, I research and I learn. I have been fortunate. I believe powerfully that we who have the power should strive to extend the gift of education to everyone. Education is the most important investment a developed society can make, and the most effective way of nurturing a developing one. The young will one day be the decision makers, the taxpayers, the voters, the explorers, the scientists, the artists and the musicians. They will protect and enhance our way of life, and make our lives worth living. They will learn about our fragility, our outrageously fortunate existence and our indescribable significance as an isolated island of meaning in a sea of infinite stars, and they will make better decisions than my generation because of that knowledge. They will ensure that our universe remains a human one.

THE END

What a piece of work is a Man. So certain, so vulnerable, so ingenious, so small, so bold, so loving, so violent, so full of promise, so unaware of his fragile significance. Someone asked me what they thought was a deep question: What are we made of? Up quarks, down quarks and electrons, I answered. That's what a Man is. Humanity is more than that. Our civilisation is the most complex emergent phenomenon in the known universe. It is the sum of our literature, our music, our technology, our art, our philosophy, our history, our science, our *knowledge*. I have a recording of Mahler's Ninth Symphony conducted by Bruno Walter made on the eve of the Anschluss. It is suffused with threat. Walter and the Vienna Philharmonic knew what was coming. Hope fades with the last vanishing note, which Mahler marked *'ersterbend'* – 'dying' – in the manuscript. It is Mahler's farewell to life, presaging Old Europe's farewell to peace. None of this depth is present in the physical score itself; those black ink dots on white paper can be digitised using a scanner and stored in a few kilobytes on a mobile phone. The fathomless power of the recording emerges from a finite collection of bits because the performance contains the sum total of the fears, dreams, concerns and anxieties of a hundred lives, played out against a backdrop of a million more. The personal history of each of the musicians, the conductor and the composer, and indeed the history of civilisation, hangs upon the supporting framework of the notes, resulting in a work of infinite complexity and power, because each human being *is* possessed of infinite faculties, emergent from a finite number of quarks and electrons. Our existence is a ridiculous affront to common sense, beyond any reasonable expectation of the possible based on the simplicity of the laws of nature, and our civilisation is the combination of seven billion individual affronts. This is what my smiling seems to say: Man certainly does delight me. Our existence is necessarily temporary and our spatial reach finite, and this makes us all the more precious. Mahler's great farewell to life can also be read as a call to value life with all your heart, to use it wisely and to enjoy it while you can.

From Brian

To George Albert Eagle:
It's your future, little boy.

From Andrew

To my soulmate Anna, my beautiful children
Benjamin, Martha and Theo, my wonderful mum
Barbara, my brothers Paul and Howard and all of
the 'small creatures' whom I am lucky enough to
have with me in the vastness.

INDEX

Entries in *italics* indicate images.

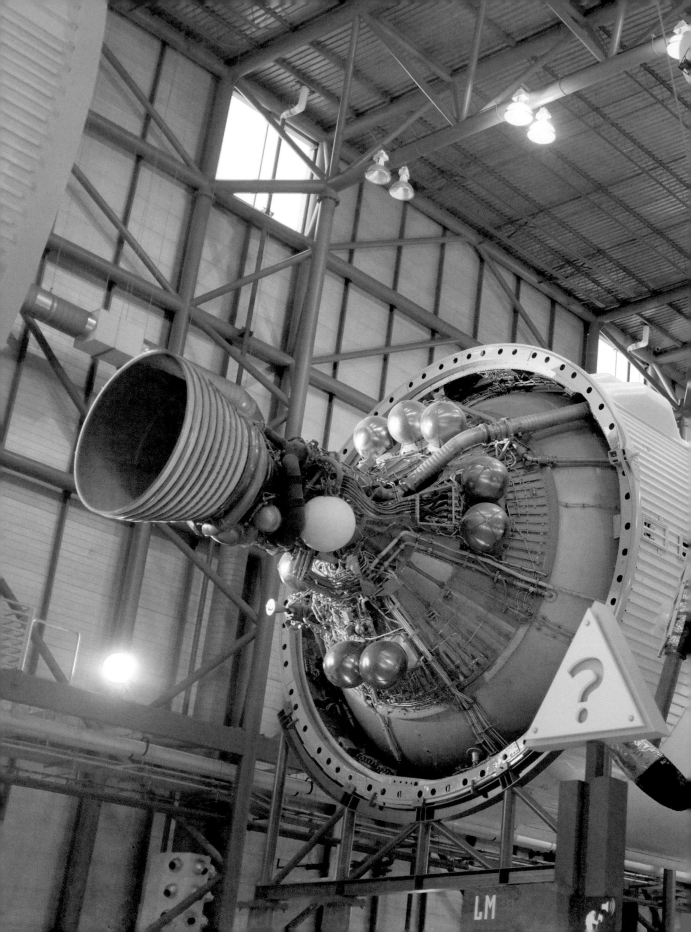

Mitochondria 113, *113*, 114, *114*,
115, 127, 143, 149
Mitosis 114, *114*
Monty Python's *Life of Brian* 10
Moon:
    Apollo missions and *see* Apollo
        missions
    Armstrong's footprints on *130*,
        131
    atmosphere 96
    dark side of the 30, *31*
    distance to the 53
    Earth's rotational rate and
        132–4
    first views of the 40
    formation of 105
    Galileo's sketches of 40, *40*
    Galileo's watercolours of 42,
        42–3
    North Pole 96
    orbit/gravity 14, 15, 16, *16–17*,
        19, 23–4, 26, 99, 132, 133,
        134, 142
    physics of getting to 253–4
Moore, Patrick 64, 145
Morphogenesis 209
Morrison, Philip 69–70, 71, 72, 74,
    117
Mount Pinatubo eruption, 1991 96
Mount Wilson Observatory,
    California *34*, 35, 36, 37
mutually assured destruction 117

N

Nabataeans 151, 152, 163
Nagasaki, nuclear attack on 68
Nakayara, Ukichiro 202
Nanorobot 119, *119*
NASA 72, 94, 239
    Apollo missions and 23, 149,
        145, 147, 149, 252 *see also*
        Apollo missions
    Aquarius Reef Base 239
    AS8-14-2383 24
    Big Ear telescope and 72
    definition of properties a planet
        needs to have chance of
        supporting life 94
    Exoplanet Archive 88
    Extreme Environment Mission
        Operations (NEEMO)
        236–7, 239
    Glenn Research Center 47
    Hubble Space Telescope 32, 59,

99, *218*, 219
Jet Propulsion Laboratory,
    Pasadena, California 78
Lunar Reconnaissance Orbiter
    96
Near-Earth Object Program
    235
NEEMO 16 *236–7*
Plum Brook Station, Ohio 46,
    47, *47*, *48–9*, 50, *51*
Project Cyclops and 72
Sentry System 235
Space Shuttle missions 122
National Academy of Sciences 70
National Ignition Facility (NIF),
    California 260, 264
National Radio Astronomy
    Observatory, Green Bank, West
    Virginia 70, 71, 72, 82, 85, 86,
    101, 116, 117, 118
'National Radio Silence Day' 69
Natufians 151
Nature 69
Neanderthals 126, 140, *140*, 142,
    143, *143*, 149, 233
NEEMO 16 *236–7*
Neptune 8, 78, 79, 118
Neumann, John von 118
neutrino 53, 179, 182
neutron stars 53, 83
neutrons 179, 182, 183, 214, 260,
    264
neutrophil 114, *114*
New Yorker 67, *67*, 68
Newman, William 118
Newton, Isaac 16, 18, 24, 25, 26, 33,
    43, 45–6, 50, 52, 53, 160, 161,
    162, 165, *165*, 198, 240, 246, 256
Newton's Constant 18, 186
Newton's Law of Gravity 18, 24,
    25, 26, 33, 45–6, 160, 161, 246
Nicholas II, Tsar 157
Nile, River 151, 165
99942 Apophis (asteroid) 235
North Star 134
nuclear fusion 33, 214, 260–1,
    264–5
nuclear reactors 68

O

Oakbank Avenue, Chadderton,
    Oldham, Greater Manchester,
    England 8, 23, 55, 64, 132, 165,
    186

Observatoire de Haute-Provence,
    France 86
Occam's razor 66
odds of our existence 176
Ohio University 72
Oliver, Barney 70, 71
Omo 1 and Omo 2 140, *141*
Omo River, Ethiopia 140
Order of the Dolphin, The 70
Orion 30, 98
'Out of Africa' model 140, *146–7*,
    149
oxygenic photosynthesis 110, 111,
    112, 113, 116, 119
Ozma 70

P

parallax, stellar 24–5, *24*, *25*, 26,
    30, 32
Paranthropus 126, 140
Pardoe, Geoffrey 145
patterns in nature, emergence of
    complex 198, 199, *199*, *200–1*,
    202, *203*, *204*, *205*, 208, *208–9*,
    209–11, *210*, *211*, *228–9*
Pauli Exclusion Principle 52, 53
Pauline Chapel, Rome 40, *40–1*, 42
Pearman, Peter 70, 71
Persepolis, Iran 162
Peru 88, *89*
Petra *150*, 151, 152, *153*, 163
Petrovich 157, 166
phagocytosis 114
Pherkad 134
photon 69, 179, 182, 183
photosynthesis 70, 96, 110–13, 115,
    116, 119
Photosystem 2 111
physics, laws of 17, 40, 65, 82, 119,
    142, 170, 173, 177, 225, 226 *see
    also under individual law name*
Pickering, Professor Edward
    Charles 30, 32
Pilbara region, Western Australia
    105
Pius XII, Pope 59
Planck epoch 170, 173
Planck length 219, 220
Planck satellite 219
Planck temperature 173
Planck's constant 53
Planetary Motion, Kepler's laws
    of 198
Plato 195

PICTURE CREDITS

Collage artworks on pp6, 20–21, 38–39, 62, 76–77, 92–93, 120, 136–137, 154–155, 168, 184–185, 206–207, 230, 244–245, 258–259 © Darrel Rees; pp2, 9, 12–13, 32, 47, 48–49, 51, 52, 54–55, 89, 102–103, 142, 150, 156, 158–159, 167, 174–175, 189, 190–191, 196–197, 215, 227, 250, 270 © Brian Cox; pp10–11 © Sheila Terry/Science Photo Library; pp15, 42/43 top © Royal Astronomical Society/Science Photo Library; p16 © British Library/Science Photo Library; p17 © Bibliothèque nationale de France; pp22, 42/43 bottom, 86, 91, 133, 144, 252–253 © NASA/Science Photo Library; pp26, 33 © Harvard College Observatory/Science Photo Library; p27 © European Space Agency/Science Photo Library; pp28–29 © Scott Smith/Corbis; p30 from the *Annals of the Harvard College Observatory*, Vol. LX, No. IV, Published by the Observatory, Cambridge, Massachusetts, 1908; pp31, 236–237 © NASA; p34 © Emilio Segre Visual Archives/American Institute of Physics/Science Photo Library; p36 © Robert Gendler/Science Photo Library; p37 Courtesy of The Carnegie Observatories; p40 © Hemis/Alamy; p41 © Jon Arnold Images Ltd/Alamy; pp44, 178–179 © Science Source/Science Photo Library; pp56/57 © Science Photo Library – Mark Garlick/Getty Images; p58 © JPL-CALTECH/NASA/Science Photo Library; p59 © NASA/ESA/STSCI/R. Williams/HDF Team/Science Photo Library; pp60–61, 219 © ESA and the Planck Collaboration; pp64–65 Courtesy of Lowell Observatory; p66 Courtesy of the National Archives at College Park, Maryland, USA; p67 © Alan Dunn/The New Yorker Collection/The Cartoon Bank; p68 Courtesy of the National Archives at Seattle, Washington, USA; p73 © Mike Hutchings/Reuters/Corbis; p74 © Jerry R. Ehman; p75 © Benjamin Crowell; pp79, 80, 216–217, 218 © NASA/JPL; p82 © NASA Ames/JPL-Caltech; pp85, 165 bottom © Science Photo Library; p87 © Eckhard Slawik/Science Photo Library; p88 © Walter Myers/Science Photo Library; p90 © NASA/Ball Aerospace/Science Photo Library; pp98/99 top © NASA/ESA/STSCI/Science Photo Library; middle © NOAA/Science Source/Science Photo Library; bottom © Royal Observatory, Edinburgh/AAO/Science Photo Library; pp100–101 © Lionel Bret/Look at Sciences/Science Photo Library; p104 © Smithsonian Institution; pp107, 242–243 © Frans Lanting, Mint Images/Science Photo Library; pp108–109 © Didier Descouens; p110 © Paul Harrison; p112 © Wim van Egmond/Visuals Unlimited/Science Photo Library; p113 © Dr. Fred Hossler/Visuals Unlimited/Science Photo Library; p114 left, 115 left © Dr. Gopal Murti/Science Photo Library; middle © Eric Grave/Science Photo Library; right © Science Photo Library; p115 middle © Professors P. M. Motta & S. Correr/Science Photo Library; right © Dr. Alexey Khodjakov/Science Photo Library; p116 © Ashley Cooper/Visuals Unlimited/Science Photo Library; p119 © Roger Harris/Science Photo Library;

pp123, 124–125, 235, 252 © Detlev van Ravenswaay/Science Photo Library; p127 © Dr. Xijun Ni, Institute of Vertebrate Paleontology and Paleoanthropology, Chinese Academy of Sciences in Beijing (China); pp128–129 © Brian Gadsby/Science Photo Library; p130 top © Horizon International Images Limited/Alamy; p130 bottom, 163 © John Mead/Science Photo Library; pp138–139 © Dr. Juerg Alean/Science Photo Library; p141 © The Natural History Museum/Alamy; p143 © John Reader/Science Photo Library; p146 © RGB Ventures/SuperStock/Alamy; p148 © bnps.co.uk; p153 © Hubert Raguet/Look at Sciences/Science Photo Library; p161 © Sergei Remezov/Reuters/Corbis; p162 © Diego Lezama Orezzoli/Corbis; p164 © Seth Joel/Corbis; p165 top © Peter MacDiarmid/Reuters/Corbis; p171 © NSF/Steffen Richter/Harvard University/Science Photo Library; pp172, 199, 249 © Middle Temple Library/Science Photo Library; p173 © Emilio Segre Visual Archives/American Institute of Physics/Science Photo Library; p176 Courtesy of Factory Records; p177 © Edelmann/Science Photo Library; pp180–181 © Maximilien Brice/CERN/Science Photo Library; p186 © Albert Einstein Archives/Hebrew University of Jerusalem; p187 © CERN/Science Photo Library; p188 © Patrick Eagar/Getty Images; p194 © David Wall/Alamy; p195 © Ryan J. Lane/Getty Images; pp200–201 © Ted Kinsman/Kenneth Libbrecht/Science Photo Library; pp203, 248 © Natural History Museum London/Science Photo Library; p204 © Chris Mattison/Alamy; p205 top left © Danita Delimont/Alamy; p205 top right © Photoshot Holdings Ltd/Alamy; p205 middle left © John Hartung/Alamy; p205 middle right © Life on white/Alamy; p205 bottom left © WaterFrame/Alamy; p205 bottom right © Frans Lanting Studio/Alamy; p208 © Nick Greaves/Alamy; pp210, 211 © Philippe Plailly/Science Photo Library; pp212–213 © ESA/DLR/FU Berlin (G. Neukum); p221 © Geoff Moore/Rex Features; pp222–223 © ATLAS Collaboration/CERN/Science Photo Library; p224 © NSF/BICEP2 Collaboration/Science Photo Library; p225 © European Space Agency/Rosetta/OsirisTeam/ Science Photo Library; pp228–229 © Alfred Pasieka/Science Photo Library; p232 © age fotostock Spain, S. L./Alamy; p238 © European Space Agency, IPMB/Science Photo Library; 241 © Mark Garlick/Science Photo Library; p244 © Ondrej Kucera/Shutterstock; pp246/247 © Gianni Dagli Orti/Corbis; p247 © Timothy Ball/iStock; lry; pp251 both images, 253 © NASA/Rex Features; pp254–255 © NASA/National Geographic Society/Corbis; p256 © Steven Hobbs/Stocktrek Images/Corbis; p257 © NASA/Retna Ltd/Corbis; p261 © EFDA-JET/Science Photo Library; pp262–263 © Lawrence Livermore National Laboratory/Science Photo Library; p265 © NASA GSFC/Science Photo Library; pp266–267, 268 © National Geographic Image Collection/Alamy.

ACKNOWLEDGEMENTS

We first began to discuss the television series that became *Human Universe* in the summer of 2012. It's the fourth major television project we have worked on together and like all of the previous series it has required the talent and dedication of a brilliant team of people. We'd like to thank them all for the endless passion and commitment they have given to the series. We'd especially like to thank Gideon Bradshaw, the Series Producer, for his outstanding leadership. Gideon has worked on many of our television projects over the years including *Horizon* and the *Wonders* series and as always his creativity, vision and passion have been ever present during the production of *Human Universe*. The team also consisted of a world-class group of directors: Stephen Cooter, Nat Sharman, Annabel Gillings and Michael Lachman. The ability to take complex scientific ideas and transform them into beautiful films is a rare talent and we are lucky to have had such expertise on the project. We would also like to thank the hugely talented Paul O'Callaghan, Director of Photography, who has brought such a vibrant beauty to the cinematography across the series, Andy Paddon, 'soundman', for his endless hard work across all of the films, Rob McGregor for his coffee machine and for shooting so many beautiful scenes both above and below the water and Phillip Sheppard for his beautiful score. We'd also like to thank Davina Bristow, Mags Lightbody, Laura Flegg, Alice Jones, Jodie Adams, Karen McCallion and Eloisa Noble for all the ideas and dedication they have brought to the series.

Editing is such an important part of the television-making process and we are hugely grateful to Darren Jonusas for his craft in shaping the series along with the other superb editors Graeme Dawson, Louise Salkow and Gerard Evans. We'd also like to thank Rob Hifle and the team at BDH for the design and visual effects they have brought to every film.

Every production also needs a brilliant team back in the office and *Human Universe* relied again and again on the leadership of Production Manager Alexandra Nicolson, Production Executive Laura Davey and the hard work and dedication of all the production team. Thank you to Louisa Reid, Viola Schwedhelm, Carly Wallis, Alexandra Osborne, and all of those who worked so tirelessly to support this complex production. We'd also like to thank Nik Sopwith and Kate Bartlett who helped shape and nurture the ideas that would form the foundation of the series during its early development.

There are of course so many others who helped make the series and we are grateful to them all, but we would like to thank Peter Leonard, Jenny Scott, Professor Nik Lane, Professor Jeff Forshaw, Professor Frank Drake, Martin West, Julius Brighton, Helene Ganichaud and Vicky Edgar.

Plus a very special thanks to Sue Rider for all of her endless support.

As always, the team at HarperCollins have been outstanding in delivering such a beautiful book against punishing deadlines. We'd particularly like to thank Zoë Bather, whose brilliant design is found in this and all three of the *Wonders* books, Michael Gray, Julia Koppitz, Chris Wright, Anna Mitchelmore and of course Myles Archibald, our patient and wise publisher.

We'd also like to thank the University of Manchester for their continued unwavering support and encouragement, in particular Dame Nancy Rothwell, President and Vice Chancellor, who allows her academics the freedom to be academics.

Cognitio, sapientia, humanitas.

FORCES OF NATURE

Professor Brian Cox
& Andrew Cohen

WILLIAM
COLLINS

SEARCHING FOR THE DEEPEST ANSWERS

TO THE
SIMPLEST
QUESTIONS

'What beauty. I saw clouds and their light shadows
on the distant dear Earth.... The water looked
like darkish, slightly gleaming spots.... When I
watched the horizon, I saw the abrupt, contrasting
transition from the Earth's light-coloured surface
to the absolutely black sky. I enjoyed the rich colour
spectrum of the Earth. It is surrounded by a light
blue aureole that gradually darkens, becoming
turquoise, dark blue, violet, and finally coal black.'
— *Yuri Gagarin*

Taking a different perspective

'The first day or so we all pointed to our countries. The third or fourth day we were pointing to our continents. By the fifth day we were aware of only one Earth.'
— *Sultan bin Salman bin Abdulaziz Al-Saud, Space Shuttle STS-51-G*

Left: On 5 May 1961, Alan Shepard's Freedom 7 launched into space from Cape Canaveral, Florida, for NASA's first ever suborbital flight.

This is a book about science. What is science? That's a good question, and there may be as many answers as there are scientists. I would say that science is an attempt to understand the natural world. The explanations we discover can often seem abstract and separate from the familiar, but this is a false impression. Science is about explaining the everyday minutiae of human experience. Why is the sky blue? Why are stars and planets round? Why does the world keep on turning? Why are plants green? These are questions a child might ask, but they are certainly not childish; they generate a chain of answers that ultimately lead to the edge of our understanding.

If you dig deep enough, most questions end with uncertainty. The sky is blue because of the way light interacts with matter, and the way light interacts with matter is determined by symmetries that constrain the laws of nature. We'll encounter these concepts later in the book. But if one keeps on digging, and asks why those particular symmetries, or why there are laws of nature at all, then we are into the glorious hazy place in which scientists live and work; the space between the known and the unknown. This is the domain of the research scientist, and it is a place of curiosity and wonder.

Grander questions lurk in the half-light. How did life on Earth begin? Is there life on other worlds? What happened in the first few moments after the Big Bang? These are questions that have a sense of depth and a feeling of complexity and intractability, but the techniques and processes by which we look for answers are no different to those deployed in discovering why the sky is blue. This is an important point. If a question sounds deep, it doesn't mean that the way to answer it is to retire to the wilderness for a year, sit cross-legged and hope for something to occur to you. Rather, the answers are often constructed on foundations generated by the systematic and careful exploration of simpler questions. This idea is central to our book. In seeking to understand the everyday world – the colours, structure, behaviour and history of our home – we develop the knowledge and techniques necessary to step beyond the everyday and approach the Universe beyond.

Planet Earth is the easiest place in the Universe to study because we live on it, but it is also confusingly complicated. For one thing, it's the only planet we know of that supports life. It is home to over seven billion humans and at least ten million species of animals and plants. Of its surface area, 29 per cent is land, and humans have divided that 148,326,000 square kilometres into 196 countries, although this number is disputed. Within these boundaries, reflecting the vagaries of 10,000 years of human history, there are over 4000 religions. Some want to increase the number of countries; others want to decrease the number of religions. For such a small world orbiting an ordinary star in such a run-of-the-mill galaxy, it's not very well organised and difficult to understand through the parochial fog. Just over five hundred humans have travelled high enough to see our home in its entirety – a small world against the backdrop of the stars – and when they do, something interesting happens. They see through the fog, and return with a description not of segregation and complexity, but of unity and simplicity.

'When you're finally up at the Moon looking back on Earth, all those differences and nationalistic traits are pretty well going to blend, and you're going to get a concept that maybe this really is one world and why the hell can't we learn to live together like decent people.'
— *Frank Borman, Gemini 7, Apollo 8*

'If somebody had said before the flight, "Are you going to get carried away looking at the Earth from the Moon?" I would have said, "No, no way." But yet when I first looked back at the Earth, standing on the Moon, I cried.'
— *Alan Shepard, Mercury 3, Apollo 14*

Left: Earthrise – possibly the most influential and best-known image in space history. Taken by astronaut William Anders in 1968 during the Apollo 8 mission.

Below: Alan Shepard being hoisted into a US Marine helicopter after completing his 15-minute suborbital flight in Freedom 7, 5 May 1961.

Right: Alan Shepard became the first American in space but didn't walk on the Moon until 15 February 1971, with Edgar Mitchell.

'ODDLY ENOUGH

THE OVERRIDING SENSATION

Above: Harrison Schmitt, of the Apollo 17 lunar mission, January 1972, stands next to the US flag on the Moon, as it points to Earth in the distance.

'When you're finally up at the Moon looking back on Earth, all those differences and nationalistic traits are pretty well going to blend, and you're going to get a concept that maybe this really is one world and why the hell can't we learn to live together like decent people.'
Frank Borman, Gemini 7, Apollo 8

'If somebody had said before the flight, "Are you going to get carried away looking at the Earth from the Moon?" I would have said, "No, no way." But yet when I first looked back at the Earth, standing on the Moon, I cried.'
Alan Shepard, Mercury 3, Apollo 14

The astronauts were not making whimsical comments. These are statements from human beings whose experience has given them a different perspective. The astronauts see simplicity because they have been forced to look at the world in a different way. We are self-evidently one species, inhabiting one planet, and it follows that we have one chance not to mess it all up. We can't all be astronauts, but we can all be scientists, and I think science provides a similar perspective to altitude. It lifts us up, mentally rather than physically, and allows us to survey the landscape below. We look for regularities and, once glimpsed, we try to understand their origin. I'll put my cards on the table right away. I want you to draw the obvious analogy. On his return from space, Scott Carpenter, officer in the United States Navy and Korean War veteran, felt that our highest loyalty should not be to our own country, but to the family of man and the planet at large. Space travel is about a shift in perspective, and so is science. The more we understand about nature, the more beautiful it appears and the more we understand what a privilege it is to be able to spend our short time exploring it. Be a child. Pay attention to small things. Don't be led by prejudice. Take nobody's word for anything. Observe and think. Ask simple questions. Seek simple answers. That's what we'll do in this book, and hopefully, by the end, you'll agree with Scott Carpenter.

'This planet is not terra firma. It is a delicate flower and it must be cared for. It's lonely. It's small. It's isolated, and there is no resupply. And we are mistreating it. Clearly, the highest loyalty we should have is not to our own country or our own religion or our home town or even to ourselves. It should be to, number two, the family of man, and number one, the planet at large. This is our home, and this is all we've got.'
— *Scott Carpenter, Mercury 7*

The Universe in a snowflake

Below: Wilson Bentley absorbed in capturing unique and delicate images of snowflakes on film in Vermont in 1885.

'Hast thou entered into the treasures of the snow?'
— *The Old Testament, Book of Job, 38:22.*

I love this photograph of Wilson 'Snowflake' Bentley; a tilt of the head, content, protected from the cold by curiosity, absorbed in Nature's detail which he holds carefully in both hands, oblivious to the snow falling on his hat. No gloves. As a 15-year-old farm boy from Jericho, Vermont, Bentley spent the snow days from November to April with a battered microscope sketching snowflakes before they melted away. Frustrated by their transience, too short-lived to capture in detail, he began experimenting with a camera and, on 15 January 1885, he took the first ever photograph of a snowflake. Over the next 45 years he collected over 5000 images and dedicated his life to carefully observing and documenting the raindrops, snowfalls and mists that swept across his farm.

These delicate snapshots of a world available to everyone but rarely seen captured the public imagination. How could they not? They are magical, even today in an age familiar with photography. I challenge anyone to look at these structures, endless and most beautiful – to paraphrase Darwin – and not be curious. How do they form? What natural mechanism could mimic the work of a crazed, impatient sculptor obsessed with similarity and yet incapable of chiselling the same thing twice?

These are questions that can be asked about any naturally occurring structure, and which Darwin famously answered for living things in *On the Origin of Species*. In May 1898 Bentley co-wrote an article for *Appletons' Popular Science* with George Henry Perkins, Professor of Natural History at the University of Vermont, in which he argued that the evidence he'd collated frame by frame revealed that no two snowflakes are ever alike. 'Every crystal was a masterpiece of design and no one design was ever repeated,' he wrote. Their uniqueness is part of their fascination and romance, yet there is undoubtedly something similar about them; they share a 'six-ness'. Which is more interesting? Perhaps it depends on the character of the observer.

Johannes Kepler is best known for his laws of planetary motion. He pored over the high-precision astronomical observations of the Danish astronomer Tycho Brahe, just as Snowflake Bentley pored over his photographs, and he noticed patterns in the data. These patterns led him to propose that planets move in elliptical orbits around the Sun, sweeping out equal areas in equal times and with orbital periods related to their average distances from the Sun. Kepler's empirical laws laid the foundations upon which Isaac Newton constructed his Law of Universal Gravitation, published in 1687; arguably (I would say unarguably, but one has to keep argumentative historians happy) the first modern scientific work.

In December 1610, shortly after the publication of two of his three laws in *Astronomia Nova*, Kepler was walking across the Charles Bridge in Prague through the Christmas dark when a snowflake landed on his coat. The evident structure of the elegant, white near-nothing interested him, and he wrote a small book entitled *On the Six-Cornered Snowflake*. It is a piece of scientific writing that transcends time and provides an illuminating and entertaining insight into a great mind at play. The title page of the book is addressed 'To the honorable Counselor at the Court of his Imperial Majesty, Lord Matthaus Wacker von Wackenfels, a Decorated Knight and Patron of Writers and Philosophers, my Lord and Benefactor'. Modern language lacks a certain flourish; I wish I had something equally magnificent with which to begin this book.

As a modern research proposal, Kepler's *Six-Cornered Snowflake* would fall at the first hurdle because it begins: 'I am well aware how fond you are of Nothing, not so much on account of its inexpensive price as for the charming and subtle *jeu d'esprit* of playful Passereau.[1] Thus, I can easily tell that a gift will be the more pleasing and welcome to you the closer it comes to nothing.' Now there's a statement of projected economic impact; the closer my research comes to nothing, the more valuable it is. Stick that on your spreadsheet… Kepler doesn't succeed in explaining the structure of snowflakes – how could he? A full explanation requires atomic theory and a good fraction of the machinery of modern physics; we will get to that later on. What he does achieve is to make vivid the joy of science; the idea that the playful investigation of Nature has immense value, irrespective of the outcome. His book explodes with excited curiosity, fizzing with speculations on snowflakes and their similarities to other regular shapes in the natural world; five-petalled flowers, pomegranate seeds and honeycombs. He covers so much ground, bouncing thrillingly from subject to subject, that eventually, with magnificent perspicacity, he has to rein himself in: 'But I am getting carried away foolishly, and in attempting to give a gift of almost Nothing, I almost make Nothing of it all. For from this almost Nothing, I have very nearly recreated the entire Universe, which contains everything!'

Kepler does have a clear question, however, which surely occurs to anyone who studies Snowflake Bentley's exquisite photographs: how do structures as ordered and regular as snowflakes form from apparently form-less origins? 'Since it always happens, when it begins to snow, that the first particles of snow adopt the shape of small, six-cornered stars, there must be a particular cause; for if it happened by chance, why would they always fall with six corners and not with five, or seven, as long as they are still scattered and distinct, and before they are driven into a confused mass?'

Kepler knew that snow forms from water vapour, which has no discernable structure. So how does the snowflake acquire structure? What is the 'six-ness' telling us about the building blocks of snowflakes and the forces that sculpt them? This is a modern way of looking at the world, one that any physicist would recognise. Kepler's insight, and his delighted frustration at not possessing the knowledge to approach an answer, echoes loudly down the centuries. 'I have knocked on the doors of chemistry,' he writes, 'and seeing how much remains to be said on this subject before we know the cause, I would rather hear what you think, my most ingenious man, than wear myself out with further discussion. Nothing follows. The End.'

Science is delighted frustration. It is about asking questions, to which the answers may be unavailable – now, or perhaps ever. It is about noticing regularities, asserting that these regularities must have natural explanations and searching for those explanations. The aim of this chapter, inspired by Kepler and Snowflake Bentley, is to seek explanations for the complex shapes in Nature; from beehives to icebergs; planets to free-diving grandmothers (honestly!). This will lead us to think about how such diversity and complexity can emerge from laws of Nature that are few in number and simple in form. At the end of the chapter, we will explain the structure of snowflakes.

[1] It is generally accepted that 'Passereau' is used here by Kepler as a pun, connecting a playful sparrow with French poet Jean Passerat, who wrote a New Year's poem on the subject of Nothing. Obscure, but fun!

IT IS ONE OF THE GREAT
ACHIEVEMENTS OF MODERN SCIENCE
THAT WE HAVE DISCOVERED LAWS
OF NATURE, AND THAT THESE LAWS
PROVIDE A COMMON EXPLANATION
FOR MANY NATURALLY OCCURRING
STRUCTURES. IT IS ONE OF THE
GREAT MYSTERIES THAT SUCH
ECONOMICAL EXPLANATIONS EXIST
AND ARE AVAILABLE TO US.

Why do bees build hexagons?

Bees have a got a tricky problem to solve. How do you store honey, the food that will sustain your colony, through the long winter months? We know that bees build honeycombs for this purpose. Kepler was interested in the structure of honeycombs precisely because they are built, as he writes, by 'an agent'. Since he was seeking the 'agency' that sculpts snowflakes, he decided to search for the reason why bees build hexagons. With the benefit of Darwin, we might propose that the answer will involve natural selection, which is a simple and powerful idea. If an inherited trait or behaviour confers an advantage in what Darwin referred to as the 'struggle for life', that trait will come to dominate in future generations simply because it is more likely to be passed on. The sum of an organism's physical characteristics, behaviours and constructions is known as the phenotype, and it is on this that natural selection operates. If natural selection is the reason for the structure of honeycombs, we should be able to understand why their hexagonal shape offers an advantage to the bees that construct them.

'Bees, then, know just this fact which is
useful to them – that the hexagon is greater
than the square and the triangle and will
hold more honey for the same expenditure
of material in constructing each.'
— *Papas of Alexandria, AD 340*

Charles Darwin was fascinated by bees and followed
precisely this path. 'He must be a dull man who can examine
the exquisite structure of a comb, so beautifully adapted to
its end, without enthusiastic admiration', he wrote in *On the
Origin of Species*. I enjoy the directness of Victorian writing;
if your mind isn't inquisitive, you are a dullard. In the same
seminal work, Darwin describes a series of experiments
he conducted in order to understand the cell-making instincts
of the hive bee.

'…*it seems at first quite inconceivable how they can make all
the necessary angles and planes, or even perceive when they
are correctly made. But the difficulty is not nearly so great as
it first appears: all this beautiful work can be shown, I think,
to follow from a few very simple instincts.*'

To identify these simple instincts, Darwin compared
the hive-making behaviours of the honeybee with a less
architecturally accomplished species of bee, the Mexican
Melipona domestica. The Melipona bees construct regular
combs of cylindrical cells which Darwin asserted to be a
simpler geometrical form, intermediate between no structure
at all and the hexagons of the honeybees. 'We may safely
conclude that if we could slightly modify the instincts already
possessed by the Melipona, this bee would make a structure
as wonderfully perfect as that of the hive bee.'

To test the hypothesis, Darwin conducted a series of
experiments in collaboration with his friend and fellow
naturalist William Bernhardt Tegetmeier. They added
different-coloured dyes to the beeswax, enabling them to
create a visual record of the construction process, and were
able to conclude that the bees first build cylindrical cells
that are subsequently modified to form hexagons. Darwin
was able to describe this in terms of natural selection:

'*Thus, as I believe, the most wonderful of all known instincts,
that of the hive-bee, can be explained by natural selection having
taken advantage of numerous, successive, slight modifications
of simpler instincts; natural selection having by slow degrees,
more and more perfectly, led the bees to sweep equal spheres at a
given distance from each other in a double layer, and to build up
and excavate the wax along the planes of intersection. The bees,
of course, no more knowing that they swept their spheres at one
particular distance from each other, than they know what are the
several angles of the hexagonal prisms and of the basal rhombic
plates. The motive power of the process of natural selection having
been economy of wax; that individual swarm which wasted least
honey in the secretion of wax, having succeeded best, and having
transmitted by inheritance its newly acquired economical instinct
to new swarms, which in their turn will have had the best chance
of succeeding in the struggle for existence.*'

Darwin concluded that bees build hexagonal honeycombs
because they are the most economical way of dividing up
their honey storage area. Hexagons use less wax, and the bees
that use less wax are more efficient and more likely to survive
and pass on their inherited behaviour to the next generation.
This makes sense, because building a wax hive is extremely
honey-intensive; for every gram of wax a bee produces it has
to consume up to eight grams of honey. There is clearly an
impetus to build efficiently, since using as little wax as possible
maximises the honey available for food – an advantage that
will have shaped the behaviour of honey bees over generations.

Is this correct? It's certainly plausible. If bees used cylinders to build their honeycomb there would be gaps between each cell and the whole structure would be less efficient. Similarly, pentagons and octagons also produce gaps and so cannot be optimal. It is possible to imagine that each cell could be constructed in a bespoke shape by each bee to fit perfectly with its neighbour. In this 'custom-made' scenario each cell would be a different shape, but the gaps in the honeycomb could still be minimised. A problem with this strategy might be that one bee has to finish before the next bee can create a cell to fit. That's an inefficient use of time. A repeatable single shape that leaves no gaps would seem to be preferred. The square, the triangle and the hexagon are the only regular geometrical figures that can fit together in a plane without leaving gaps.[2]

Why do bees use hexagons? Sometime around 36 BC, the Roman scholar Marcus Terentius Varro wrote down the earliest-known description of the honeycomb conjecture. This states that the most efficient way to divide a surface into regions of equal area (cells) with the least total perimeter (wax) is to use a regular hexagonal grid or honeycomb. No proof was offered, and the assertion remained conjecture for the next 2000 years until, in 1999, a mathematician at the University of Michigan named Thomas Hales found a proof: a hexagonal pattern is the most efficient engineering design. Natural selection, selecting for efficiency and creating structures are a shadow of an elegant underlying mathematical law. What a beautiful answer to a simple question.

Right: Beyond just the simple fear of a thousand honeybees' excruciating stings, humans go to extraordinary lengths to gather the precious commodity that lies within. Perhaps nowhere is this risk more extreme than in the Himalayan cliffs of central Nepal where the world's largest honeybee, the Himalayan Cliff honeybee, makes its home.

[2] There are many ways of tiling a plane using tiles of more than one shape; Penrose tiling is a particularly interesting example, in which the plane can be tiled by a set of 'aperiodic' tiles that form a pattern that never repeats.

Well … possibly, but there may be more to it. In 2013, three engineers – Karihaloo, Zhang and Wang – published an article entitled 'Honeybee combs: how the circular cells transform into rounded hexagons'. The claim is that honeybees, just like the Melipona bees that Darwin dismissed as inferior architects, make cells that are initially circular in cross section. The hexagons appear because the bees' body heat softens the wax until it reaches 45 degrees Celsius, a temperature at which wax begins to flow like a viscous fluid. The circular cells of molten wax then act in a similar way to soap bubbles, joining together at an angle of 120 degrees wherever they meet. If all the bubbles or wax cells are identical in size and spacing, the circular cells spontaneously reform into a sheet of hexagons. Karihaloo and his team demonstrated this by using smoke to interrupt honeybees in the process of making a hive, revealing that the most recently built cells were circular, whilst the older ones had developed into hexagons. This transition from cylindrical to hexagonal structure appears to be what Darwin observed, but the explanation for the transition is different.

Natural selection is still the basic explanation for the hexagons, but the bees don't have to go to the trouble of building the most efficient packing shape because physics will

The circular cells of molten wax then act in a similar way to soap bubbles, joining together at an angle of 120 degrees wherever they meet.

do that for them, given a nice sheet of circular cells of similar size and spacing and some body heat. To me, this is even more elegant and efficient; the bees allow physics to finish their work! As the authors of the study write: 'We cannot ... ignore, nor can we not marvel at the role played by the bees in this process by heating, kneading and thinning the wax exactly where needed.' Is this the solution to a problem that has fired the imagination of so many for so long? The origin of the hexagons continues to be debated, and Karihaloo *et al.* will probably not be the last word in the literature.

This is as it should be, and illustrative of something that is often missed in the presentation of science. Scientific results are always preliminary. No good scientist will believe that they have offered the last word on a given subject. A result is published if the authors and a group of their peers consider it to be a valuable contribution to the field. Crucially, this does not mean that it's correct; it means that it's not obviously wrong. Rather than closing down a question, publication is intended to be a red flag to bullish colleagues. As one reads in Kepler's partial, yet evident, delight in not discovering a satisfactory explanation for the structure of a snowflake, there is joy in hearing what you think, my most ingenious colleague.

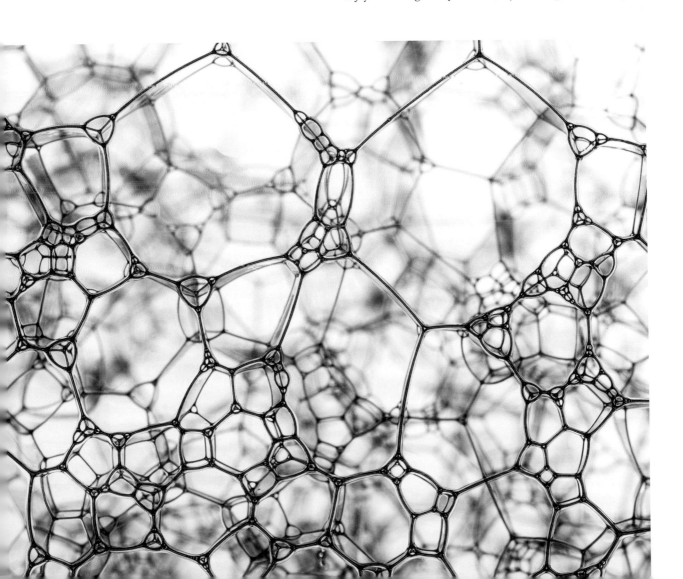

Knocking on the doors of chemistry

In the final lines of *The Six-Cornered Snowflake*, Kepler writes with lovely regret that he is 'knocking on the doors of chemistry'; the implication being that those doors would be opened by future generations. He asserts, correctly, that the structure of the snowflakes must be due at least in part to some underlying structure or shape, but given that atomic theory didn't move into the realm of experimentally testable science until the early nineteenth century, and the structure of atoms themselves was a twentieth-century discovery, Kepler had no way of unlocking the doors. We now know that the building blocks of snowflakes are water molecules, and water molecules are capable of extremely complex behaviour when they get together. That may be a surprising statement if we think of water as the colourless, odourless liquid in a glass. Perhaps it shouldn't be so surprising if we think of water molecules as the objects that come together spontaneously to produce the romantic flourishes of form and exquisite diversity of snowflakes.

Single water molecules aren't particularly complicated. They are molecules of hydrogen and oxygen, bonded together. Oxygen was first isolated in 1774 by Joseph Priestley, the son of a Yorkshire woollen cloth maker, and Henry Cavendish first identified hydrogen in 1766. The Nobel Prize in Physics in 1926 was awarded to Jean Baptiste Perrin for the confirmation of the physical reality of molecules, just about within living memory, which demonstrates how difficult it is to study the microscopic world and how quickly cutting-edge science can become common knowledge.

A water molecule consists of two hydrogen atoms bonded to a single oxygen atom: H_2O (see illustration opposite). The water molecule isn't linear – the hydrogen atoms are displaced at an angle of 104.5 degrees. The reason for this is the presence of two extra pairs of electrons that sit on the opposite side of the oxygen atom. To see why that is, let's have a very brief tutorial on atomic physics and quantum mechanics.

Atoms are made up of three constituents, as far as chemists are concerned (we'll dig more deeply into this later on); they consist of a small, dense, atomic nucleus made up of protons and neutrons, with electrons orbiting a long way away. If the nucleus were the size of a tennis ball, the outer electron orbits would be several kilometres across. Hydrogen is the simplest element; its nucleus consists of a single proton. Next is helium, which contains two protons and two neutrons. Oxygen has eight protons and eight neutrons. The nucleus is surrounded by electrons, which are held in place by one of the four fundamental forces of nature: electromagnetism. Electrons are negatively charged and protons are positively charged, and the negative electric charge of the electron is precisely equal in magnitude but opposite in sign to the positive electric charge of the proton. Nobody knows why these charges are precisely equal in magnitude; it's one of the great mysteries of fundamental physics. The atoms of each chemical element are electrically neutral, which means that the number of protons in the nucleus is equal to the number of electrons that surround it. Hydrogen atoms have a single electron, therefore, whilst oxygen atoms have eight electrons.

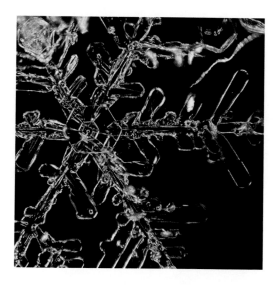

Atoms consist of a small, dense, atomic nucleus made up of protons and neutrons, with electrons attached a long way away. If the nucleus were the size of a tennis ball, the atom would be several kilometres across.

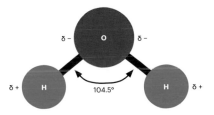

δ − O δ −

δ + H 104.5° H δ +

Above: At the northern tip of Alexander Island, in the Antarctic Peninsula, every one of these icebergs begins its life far from the oceans as the lightest of snowfalls on the icecaps of Greenland. For an iceberg born in the twenty-first century that may mean that the snow that made it fell from the sky whilst the Egyptians were still building the pyramids. These ancient fragile flakes of snow are then slowly transformed as layer after layer of snow is lain down in the same area.

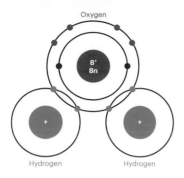

Above: The structure of a water molecule, showing oxygen's eight electrons, two of which are shared with the hydrogen atoms.

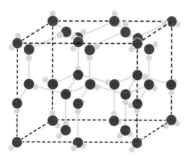

Above: The hexagonal crystalline structure of ice 1_h. Water molecules are attached together by hydrogen bonds, with oxygen atoms from one water molecule lining up with hydrogen atoms from another.

[3] The details of where the electrons reside in any particular molecule are generally very hard to compute. The details follow from solving the Schrödinger equation in the spherically symmetric potential generated by the atomic nucleus. If you'd like more details, and are interested in delving more deeply into quantum theory, there is much more in my book with my colleague Jeff Forshaw entitled *The Quantum Universe*.

Now we need a little sprinkle of quantum theory. You can picture the electric charge of the atomic nucleus as creating a kind of box within which the electrons are trapped. Electrons, along with all of the fundamental building blocks of the Universe, obey the laws of quantum theory, which describe how they move. It turns out that the basic rules of quantum theory are counterintuitive and fly in the face of common sense. But that is okay because there is no reason at all to expect the laws that govern the Universe to be in accord with 'common sense'. The most fundamental rule governing the behaviour of subatomic particles is that they don't like to stand still. Unfettered, they are very likely to wander off, and the more we try to pin them down, the more they are inclined to wander. The presence of the nucleus tames the anarchic electrons somewhat, by confining them to the 'nuclear box'.

Another rule governing the behaviour of electrons is that they don't much like each other's company. This is known as the Pauli exclusion principle, also a consequence of the laws of quantum theory. Electrons will arrange themselves around the nucleus such that they stay away from each other, as best they can. There is a caveat, though, which is important for understanding the structure of atoms. Electrons of opposite spin are allowed to get close together (or 'pair up'). Of course they cannot get too close because they have the same electric charge and 'like-charges repel'. Spin is a property of subatomic particles that is easy to name but hard to picture. You could think of electrons as little spinning tops, if you like, but that's a bad analogy on many levels, so you probably shouldn't. Having said that, spin is a measure of how much an electron is spinning – it is just that the notion of a spinning point is not something we can easily imagine. For particles such as electrons, which are known as 'spin ½' particles or fermions, spin can have only two values; these are known as spin-up and spin-down. Spin is a direct, if rather subtle, consequence of the merger between Einstein's Theory of Special Relativity and quantum theory, achieved by physicist Paul Dirac in his equation describing the electron in 1928. The details don't matter here; what matters is that the negatively charged electrons get trapped by the positive electric charge of the protons in the atomic nucleus and that electrons tend to keep away from each other, although opposite-spin electrons can get closer together than same-spin electrons can. This is enough information for us to get a basic understanding of a water molecule. Oxygen has eight electrons. Two of the electrons sit close to the nucleus and do not play much of a role in binding the two hydrogen atoms to the oxygen. The remaining six are shared out as in the diagram above.[3]

One of the basic concepts in chemistry, which again goes all the way back to the fundamental laws of quantum theory, is that electrons can be shared between atoms. This results in the formation of a chemical bond. Two hydrogen atoms will share their single electrons with an oxygen atom if they can, pairing up to fill the two remaining outer slots around the oxygen nucleus; the result is a water molecule, which is shown in the top illustration. The reason for the 104.5-degree 'kink' is the presence of the other two pairs of electrons in the outer level of the oxygen atom. They take up residence on the opposite side of the oxygen atom to the hydrogen atoms, giving the water molecule its distinctive shape, and its many unusual properties.

The regular crystalline structure leads to one of water's most bizarre properties: ice floats … Every other commonly occurring solid is denser in the solid phase than in the liquid phase, and therefore does not float on its own liquid.

Below: Because solid H_2O – ice – is less dense than its liquid form, even in the most compressed forms of ice like glacial ice, where most of the air bubbles have been squeezed out, this huge solid will still float in its own liquid form.

The water molecule, like its constituent atoms, is electrically neutral, but the uneven distribution of electrons means that the hydrogen atom 'legs' have a very small net positive charge, whilst the oxygen end of things has a slight net negative charge. Water is known as a polar molecule for this reason – it has a negative end and a positive end. This opens up a world of complexity.

An important consequence of water's polarity is that water molecules like to stick together. The negatively charged oxygen ends of water molecules attract the positively charged hydrogen ends of other water molecules and they attach together through what is known as a hydrogen bond. This happens to an extent in liquid water, resulting in quite large and complex structures.

The effects are even more dramatic when temperatures drop and water freezes to form ice. Water ice is very weird stuff. There are seventeen known forms of ice, the most common of which on Earth is called Ice 1_h (the structure of which is shown in the lower illustration opposite). The regular crystalline structure leads to one of water's most bizarre

properties: ice floats. This is very unusual behaviour. Every other commonly occurring solid is denser in the solid phase than in the liquid phase, and therefore does not float on its own liquid. The crystalline structure of ice, however, is so open that at atmospheric pressure and 0 degrees Celsius it is 8 per cent less dense than liquid water. This is why icebergs float on the oceans.

This is interesting, and it isn't necessarily a trivial observation. It has been suggested that this unusual behaviour may have played a vital role in the evolution and persistence

Below: In Antarctica, Emperor penguins exploit the fact that ice is less dense than liquid water, diving and swimming underneath icebergs.

Quantum theory is simple in the sense that it consists of a concise set of mathematical rules that describe a wide range of natural phenomena of all sizes, from the structure of atoms and molecules to the nuclear reactions in the Sun.

of life on Earth. If ice were denser than liquid water, sea ice would sink to the ocean floor. In such a scenario, particularly during Earth's great glaciations, the lakes, seas and oceans of Earth could have frozen from the bottom up, perhaps becoming permanently solid. This would have had a dramatic impact on the ecosystems and food webs that rely on the bottom-dependent animal and plant life in fresh and seawater.

The complex structure of ice is a consequence of the laws of quantum theory, which are small in number and simple. By simple, we don't mean to suggest that quantum theory is a simple thing to learn and apply; it isn't. The mathematics can be technically difficult. Quantum theory is simple in the sense that it consists of a small number of mathematical rules that describe a wide range of natural phenomena of all sizes, from the structure of atoms and molecules to the nuclear reactions in the Sun. They also describe the action of real-world devices such as transistors and lasers and, more recently, exotic pieces of technology such as quantum computers.

A tremendous economy of description is one of the defining and most surprising features of modern science; it is not *a priori* obvious that a small collection of fundamental laws should be capable of describing the limitless complexity of objects that populate our universe, and yet this is what we have discovered over the last few centuries. Perhaps a universe regular enough to permit the existence of natural objects as complex as the human brain must be governed by a simple set of laws, but since we do not yet understand the origin of the laws, we do not know. It is interesting that such complexity can emerge from underlying simplicity, however, and the humble water molecule is a good example. Its asymmetrical 'kinked' structure, which is ultimately responsible for the complex structure of ice, is a consequence of the laws of quantum theory, but these laws do not have 'kinks' built into them. Indeed, a physicist would say that the laws are possessed of a high degree of symmetry, as are the nuclei of hydrogen and oxygen; they form nicely spherical 'nuclear boxes' to trap the electrons. But bring them together and they form an asymmetrical structure.

The concept of symmetry is central to modern physics, and we'll meet it throughout this book. For now, let us simply note that the asymmetric structure of the water molecule is a consequence of the way that electrons fit around the nucleus of an oxygen atom. It is because there are four available outer slots and six electrons to fill them that an asymmetric molecular structure results when two hydrogen atoms approach the oxygen, and that structure emerges spontaneously. Nobody had to design the water molecule and make an aesthetic choice about the 104.5-degree bond angle! It's a consequence of, but not arbitrarily inserted into, the laws of quantum theory.

The properties of water are ultimately a result of the interactions between molecular building blocks. In turn, the properties of water molecules are a result of the interactions between their constituents – hydrogen and oxygen atoms. The properties of hydrogen and oxygen atoms are a result of the interactions between their constituents – protons, neutrons and electrons – and these interactions are governed by a simple set of rules. Is this infinite regression? How far can we go, digging deeper and deeper for more fundamental explanations for the properties of matter in general?

The fundamental building blocks and the forces of Nature

It was twenty years ago today that I began my PhD. Today is 1 October 2015. Three years later I submitted my thesis 'Double Diffraction Dissociation at Large Momentum Transfer'. I was interested in the behaviour of an object known as the Pomeron, named after the Russian physicist Isaak Pomeranchuk. I looked for it in the debris of high-energy collisions between electrons and protons, generated by a particle accelerator known as HERA. HERA is the wife of Zeus, and also the Hadron-Electron Ring Accelerator. The machine was 6.7 kilometres in circumference, located below the streets of northern Hamburg, which is a beautiful city in which to be a student. In the winter, the River Elbe freezes, but icebreakers clear a path to the port and the city feels proximate to the Baltic. In summer the small beaches that line the river beneath the old houses of Blankenese are busy and the city feels Mediterranean. In the early mornings at any time of year, a deracinated twenty-something from Oldham can be distracted on the Reeperbahn. It's a remarkable thing that someone can spend three years looking at the fine detail of high-energy collisions between electrons and protons, hunting for a thing called a Pomeron.

Why was I interested in Pomerons? I was engaged in testing our best theory of one of the four fundamental forces of Nature. We've met one of these forces already – electromagnetism – which holds electrons in orbit around the atomic nucleus and water molecules together via hydrogen bonds. My investigations of the Pomeron were concerned with exploring another of the four – the strong nuclear force. The need for such a force is clear if you think about our description of the oxygen nucleus. It is a tightly knit ball of eight positively charged protons and eight uncharged neutrons. One of the fundamental properties of the electromagnetic force is that like-electrical charges repel each other; in which case, why doesn't the atomic nucleus blow itself apart? The answer is that the strong nuclear force sticks the nucleus together, and it is far stronger than the electromagnetic repulsion between the protons.

Protons are small, but they make up just over half of you by mass. Most of the rest of you is made of neutrons. There are around twenty thousand million million million million protons in the average human being. In scientific notation, that's 2×10^{28}, which means 2 followed by 28 zeros. You are pretty simple at this level.

When you look deeper into the heart of the protons and neutrons themselves, things appear to get more complicated. Protons are small by everyday standards, but it is well within our current scientific and engineering capabilities to measure their size and look inside them. This is what HERA was designed to do. The machine was a giant electron microscope, peering deep into the heart of matter. You have to define what is meant by size carefully, because a proton doesn't have a hard edge to it, but recent measurements put its radius at just over 0.8 femtometres, which is just under 10^{-15} m – a thousand million millionths of a metre.[4]

Left: HERA (Hadron-Electron Ring Accelerator) under construction in 1983. I worked with HERA in the 1990s to uncover the behaviour of the Pomeron as part of my thesis.

[4] There is currently some discrepancy between different measurements of the proton radius, which may signal something interesting that we don't understand. See, for example, http://arxiv.org/pdf/1502.05314.pdf, which is a technical paper, but I recommend a glance because it demonstrates rather beautifully the precision of modern particle physics.

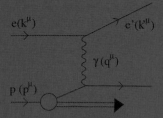

(a)

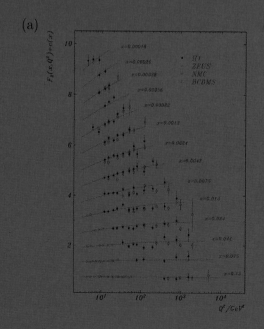

(b)

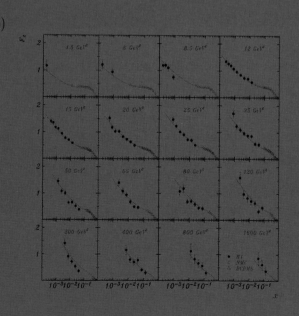

Because I'm getting old and sentimental, but also in service of the narrative, I've indulged myself and included two plots from the thesis I wrote in Hamburg twenty years ago. After all, this was my snowflake. The first one shows a drawing I made using a 1990s UNIX computer program called *xfig* (see illustration, opposite). Happy days. It shows an electron colliding with a proton. The language of modern physics is superficially opaque, as evidenced by the caption of my thesis figure, but the language isn't designed to make physicists appear clever. To be honest, I never thought a non-physicist would read it. Every word is necessary and means something. George Orwell would approve. 'A man may take to drink because he feels himself to be a failure, and then fail all the more completely because he drinks. It is rather the same thing that is happening to the English language. It becomes ugly and inaccurate because our thoughts are foolish, but the slovenliness of our language makes it easier for us to have foolish thoughts'.[5] Physics is about precision of thought, which is aided and evidenced by precision of language.

Here is the meaning of the caption. Neutral current means that the electron bounces off the proton by exchanging an electrically neutral object with it – in this case, a photon; a particle of light. The photon is shown in the diagram as the wavy line, labelled by the Greek letter γ. DIS stands for 'Deep Inelastic Scattering', which means that the photon is hitting something deep inside the proton, resulting in the proton being broken into pieces. This is how a modern particle physicist would describe the interaction between any two particles; interactions involve the 'exchange' of some other particle that carries the force. In this case, the force is electromagnetism and the force-carrying particle is a photon. The most fundamental description of the mechanism by which water molecules stick together to form ice is that photons are being emitted and absorbed by electrons in the water molecules, with the net result that water molecules stick together.

There is another way of thinking about this electron–proton collision. You can imagine the photon emitted from the electron smashing into the proton and revealing its inner structure. That structure is shown in the second figure from my thesis, shown opposite.

Allow me a single paragraph of postgraduate-level physics. I want to take this liberty for two reasons. The first is that there is great joy to be had in understanding a complex idea, and in doing so glimpsing the underlying simplicity and beauty of Nature. The biologist Edward O. Wilson coined the term 'Ionian Enchantment' for this feeling, named after Thales of Miletus, credited by Aristotle as laying the foundations for the physical sciences in 600 BC on the Greek island of Ionia. The feeling is one of elation when something about nature is understood, and seen to be elegant. The second reason is to revisit and enhance an idea we've been developing. Science is all about making careful observations and trying to explain what you see. That might be the hexagonal structure of a beehive, the jagged symmetry of a snowflake, or the details of how electrons bounce off protons. Careful observations lead to Ionian Enchantment.

At HERA, we measured the angle and energy of the electrons after they hit the protons. This is a simple thing to do, and it allowed us to build up a picture of what the electron 'bounced off' – the fizzing heart of matter. Two different ways of visualising the inside of a proton are shown in the figure. The thing called F2 (x,Q^2) is known as the proton structure function. Now for the precise bit of observation that requires thought. Have a look at illustration (a) opposite and focus on the bottom line of the graph labelled $x = 0.13$. The points along this line tell you the probability that an electron will bounce off something inside the proton that is carrying 13 per cent of the proton's momentum – this is what $x = 0.13$ means. The quantity Q^2 is known as the virtuality of the photon that smashes into the proton. One way to think about this quantity is as the resolving power of the photon. High Q^2 corresponds to short wavelength, which means that high Q^2 photons can see smaller details. The $x = 0.13$ line is pretty flat, which means that whatever the photon is bouncing off, it behaves as if it has no discernable size. This is because what we see does not change as we crank up the resolving power of the microscope (which corresponds to going to higher Q^2), and this is what would happen if the photon were scattering off tiny dots of matter inside the proton. The dot is known as a quark, and as far as we can tell, it is one of the fundamental building blocks of the Universe. Together, these two plots describe in detail the innards of the proton as revealed by years of experimental study by many hundreds of scientists at the HERA accelerator.

The proton is a seething, shifting mass of dot-like constituents, continually evolving around scaffolding. The scaffolding consists of three quarks; two 'up' quarks and one 'down' quark. The quarks are bound together by the strong nuclear force, which is carried by particles called gluons in much the same way that the electromagnetic force is carried by photons. Unlike photons, however, the gluons can interact with each other through the exchange of more gluons, and that results in the proton having an increasingly complex structure as we dial up the resolving power. Illustration (b) on page 36 shows this behaviour; the rising curves towards smaller x are telling us that there is a proliferation of gluons, each carrying very small fractions of the proton's momentum. Illustration (a) also shows this. The lines are not flat at smaller x. In the jargon, this behaviour is known as 'scaling violation', which means that as we dial up the resolving power the dot-like constituents appear to be increasingly numerous. In other words, at low resolving power we tend to resolve only the scaffolding, i.e. the three quarks, while at high resolving power the full glory of the proton's gluonic structure is revealed to us. Roughly speaking, gluons carry around half of the momentum of a proton, because there are so many of them buzzing around between the quarks. The lines on these graphs, which go pretty much through the data points, are calculated using our best theory of the strong nuclear force: Quantum Chromodynamics, or QCD. QCD is a set of rules that specifies the probability that a quark will emit a gluon, and also how gluons interact with other quarks and gluons. It's a quantum theory – the same basic framework we referred to when we discussed the structure of the water molecule. When we are dealing with electric charges – for example, the interactions between electrons and the atomic nucleus – we use our quantum theory of electromagnetism called Quantum Electrodynamics, or QED.

[5] George Orwell, *Politics and the English Language*.

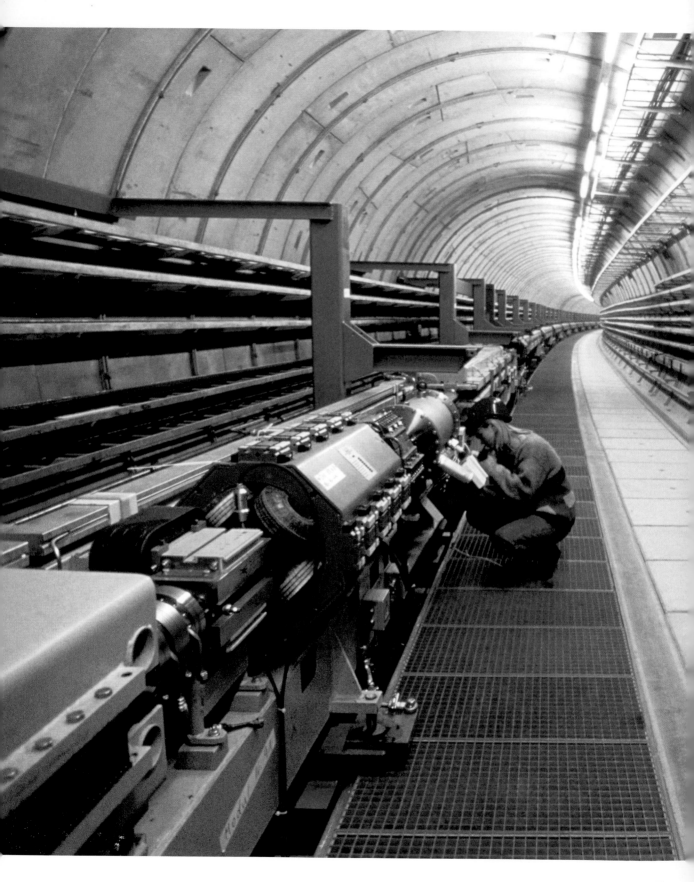

I remember writing computer programs to skim through vast amounts of data about individual electron-proton collisions and make figures like the one above. On the computers we had in the 1990s these programs took days to run. Even now, looking at these plots, I find it exhilarating to consider that I'm looking at the structure of an object a thousand million millionths of a metre in size, measured using a machine 6.7 kilometres in circumference beneath the city of Hamburg, and that we have a theory that allows us to understand and describe what we see. Industrial engineering and subatomic beauty in concert. The Ionian Enchantment.

On the next page you will find a snapshot of the deep structure of ordinary matter. You are this, at the level of accuracy we can measure today. Two sorts of quarks, stuck together by gluons, to make protons and neutrons that are stuck together by more gluons to make atomic nuclei. Electrons are stuck in orbit around the nuclei by photons to make atoms and atoms stick together by exchanging photons between their electrons to make molecules. And so it goes! This simple picture is the result of a hundred years of experimental and theoretical investigation. The structure of everything can be explained using a set of building blocks and some rules. We've met three of the building blocks; up quarks, down quarks and electrons. We've also met two forces; the strong nuclear force and the electromagnetic force. There is another force called the weak nuclear force that can convert up quarks into down quarks, with the simultaneous emission of another sort of particle called the electron-neutrino. In total that makes four matter particles. The weak force is carried by particles known as the W and Z bosons. There is also the Higgs boson, discovered in 2012 at the Large Hadron Collider (LHC) at CERN, in Geneva, which gives the building blocks their mass.

Left: The 6.7km-long tunnel of the HERA collider in Hamburg. The machine is a giant electron microscope that is designed to allow us to look inside Pomerons and measure their size.

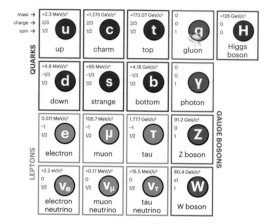

The fourth and final fundamental force is the most familiar – gravity. It is so weak that its effects on the subatomic world are invisible even in our most high-precision experiments, like those at HERA. If this statement seems a little mystifying, particularly if you've ever fallen off a ladder, then park it in your memory for a while; we'll get back to gravity later when we discuss the shape of planets and galaxies.

These four particles, four forces and the Higgs boson appear to be all that is needed to make a water molecule, a honeybee, a human being, or planet Earth. This is a dazzlingly elegant and simple structure. For some reason, Nature didn't adopt this economical scheme but instead made two further copies of the family of up quarks, down quarks, electrons and electron neutrinos. These two extra families are identical to the first family in every way except that they are more massive, possibly because they interact with Higgs particles in a different way. The existence of the three families of particle is another of the great mysteries, and discovering why Nature appears to have been unduly profligate is one of the most important goals of twenty-first-century particle physics. She won't have been unduly profligate, of course! We know that three families is the minimum number to accommodate a process known as CP violation, which is needed to explain why, if the Universe started out with equal amounts of matter and anti-matter, there is matter left over in the Universe today to make stars and people. But that's not an answer to the 'Why?' question, and it would be nice to know if the existence of planets, stars and galaxies is down to more than blind luck.

With these extra families, there are twelve fundamental particles of matter, four different sorts of force-carrying particle and the Higgs particle. That's it, as far as we know – although I wouldn't be surprised if some more pop up at the Large Hadron Collider over the next few years. This is fuelled by the fact that we already have good evidence from many independent astronomical observations that there is another form of matter in the Universe known as dark matter. There is five times more dark matter than 'normal' matter in the Universe by mass, and the dark matter cannot be made up out of the twelve particles that we've seen in experiments at particle accelerators such as HERA or the LHC. The collection of fundamental building blocks, circa 2015, is shown in the illustration opposite.

This isn't intended to be a complete course on particle physics, much as I'd like to deliver that; rather, it is a chapter about shapes and patterns in Nature and what they reveal about the way in which the Universe works. Having said that, if you'll allow me one last foray into particle physics, the story of the discovery of the quarks inside the proton and neutron is a very beautiful example of the way physicists notice patterns and attempt to explain them. The remarkable thing is that quarks were predicted *before* they were discovered experimentally.

Below: A baryon
'super-multiplet'
showing the quark
content of each baryon.

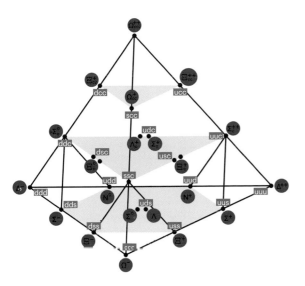

The theoretical prediction that building blocks exist beneath the level of protons and neutrons was made by Murray Gell-Mann and George Zweig in 1964. It was based on a pattern in the subatomic particles known at the time. By the early 1960s, an inelegant, profligate and seemingly ever-expanding list of subatomic building blocks had been discovered. The proton and neutron are part of a whole family of particles known as baryons; there are Lambdas, Sigmas, Deltas, Cascades and a host of others. There is also a family of particles known as mesons: Pions, Kaons, Rho and so on. There are thirteen different types of Lambda particle alone, nine Sigmas and eight Kaons. Particle physics was looking increasingly like a subatomic branch of botany. Then Gell-Mann and Zweig noticed a beautiful pattern. The particles could be arranged according to their observed properties in geometrical patterns. Two such patterns are shown in the illustration (left). Today, these are known as 'super-multiplets'.

As Kepler suspected when he considered the six-fold symmetry of snowflakes, patterns in nature are often a clue that there is a deeper underlying structure. The patterns may or may not be easy to recognise – Gell-Mann received the Nobel Prize in Physics in 1969 for noticing the pattern amongst the particles – but they are the Rosetta Stone that allows Nature's language to be deciphered. In this case, the pattern in the particles suggested to Gell-Mann and Zweig that the baryons are all constructed out of three smaller building blocks, that Gell-Mann called quarks. When they first recognised the pattern, they included three quarks in their scheme: up, down and strange. The different baryons on the lower planes of the super-multiples are the possible three-fold combinations of the three building blocks. Adding a fourth quark – charm – constructs the higher layers. The quark constituents of the particles are shown in the illustration opposite: for example the Δ^{++} contains three up quarks.

The particle on the base of the pyramid in the illustration (left) known as the Omega-minus, is of particular historical interest because its existence was predicted by Gell-Mann at a meeting at CERN in 1962, based solely on the pattern of the base of the pyramid. It was subsequently discovered at the Brookhaven National Laboratory in the United States in 1964. When a theory predicts the existence of something new that is subsequently discovered, we can have particular confidence that we are on the right track.

We've met three of the four fundamental forces of nature; the strong and weak nuclear forces and electromagnetism, and the twelve building blocks of nature. We will now turn to the final, weakest and most familiar force – gravity – and investigate it by thinking about the size and shape of the objects it sculpts. These are not tiny things like subatomic particles, or small things like snowflakes, but very much larger structures: planets, stars and galaxies.

Why is the Earth a sphere?

This picture of Earth is known as the Blue Marble. It was taken on 7 December 1972 by the crew of Apollo 17 during their journey to the Moon. Close to the winter solstice, Antarctica is a continent of permanent light, and Madagascar, the island of lemurs, takes centre stage. Ochre deserts set against blue oceans, green hues hinting at life.

On 5 December 2012, NASA released the Black Marble, an image of the Americas at night. Now we see a civilisation on the planet; the lights herald the dawn of the Anthropocene – the age of human dominance. What do you see in these images? What is the most basic property of Earth? Alexei Leonov, on completing the first human spacewalk on 18 March 1965, had an answer.

'I never knew what the word round meant until I saw Earth from space.'

Alexei Leonov, Voskhod 2, Soyuz 19/ASTP

Seen from space, the Earth is a near-perfect sphere. All the planets in the Solar System, all the large moons and the Sun itself share this property, as does every star in the Universe. Why? If lots of different objects share a common feature, there must be an explanation. To make progress, let's think about what could affect the shape of a planet, moon or star. It can't be much to do with their composition because planets are made of different stuff to stars. The Earth is made up of heavy chemical elements such as iron, oxygen, silicon and carbon. The Sun, on the other hand, is primarily hydrogen and helium; it's a giant ball of plasma with no solid surface. Giant planets such as Jupiter have more in common with stars than with Earth, at least in terms of their composition. They too are primarily composed of hydrogen and helium. Stars and planets are united, however, by the force that formed them and holds them together – gravity. So to understand why they are all spherical, we should explore the nature of the gravitational force further.

Defying gravity

For most of the time Tarragona is a quiet Mediterranean port on the northeastern coast of Spain, but each September it explodes into vivid, violent colour as teams compete against gravity in the Tarragona *Castells* competition. *Castells* are human towers, reaching ten people high and involving an intricate mix of strength, balance, strategy and teamwork to be built up to the top. Each team begins by forming the foundations of the tower, with up to two hundred people creating the *pinya*. Once the foundation is in place, a variety of human geometries are used to build as high as possible, with each level taking shape before the next is added. The most successful team is the Castellers de Vilafranca, having won the Tarragona competition eight times since 1972. A mass of green shirts acting in unison flows from one level to the next, with higher levels consisting of fewer people, until two children form a final stable platform for the *exaneta* – the *castellar* who ascends daringly to the summit; since low mass, agility – and perhaps a lack of fear – are called for, the *exaneta* will be as young as 6 or 7 years old. This is what the crowds have come to see. Towers give way, human buildings come tumbling down, falls softened by the elbows, knees, heads and shoulders, colliding and crashing, usually delivering only bruises, bumps and the occasional lost tooth. Serious injuries are very rare.

Below: Soviet astronaut Alexei Leonov taking Man's first steps into space on 18 March 1965.

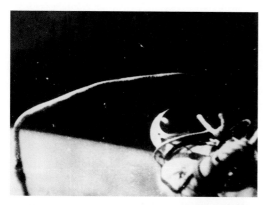

Left: The iconic Blue Marble – Earth as seen from Apollo 17 on 7 December 1972.

Left: The Black Marble. Released by NASA on 5 December 2012. This image, taken 40 years after the Blue Marble, shows the presence of human civilisation through the illuminated city lights.

'*Força, equilibri, valor i seny*'
(Strength, balance, courage and
common sense)

It is obvious why people fall to the ground if they lose their balance: gravity. But how precisely do objects behave under the influence of gravity? We have two theoretical frameworks, both of which are still in use, depending on what we wish to calculate. Here we see an idea central to the success of science; there are no absolute truths! Usefulness is the figure of merit; if a theory can be used to make predictions that agree with experiment in certain circumstances, then as long as we understand the restrictions, we can continue to use the theory. The first theory of gravity was written down by Isaac Newton in 1687 in his *Philosophiae Naturalis Principia Mathematica* – the mathematical principles of natural philosophy, inspired at least in part by the work of our curious companion, Johannes Kepler.

A more precise description of gravity was published in 1915 by Albert Einstein. Newton's theory doesn't have anything to say about the mechanism by which gravity acts between objects, but it does allow us to calculate the gravitational force between any objects, anywhere in the Universe. Einstein's more accurate Theory of General Relativity provides an explanation for the force of gravity. Space and time are distorted by the presence of matter and energy, and objects travel in straight lines through this curved and distorted spacetime. Because of the distortion, it appears to us as if the objects are being acted upon by a force, which we call gravity. But in Einstein's picture there isn't a force; there is curved spacetime and the rule that everything travels in a straight line through it. We will encounter spacetime in much more detail in Chapter Two.

To answer the question about spherical planets, we don't need Einstein's elegant but significantly more mathematically challenging Theory of General Relativity. It is a sledgehammer to crack a nut. We'll therefore confine ourselves to Newton's simpler theory; General Relativity would give the same answer. Here is Newton's Law of Universal Gravitation:

$$F = G \, m \, M / r^2$$

In words, this equation says that there is a force between all objects, F, which is equal to the product of their masses, m and M, and inversely proportional to the square of their distance apart, r. If you double the distance between two objects, the gravitational force between them falls by a factor of 4. G is known as Newton's Constant, and it tells us the strength of the gravitational force. If we measure mass in kilograms, distance in metres and wish to know the gravitational force in Newtons, then $G = 6.6738 \times 10^{-11} \, m^3 \, kg^{-1} s^{-2}$.

Newton's Gravitational Constant is one of the fundamental physical constants. It describes a property of our Universe that can be measured, but not derived from some deeper principle, as far as we know. One of the great unsolved questions in physics is why Newton's gravitational constant is so small, which is equivalent to asking why the gravitational force between objects is so weak. Comparing the strengths of forces is not entirely straightforward, because they change in strength depending on the energy scale at which you probe them; very close to the Big Bang, at what is known as the Planck temperature – 1.417×10^{32} degrees Celsius – we have good reason to think that all four forces had the same strength. To describe physics at such temperatures we require

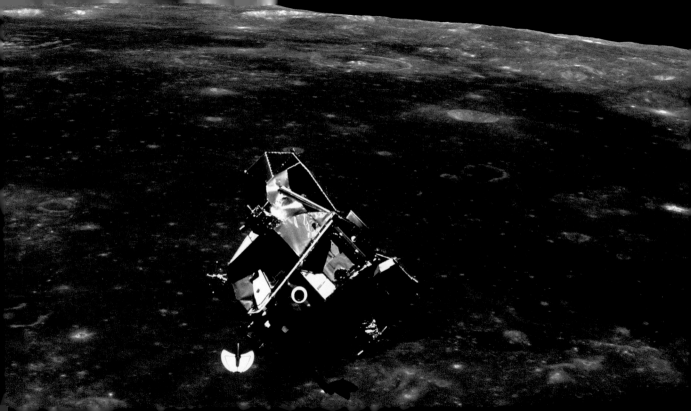

a quantum theory of gravity, which we don't currently possess in detail. But at the energies we encounter in everyday life, gravity is around forty orders of magnitude weaker than the electromagnetic force; that's 1 followed by 40 zeroes. This smallness seems absurd, and demands an explanation. Physicists speculate about extra spatial dimensions in the Universe and other exotic ideas, but as yet we have no experimental evidence to point the way. One possibility is that the constants of nature were randomly selected at the Big Bang, in which case they are simply a set of incalculable fundamental numbers that define what sort of Universe we happen to live in. Or maybe we will one day possess a theory that is able to explain why the fundamental numbers take on the values they do.

Newton discovered his law of gravity by looking for a simple equation that could describe the apparent complexity of the motions of the planets around the Sun. Kepler's three empirical laws of planetary motion can be derived from Newton's Law of Gravitation and his laws of motion. This is why we might describe Newton's theory as elegant, in line with our discussion of quantum theory earlier in the chapter. Newton discovered a simple equation that is able to describe a wide range of phenomena: the flight of artillery shells on Earth, the orbits of planets around the Sun, the orbits of the moons of Jupiter and Saturn, the motion of stars within galaxies. His was the first truly universal law of Nature to be discovered.

The answer to our question 'why is the Earth spherical?' must be contained within Newton's equation, because the Earth formed by the action of gravity. The gravitational force is the sculptor of planets. Our solar system formed from a cloud of gas and dust, collapsing due to the attractive force of gravity around 4.6 billion years ago. The Sun formed first, followed by the planets. Let's fast-forward a few million years to a time when the infant sun is shining in the centre of a planet-less solar system. Circling the young sun are the remains of the cloud of dust and gas out of which the Sun formed, containing all the ingredients to make a planet. This is known as a protoplanetary disc. The fine details of the formation of planets are still a matter of active research, and the mechanisms may be different for rocky planets such as the Earth and gas giants such as Jupiter. For Earth-like planets, random collisions between dust particles can result in the formation of objects of around 1 kilometre in diameter known as planetesimals. These grow larger as they attract smaller lumps of rock and dust by their gravitational pull, increasing their mass, which increases their gravitational pull, attracting more objects, and so on. This is known as runaway accretion, and computer simulations using Newton's laws suggest that through a series of collisions between these ever-growing planetesimals, a small number of rocky planets emerge from the protoplanetary disc orbiting the young star.

The gravitational force is the sculptor of planets. Our Solar System formed from a cloud of gas and dust, collapsing due to the attractive force of gravity around 4.6 billion years ago.

Models of planetary formation can be checked using the telescopic observation of young star systems. In 2014 the ALMA (Atacama Large Millimeter/submillimeter Array) observatory in Chile captured a beautiful image of a planetary system forming inside a protoplanetary disc around HL Tauri, a system less than 100,000 years old and only 450 light years from Earth. A series of bright concentric rings is clearly visible, separated by darker areas. It is thought that these dark gaps are being cleared by embryonic planets orbiting around the star and sweeping up material – they are the shadow of the planetary orbits. It is interesting to note that planetary formation appears to be well advanced in this very young system. This image is perhaps a glimpse of what our Solar System looked like 4.5 billion years ago.

All objects in the Solar System are not spheres. The Martian moon Phobos is a misshapen lump. Smaller still are the asteroids, comets and grains of dust that formed at the same time as the planets.

Opposite: Comet 67P/Churyumov–Gerasimenko, as photographed by the Rosetta spacecraft from cometary orbit on 2 August 2014.

Below: Planetary formation in motion; the birth of a planetary system was captured by the ALMA observatory in Chile in 2014.

Rocky planets begin life as small, irregular planetesimals and evolve over time into spheres. To make progress in understanding why, we might make an observation; all objects in the Solar System are not spheres. The picture on page 57 shows the Martian moon, Phobos, which has a radius of approximately 11 kilometres. It is a misshapen lump. Smaller still are the asteroids, comets and grains of dust that formed at the same time as the planets. The picture bottom left shows Comet 67P/Churyumov–Gerasimenko, which is less than 5 kilometres across and is an intriguing dumbbell shape. Analysis of data from the Rosetta spacecraft, in orbit around the comet at the time of writing, has shown that 67P was formed by a low-velocity collision of two larger objects. Perhaps this is a snapshot of the processes that previously resulted in the formation of much larger objects such as planets and moons. Smaller lumps of rock merge together under the influence of gravity, and if there is enough material in the vicinity, as there would have been early in the life of the Solar System, the objects will undergo many such collisions and grow. Why isn't comet 67P spherical?

Let's return to the human towers. What sets the maximum height of a tower? Consider an artificial situation in which the tower is a vertical stack of humans, one on top of the other. If there are only two people in the stack, then the force on the person at the base is the weight of the person above. Let's understand that sentence. What is weight? Your weight at the Earth's surface is given by Newton's equation; it is defined to be the force exerted on you by the Earth. What numbers should we put into the equation to calculate it? Your mass: *75kg*. The mass of the Earth: *5.972 x 10²⁴ kg*.[6] Newton's gravitational constant, *G: 6.6738 x 10⁻¹¹ m³ kg⁻¹ s⁻²*. What should we use for *r*? This is the distance from the centre of the Earth to the centre of you. That sounds a bit vague. More precisely, *r* is the distance between the centre of mass of the Earth and your centre of mass, but it's a very good approximation to simply insert the radius of the Earth into Newton's equation. This is because you are only around a couple of metres tall, and the average radius of the Earth is 6,371,000 metres, so moving your centre of mass around by a few tens of centimetres isn't going to change the calculation much.

Plugging in the numbers, Newton's equation tells us that the force on you at the Earth's surface – your weight – is approximately 736 Newtons (a force of 1 Newton produces an acceleration of 1 m/s^2 on a 1kg mass).

We now need to introduce another of Newton's laws – his third law of motion, also published in the *Principia*: To every action, there is an equal and opposite reaction. This says that the Earth exerts a force on you and you exert an equal and opposite force on the Earth. We can now understand what happens when the human towers get higher and higher. If one person stands on another's shoulders, there is a downward force on the lower person of around 730 Newtons. If another person of the same mass climbs up, the force on the person at the base doubles to 1460 Newtons. If another two people climb up to form a tower five people high, the force on the base person is 2920 Newtons, and so on. Clearly, at some point, the person at the base isn't strong enough to hold the tower up, and the whole thing will collapse. This is where the skill of the Castellars comes in. By having a base, made up of many

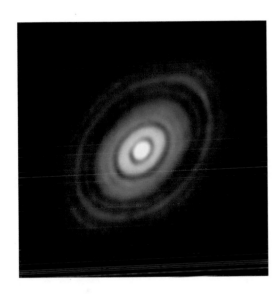

---

[6] 10²⁴ means 1 followed by 24 zeros. So we could write the number 100 as 10², 1000 as 10³ and so on. Notice how big a number 10²⁴ is. 10² is 10 x 10. 10³ is 10 x 10 x 10. So 10²⁴ is 10 x 10 x 10 …. 24 times.

individuals, the forces can be distributed across the human
structure, and this allows the towers to get higher before
catastrophe strikes. There is clearly a trade-off; a larger base
can support a larger layer above, which in turn can support a
larger layer above, and so on. But a larger layer weighs more,
and exerts a larger force on the layer below. The ingenious
geometrical solutions to this gravitational conundrum emerge
through a combination of trial and error, instinct and skill,
and this is what makes the Tarragona Castells competition so
compelling. For our purposes, it is the principle that matters.
As the tower gets higher, the forces on the base increase, and
ultimately a limit will be reached.

Perhaps you can see where this is leading. High human
towers are more difficult to sustain because the force on the
base becomes increasingly large as the mass of the tower
increases. This suggests that the size of structures that rise
above the surface of a planet is limited by the structural
strength of the rock out of which the planet is made, and
the mass of the planet, which sets the gravitational pull and
therefore the weight of the structure. On Earth, the tallest
mountain as measured from its base on the sea floor is Mauna
Kea, on the island of Hawaii. This dormant volcano is
10 kilometres high, over a kilometre higher than Mount
Everest. Mauna Kea is sinking because its weight is so great
that the rock beneath cannot support it. Mars, by contrast,
is a less massive planet. At a mere 6.39×10^{23} kg, it is around
10 per cent of Earth's mass and has a radius about half that of
Earth. A quick calculation using the equation on page 47 will
tell you that an object on the surface of Mars weighs around

40 per cent of its weight at the Earth's surface. Since Mars has a similar composition to Earth, its surface rock has a similar strength, and this implies that more massive mountains can exist on Mars because they weigh less – and this is indeed the case. The Martian mountain Olympus Mons is the highest mountain in the Solar System; at over 24 kilometres in altitude, it is close to the height of three Everests stacked on top of each other. Such a monstrous structure is impossible on Earth because of the immense weight – a result of the Earth's greater mass and therefore stronger gravitational pull at the surface.

We see that there must be a limit to the height to which a structure can rise above the surface of a planet. The more massive the planet, the stronger the gravitational pull at its surface, and the lower the height of structures that the surface can support. As the planets get more and more massive, their surfaces will get smoother and smoother because of the stronger gravity. Less-massive planets can be more uneven. We are approaching an answer to our question; we have a mechanism for smoothing out the surface of a planet, but why should this mean that planets get smoothed into a sphere?

Imagine a mountain on the surface of a planet. Let's say it is at the North Pole. Now, in your mind's eye, imagine rotating the planet through, say, 90 degrees, so the mountain sits on the Equator. Has anything changed? All the arguments about the maximum height of the mountain still apply, because the gravitational force at the surface depends *only* upon the radius and mass of the planet and the mass of the mountain. There is no reference to any angle in Newton's equation (page 47).

There must be a limit to the height to which a structure can rise above the surface of a planet, assuming that the height of a hill or mountain is proportional to its mass.

Above: Artist Gordon Legg created this image of Olympus Mons using photos taken by the Viking 1 orbiter in 1975 to show its vast scale.

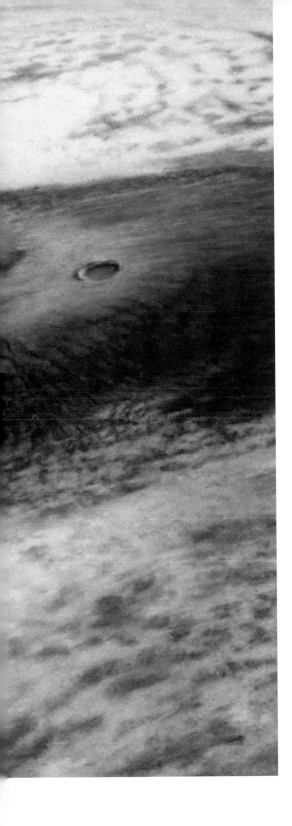

In more sophisticated language, we can say that Newton's law of gravitation possesses a rotational symmetry. By that, we mean that it gives the same results for the gravitational force between any two objects regardless of their orientation. This is an example of what physicists and mathematicians mean when they speak of the symmetries of an equation or law of Nature, and it means that the calculation for the maximum height of a mountain at any place on the Earth's surface must give the same answer irrespective of the position of the mountain *because* Newton's law of gravitation is symmetric under rotations. The symmetry of the law of gravity is reflected in the symmetry of the objects it forms. Gravity smooths mountains democratically, symmetrically, with the result that lumps of matter with a gravitational pull strong enough to overcome the rigidity of the substance out of which they are made end up being spherical. This is the reason why the Earth is spherically symmetric.

There is a deep idea lurking here that lies at the heart of modern theoretical physics. Thinking of things in terms of symmetry is extremely powerful, and perhaps fundamental. Consider the possibility that the laws of Nature possess certain symmetries, which are the fundamental properties of the Universe. This would be reflected in the physical objects they create. For example, imagine a Universe in which only laws of Nature that are symmetric under rotations through 90 degrees are allowed. In such a Universe, objects that remain the same under rotations through 90 degrees are created; cubes exist but spheres are forbidden. This isn't quite as crazy as it sounds. As far as we can tell, our Universe does possess a set of extremely restrictive symmetries, and the subatomic particles that exist and the forces that act between them are determined by these underlying symmetries.[7] In fact, *all* of the laws of Nature we regard as fundamental today can be understood by thinking in this way. There is certainly a strong case to be made that Nature's symmetries can be regarded as truly fundamental. The Nobel Prize-winning physicist Steven Weinberg wrote, 'I would like to suggest something here that I am not really certain about but which is at least a possibility: that specifying the symmetry group of Nature may be all we need to say about the physical world, beyond the principles of quantum mechanics.' Nobel laureate Philip Anderson wrote, 'It is only slightly overstating the case to say that physics is the study of symmetry.' Nobel laureate David Gross wrote, 'Indeed, it is hard to imagine that much progress could have been made in deducing the laws of Nature without the existence of certain symmetries … Today we realise that symmetry principles are even more powerful – they dictate the form of the laws of nature.' The complexity we perceive when casually glancing at the Universe masks the underlying symmetries, and it is one of the goals of modern theoretical physics to strip away the complexity and reveal the underlying simplicity and symmetry of the laws of Nature.

Returning to the task in hand, this reasoning leads to a prediction about the size and shape of planets and moons that can be checked: they should be spherical if they are large enough, and therefore massive enough, for their gravitational pull to overcome the structural strength of the rock out of which they are made. The strength of rock is ultimately related to the strength of the force of Nature

[7] These are not symmetries of three-dimensional space, like the rotational symmetry of a cube. They are more abstract symmetries.

Imagine a big cube of rock sitting on the surface of a second much bigger ball of rock, like a planet maybe (we are thinking of a cube for the sake of being specific but any shape will do). If the cube is too big then its weight will cause the rock underneath to fail and the cube will sink. Obviously it takes a lot of weight before rock starts to deform and give way. For granite, the maximum pressure before failure is around 130 million Newtons /m^2 (written 130 MPa), which is a little more than 1000 times atmospheric pressure. We will assume that our big ball of rock has compressive strength of around 100 MPa, and we label it using the symbol P. Now we need to know how heavy the cube is, given that its height is h. Its weight is equal to its mass multiplied by GM/R^2 (from Newton's law), where M is the mass of the big ball and R is its radius. If the density of the cube is d = 3000kg/m^3 (typical of rock) then its mass is d x h^3. The mass of the ball will likewise be M = 4/3 x 3.14 x R^3 x d (3.14 is the mathematical number pi, and we have used the formula for the volume of a sphere). For our purposes 3.14/3 is close enough to 1 as to make no difference (the goal here is to make a rough estimate, not a highly accurate computation). Together, these results mean that the weight of the cube is d x h^3 x G x 4R x d. Now, this weight bears down on the ground below, which will give way if the weight is bigger than the compressive strength of the rock supporting it, which is P x h^2. In other words, the ground will give way under the cube if h^3 x G x 4R x d^2 is bigger than P x h^2. This implies that h must be smaller than P/G/4/R/d^2. If this maximum value for h is less than 10 per cent of the radius of the ball, the surface of the ball will not be too much deformed from spherical by the cube. (i.e. the cube will be a small bump on the surface of a bigger ball). Putting h/R = 0.1 tells us that the planet's radius R must be bigger than the square root of P/G/4/d^2/10 per cent. Putting in the numbers gives a radius equal to just over 600 kilometres. This number should not be taken too literally, because we used typical numbers for the density and the compressive strength and these will vary across the variety of planets, asteroids and comets. But that should not detract from what we have achieved. Our calculation is telling us that lumps of rock larger than about 600 kilometres in radius will tend to look pretty smooth because big structures on their surface will tend to sink down and be absorbed. While we are at it, we can quickly go ahead and estimate the size of the biggest mountains on Earth and Mars. We have already worked this out above. The maximum size of a cubic mountain on Earth would be P/G/4/R/d^2. On Earth, the combination GM/R^2 (where M is the mass of the Earth and R is its radius) is called the acceleration due to gravity, g, and it is close to 10 m/s^2. This means that our cubic mountain would sink if it were taller than P/d/g, which is around 3.3 kilometres. If the mountain is cone shaped instead of cubic then this number increases by a factor of 3 to around 10 kilometres, which is very close to the height of the largest mountains on Earth. On Mars, the surface gravity is around 40 per cent that of the Earth, which means that its tallest mountains should be more like 10 kilometres/40 per cent = 25 kilometres high, which is the height of Olympus Mons.

that holds the constituents of rock together – molecules of silicon dioxide, iron and so on. This is the electromagnetic force; what other force could it be? There are only four forces, and the two nuclear forces are confined within the atomic nuclei themselves. Big things like planets are shaped by the interplay between gravity, trying to squash them into spheres; and electromagnetism, trying to resist the squashing. We can perform a calculation to estimate the minimum size that a lump of matter must be to form into a near-spherical shape by equating the weight of a mass of rock near its surface to the structural strength of the rocks below.[8] Our answer is approximately 600 kilometres.

We can check this by direct observation of the Solar System. Phobos fits with our prediction; with a mean radius of just over 11 kilometres and a mass of only 10^{16} kilograms, the gravitational force at its surface is far too weak to overcome the rigidity of rock and act to flatten the surface and sculpt Phobos into a sphere. At around 550 kilometres across, the asteroid Pallas is the largest known non-spherical object. Saturn's moon, Mimas, with a radius of just under 200 kilometres, is the smallest known body in the Solar System that is spherical. It is made mostly of ice, which is much easier to deform than rock – this is why it is so small and still round. Our estimate is certainly in the right ballpark.

As an important aside, 'back-of-the-envelope' estimates such as these are very important in physics; they tell us that we are on the right track, without overcomplicating things unnecessarily. We could have refined our calculation by taking into account the different compositions of different objects, and by computing the gravitational pull at different depths more carefully. We could even have tried to use General Relativity instead of Newton's laws, but we wouldn't have learnt a lot by doing so. Learning what to ignore and what to include is part and parcel of becoming a professional scientist – one might call it physical intuition. There is no precise size above which a body will be spherical; the limit depends on the object's composition; a mixture of rock and ice is easier to deform than solid rock. As a general rule, any icy moon over 400 kilometres in diameter will be a sphere. Objects made of rock need to be larger, because the gravitational force needed to deform rock is greater. If a rocky moon has an internal heat source, perhaps as a result of the presence of large amounts of radioactive material in its core or tidal heating, the body is easier to deform and may be spherical at a smaller size than would be expected for a less active object. The Solar System is full of examples of this interplay of rigidity and gravity in action, but, very roughly, we have deduced that anything with a radius in excess of a few hundred kilometres must be spherical because the gravitational forces will overcome the strength of the rock.

When gravity wins, the shape of the objects it creates reflects the underlying symmetry of the physical law, and this is why large single objects such as planets and stars are always spherical.

At larger scales, however, things change. The picture below shows our nearest galactic neighbour, Andromeda, which contains around 400 billion stars, formed and bound together by gravity. It is disc-shaped, not spherical. The Solar System itself is also a disc and not a sphere. Why?

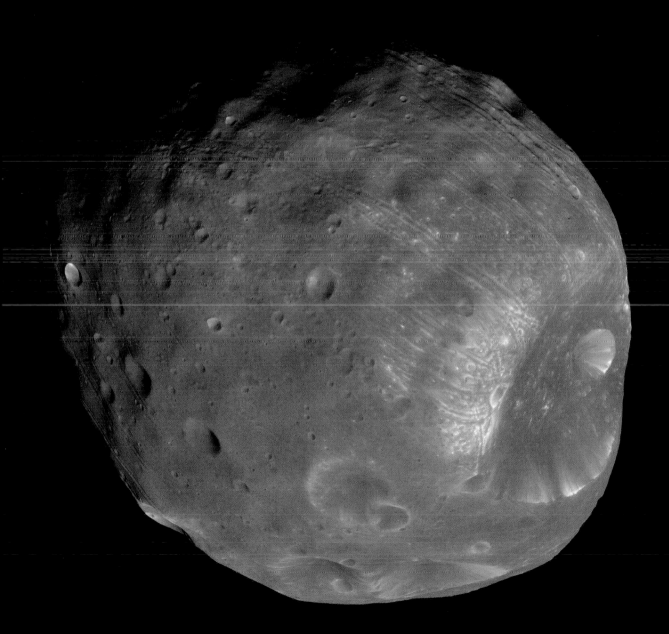

Below: Phobos, Mars's largest moon, has a gravitational force at the surface that is too weak to sculpt its craters into a smooth sphere, giving it a pockmarked appearance.

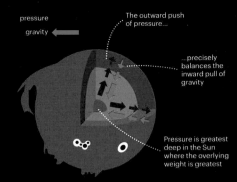

pressure

gravity

The outward push of pressure...

...precisely balances the inward pull of gravity

Pressure is greatest deep in the Sun where the overlying weight is greatest

Why are there discs as well as spheres in the Universe?

We argued above that planets and large moons are spheres because, if the gravitational forces are large enough to overcome the electromagnetic forces that keep matter rigid, the underlying symmetry of the gravitational force is made manifest in the objects it creates. Because there is no special direction in Newton's Law of Gravitation, there will be no special direction in the objects that it creates. This is not entirely true, however, even for planets, because they spin.

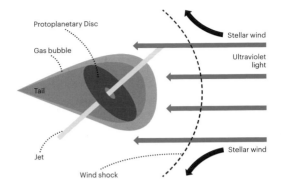

Above: Some of the many properties that have resulted in partial loss of the symmetry in the Solar System disc.

Protoplanetary Disc

Gas bubble

Tail

Jet

Wind shock

Stellar wind

Ultraviolet light

Stellar wind

Below: Messier 80, in the constellation of Scorpius, a spherical cluster of hundreds of thousands of stars 30,000 light years from the Sun.

Our planet turns on its axis once every 24 hours. The spin axis marks out a special direction, which means that all points on the Earth are not the same. Someone standing on Earth's Equator is rotating at a speed of 1670 km/hour, whilst someone in Minnesota is rotating at a speed of 1180 km/hour. The spherical symmetry is broken – the two points are different. As we'll see in Chapter Two, this difference leads to observable effects such as the rotation of storm systems and the deflection of artillery shells in flight. It also leads to a very slight flattening of the Earth – the equatorial circumference is 40,075 kilometres and the polar circumference is 40,008 kilometres. The Earth is not spherical, but an oblate spheroid, because of its spin. If it were spinning faster, the Earth would be more oblate. When our Solar System formed, the spin – or more correctly angular momentum – was 'exported' outwards from the newly forming Sun, primarily through collisions and magnetic interactions in the protoplanetary disc, resulting in the system becoming flattened into a disc.

The transfer of spin outwards from the centre also results in the flattening of some galaxies; for example, Andromeda. Globular star clusters, such as the spectacular Messier 80, remained spherical because they were too diffuse for angular momentum to be transferred outwards. The shapes of objects that are bound together by gravity are therefore dependent on the amount and location of the 'spin'. For the experts, the ratio of angular momentum L to gravitational potential energy E is the figure of merit. Large L/E = disc. Small L/E = spherical.

There is a very important idea hiding here. We used the term 'symmetry breaking' to describe how the presence of a spin axis marks out a particular direction, resulting in an object deviating from the 'perfect' spherical shape that reflects the symmetry of the underlying law of Nature – in this case gravity. The disc of our solar system is less symmetric than a sphere because it only remains the same when rotated about a particular axis in space – the spin axis. The symmetry has been partially lost. We might say that the symmetry of the law of gravity that created our solar system has been hidden by the presence of a special direction in space – the spin axis. The spin itself came from the precise details of the collapse of the initial dust cloud almost 5 billion years ago, and the distribution of the spin between the Sun and planets depended on the precise speed of collapse, the density of the protoplanetary disc and myriad other subtle details over the history of the Solar System's formation. This highlights one of the central challenges in modern science: which properties of the structures we see in Nature are reflections of the underlying laws of Nature, and which properties are determined by the history of formation or other influences? This is particularly difficult to answer when the physical systems in question are complicated. The shapes of planets, solar systems and galaxies, whilst astronomical in size, are easier to explain than the shapes of more mundane objects that we encounter every day. Let's jump from simple planets to the most complex of all physical structures – living things. By exploring the symmetries and structures of living organisms, we can further explore the idea that the shape and form of physical objects are the result of a complex interplay between deep physical principles and the history of their formation.

Why does life come in so many shapes and sizes?

The competition between the force of gravity and the electromagnetic force is responsible for smoothing the surface of planets and moons into spheres and limiting the maximum size of mountains on their surfaces. One of the central ideas in this book, which we will expand on in Chapter Three, is that there is no fundamental difference between inanimate things, such as planets, and living things, such as bacteria or human beings; all objects in the Universe are made of the same ingredients and are shaped by the same forces of Nature. We should therefore expect to see limits on the form and function of living things imposed by the laws of Nature. Basic physics is not the only driver of the structure of organisms, of course; there is also the undirected hand of evolution by natural selection, which moulds living things over time in response to their changing environment, their interaction with other living things, and the myriad available environmental niches. This creative interplay between the relentless determinism of physical laws and the seething, infinitely intertwined, ever-shifting genetic database of life on Earth is beautifully captured in Darwin's closing lines of *On the Origin of Species*;

> *'There is grandeur in this view of life, with its several powers, having been originally breathed into a few forms or into one; and that, whilst this planet has gone cycling on according to the fixed law of gravity, from so simple a beginning endless forms most beautiful and most wonderful have been, and are being, evolved.'*

Another of our recurring themes is a celebration of the energetic curiosity of the early scientists. There is a breathless lyricism in their descriptions of ideas that remains relevant and essential; yet their presentation seems somehow unencumbered by the more serious and confining demands of modern professional science. There are great writers from the modern era who capture the logic, clarity and wonder of science – Richard Feynman, Richard Dawkins and Carl Sagan spring immediately to mind – but there is something exhilarating in

We should expect to see limits on the form and function of living things imposed by the laws of Nature. Basic physics is not the only driver of the structure of organisms; there is also the undirected hand of evolution by natural selection.

seeing science evolving in words. The limits of the Renaissance authors are so often coterminous with the limits of all human knowledge that the investigations on the page are near real-time explorations rather than reminiscences from a well-trodden intellectual road. Perhaps this is what gives the old masters' writings such exhilarating intellectual pace.

Just as the force of gravity limits the maximum size of Earth's mountains, so it limits the range of forms that natural selection can create, restricting the overall size of organisms that live on its surface. Four hundred years ago, Galileo Galilei explored the factors that define how big an animal can be; in common with Kepler and his snowflakes, he was operating at the edge of knowledge and ahead of his time. *Discourses and Mathematical Demonstrations Relating to Two Sciences* was Galileo's final book, written whilst under house arrest and published in 1638 by the Dutch publisher Lodewijk Elzevir, because no country in the grip of the Inquisition would touch it. Any scientist reading this book will recognise the name: the Elsevier company, which took the publisher's name, is today a leading scientific publisher. Galileo's book is written in the style of a conversation between three men, Simplicio, Sagredo and Salviati, who each represent the author at a different age, and with a different level of knowledge. The characters wander from question to question during a conversation lasting four days, discussing and debating each subject before moving on to the next. The book has something of the voyeuristic pleasure of overhearing a conversation on a park bench – albeit in a park frequented by unusually thoughtful individuals. Galileo covers large swathes of the physics of the day, including a critical look at Aristotelian physics, accelerated motion, the motion of projectiles and the nature of infinity. His investigations also turned to the strength of materials and the limits placed on the size and form of structures, both animate and inanimate, by the laws of Nature.

From what has already been demonstrated, you can plainly see the impossibility of increasing the size of structures to vast dimensions, either in art or in nature. Likewise the impossibility of building ships, palaces or temples of enormous size in such a way that their oars, yards, beams, iron-bolts and, in short, all their other parts will hold together. Nor can Nature produce trees of extraordinary size, because the branches would break under their own weight; so also it would be impossible to build up the bony structures of men, horses or other animals so as to hold together and perform their normal functions if these animals were to be increased enormously in height. For this increase in height can be accomplished only by employing a material which is harder and stronger than usual, or by enlarging the size of the bones, thus changing their shape until their form and appearance suggest a monstrosity.

Galileo states, for the first time, the relationship between volume and area, known today as the square–cube law; as an object grows in size, the volume grows faster than the surface area. Consider the example of a cube of sides measuring 2cm. The surface area is 6 x 2 x 2 = 24cm². The volume is 2 x 2 x 2 = 8cm³. If we double the length of the sides, the surface area is 96cm² and the volume is 64cm³. Double the length of the sides again and the surface area increases to 384cm² whilst the volume is 512cm³. And so on.

This means that, as animals get larger, their volume, and therefore their mass, increases more rapidly than their surface area and the cross-sectional area of their bones. The consequence of this is that animals can't simply be 'scaled up' in size. A mouse can't be expanded to the size of an elephant because its skeleton would give way; that's why an elephant has thicker legs relative to the rest of its body than a mouse. This ultimately places a fundamental limit on the maximum size of living things on land; the structural strength of bone, or wood in the case of trees, limits the mass of the organism in the same way that the structural strength of the rocks of the Earth's crust limits the size of a mountain. On Mars, elephants could have thinner legs.

Galileo realised there was an exception to this rule. Whereas gravity imposes a limit to the size and shape of animals on land, the constraints placed on living things by physical laws are different in water. Marine animals float, which means the effects of gravity are not relevant. With the necessity for strong bones to support their weight removed, their forms are freed from this particular constraint. Here is how Simplicio, Sagredo and Salviati put it, from their metaphorical park bench. I can't help but hear them as a sort of three-way Renaissance version of Pete and Dud…

> *Simplicio: This may be so; but I am led to doubt it on account of the enormous size reached by certain fish, such as the whale which, I understand, is ten times as large as an elephant; yet they all support themselves.*

You read that in a Dagenham accent, didn't you?

> *Simplicio: A very shrewd objection! And now, in reply, tell me whether you have ever seen fish stand motionless at will under water, neither descending to the bottom nor rising to the top, without the exertion of force by swimming?*

> *Simplicio: In aquatic animals therefore circumstances are just reversed from what they are with land animals inasmuch as, in the latter, the bones sustain not only their own weight but also that of the flesh, while in the former it is the flesh which supports not only its own weight but also that of the bones. We must therefore cease to wonder why these enormously large animals inhabit the water rather than the land, that is to say, the air.*

> *Sagredo: I am convinced and I only wish to add that what we call land animals ought really to be called air animals, seeing that they live in the air, are surrounded by air, and breathe air.*

> *Salviati: I have enjoyed Simplicio's discussion, including both the question raised and its answer. Moreover I can easily understand that one of these giant fish, if pulled ashore, would not perhaps sustain itself for any great length of time, but would be crushed under its own mass as soon as the connections between the bones gave way.*

You can plainly see the impossibility of increasing the size of structures to vast dimensions, either in art or in Nature.

Every winter the warm waters of Florida are home to one of Nature's apparently less elegant shapes. The caveat is important, because the clumsy-looking manatee is as well adapted to its environment as the most aesthetically refined butterfly.

Freed from the tyranny of gravity, aquatic animals can be larger than their land-based cousins, but they don't have complete freedom from the laws of physics.

Every winter the warm waters of Florida are home to one of Nature's apparently less elegant shapes. The caveat is important, because the clumsy-looking manatee is as well adapted to its environment as the most aesthetically refined butterfly. The West Indian manatee is the largest living example in the Sirenia order of wholly aquatic, herbivorous mammals. A less-than-taxonomically accurate but nonetheless accurate image can be conjured by imagining a 4m-long aquatic cow with no legs, unhurriedly grazing on the sea grasses that grow in the slow-moving waterways along the Floridian coast.

During the summer months the manatee roam as far north as Massachusetts, but as the seasonal temperatures fall they must return to warmer seas. They are unable to survive in waters below 20 degrees Celsius for long. The need for warm winter waters drives the manatees to congregate in large groups around the warm springs that dot the Florida coast, where temperatures remain above 22 degrees Celsius all year round. They also take advantage of human activity, gathering in the outflows of power plants near Apollo Beach and Fort Myers. The manatee is a strange animal indeed; it is more closely related to an elephant than to the other marine mammals – they share a common ancestor around 60 million years ago, not long after the dinosaurs became extinct. The ancestor may have looked like the modern-day hyrax, which at around 50cm in length looks nothing like an elephant or a manatee; 60 million years is plenty of time for the un-directed tinkering sieve of natural selection to sculpt an animal to take advantage of an environmental niche.

The elephant's niche is to be the biggest land animal, which undoubtedly gives it an advantage against predators, but it also displays the anatomical evidence of a tussle with gravity. As dictated by the square-cube law, the elephant has evolved with exceptionally thick legs to support its substantial weight. There is also the matter of cooling; heat escapes from an organism through its surface. As the volume of the animal increases, so does the amount of heat it generates, but its surface area decreases in proportion, according to the square-cube law. This presents a problem for a land-dwelling animal, and the elephant has solved it by developing an ingenious cooling system – its big ears.

The manatee filled a different niche. The transition from a coastal land-dweller to an aquatic mammal saw their front limbs evolve into flippers, although they still possess their ancient finger-bone structure and fingernails. The rear limbs have become a giant paddle-shaped caudal fin, a gradual evolutionary change wonderfully documented in the fossil record. The limbs of the ancient ancestor that grew thick to resist gravity in the elephant have become streamlined to allow the manatee to swim at up to 12 km/hour. The manatee can dive deep, for up to twenty minutes at a time, but being an air-breathing mammal it must surface for air eventually. Its time under water is maximised by slowing down its heartbeat and metabolic rate, reducing the need for oxygen; but this is where biology comes into conflict with physics. A low metabolic rate means limited heat production, and water is an

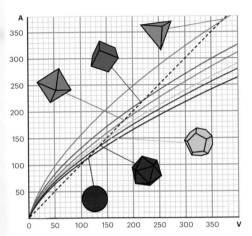

extremely good conductor of heat away from the body, so there is a danger of becoming too cold. The compromise solutions discovered, naturally, by natural selection, are to get bigger, which reduces the surface-area-to-volume ratio and therefore decreases the rate of heat loss per unit volume, and to get spherical (see illustration, left).

This is a beautiful example of a naturally occurring shape reflecting a deeper mathematical reality. The sphere is the three-dimensional shape with the lowest surface-area-to-volume ratio. If you want to generate lots of heat by having a large volume, but lose as little through your surface as possible, you'll be spherical – and the manatee is the most spherical mammal on Earth. What a wonderful thing to be – unless you are an astronomer. The astronomer Fritz Zwicky is credited with calling a group of his colleagues Spherical Bastards, because they are bastards, whichever way you look at them. Which brings us nicely back to the subject of symmetry. If a physicist designed a manatee it would be spherically symmetric. Symmetrical shapes such as planets tend to be the result of the action of symmetrical laws of Nature, unless there are reasons for the symmetry to be broken. There are no perfectly symmetric large organisms in biology. Why?

Imp. Eudes.

Symmetry and symmetry breaking in biology

Leonardo da Vinci's 'Vitruvian Man' is perhaps the most famous drawing of the human form in history. It depicts a man in two superimposed positions within a circle and a square. The proportions are carefully calculated in an attempt to represent the underlying perfection of Man and to link him directly to the Universe. Da Vinci was inspired by one of the great classical works, *De architectura*, written by the Roman architect Vitruvius. The relationship of the human form to a circle and square reflects ancient ideas – dating back to Plato, Pythagoras and earlier mystic traditions – which attempted to forge a link between Nature and geometry. Kepler's early work on the motion of the planets was firmly rooted in this tradition, and he only jettisoned the idea that the motion of the planets could be described in terms of the perfect 'Platonic' solids when the data forced him to conclude that planets actually move in elliptical orbits rather than circular ones. It is interesting to reflect on the fact that the explanation for the motion of the planets is more elegant and beautiful than Kepler's hoped-for geometrical perfection. As we've seen, the motion of all the planets and moons in the Solar System, and indeed every solar system in the Universe, can be described by the application of Newton's laws of motion and Universal Gravitation; a profound simplification that would surely have appealed to Kepler, and to Plato before him, because Newton's laws do embody a 'perfect' spherical symmetry, which is hidden but still evident in the structures it creates.

Similarly, from a modern perspective, the interesting thing about the human form is not its symmetry but its partial symmetry. As we've discussed, a sphere is a perfectly symmetrical 3-dimensional form, in that it looks precisely the same from any angle. Humans, in common with most, but not all, large animals, have a head at one end and an anus at the other, and they have very different functions in the majority of sensible individuals. Humans exhibit what is known as bilateral symmetry, at least externally. This means that there is a symmetry axis, running downwards from our heads to our anus, about which we exhibit mirror symmetry; we have left and right halves. Why?

This book is based on a television series. Part of the challenge of making a documentary that aims to explain or describe abstract scientific concepts is to work out what to point the camera at. The days when an audience would watch a middle-aged academic in a tank top with unkempt hair and a pencil are long gone. I regret this, because I was born in 1968, I have naturally bizarre hair and a big pencil case. Someone at the BBC had a very good idea for illustrating the range of symmetries of living things; on the island of Marado off the southernmost coast of South Korea they found a community of free-diving grannies.

Left: Leonardo da Vinci's drawing, 'Vitruvian Man', circa 1490, is one of the most famous anatomical drawings, showing the artist's understanding of the proportions of the human form.

Above: The Haenyeo – a group of free-diving grannies who defy biology and dive to depths of beyond 20 metres for up to two minutes at a time.

> The interesting thing about the human form is not its symmetry but its partial symmetry. Humans exhibit what is known as bilateral symmetry, at least externally.

For centuries the women in this region of Korea have been free divers, harvesting the seabed for valuable abalone, conch, sea urchin and octopus. Their bounty is so important that Marado has become one of the world's rare matriarchal societies; the women traditionally work in the ocean, while the men bring up the children and run the home. In the cold waters of the East China Sea, becoming a Haenyeo or 'sea woman' is not easy. Girls start their training as young as 11, but once proficient many continue to dive for their whole working lives. It is not clear how the tradition began, but from a biological perspective it makes sense; women are better adapted for work in cold water than men. Before the arrival of wetsuits the Haenyeo would have dived with little protection, and the additional body fat in the female body would have been an advantage. The divers often remain in the water for several hours, free diving for up to two minutes each time to depths beyond 20 metres. Today, the average age of a Haenyeo is 65, and some of the divers are in their 80s. This demographic cliff reflects a changing world. There are now fewer than 2000 Haenyeo; once there were 50,000. The riches of the deep appeal less to the twenty-first-century generation, although the Haenyeo are still highly respected in Korean culture and tourists come from far and wide to watch the women dive and to eat the seafood they catch.

The oceans are home to the most visible assortment of different body plans. Starfish, sea anemones and jellyfish exhibit radial symmetry, at least superficially; they have a top and bottom, which can be defined by the position of their mouth, but they do not have 'left' and 'right' sides. A jellyfish has continuous rotational symmetry about a central axis, whereas a five-armed starfish looks the same if it is rotated through an angle of 72 degrees. The octopus exhibits bilateral symmetry as we do: mirror symmetry around a central axis, notwithstanding the fact that it has eight arms. Some sponges have no symmetry at all. What is the origin of this great range of symmetries in living things? This is a very good question, and it is also a topic of ongoing research. The oldest widely accepted fossil evidence of bilateral symmetry dates back 555 million years ago to a slug-like creature called Kimberella, a rock-dwelling organism that has been found in both Southern Australia and most numerously near the White Sea in Russia. This is just before the Cambrian explosion, the great diversification of life that follows the earliest evidence of multicellular organisms in the fossil record during the Ediacaran period 600 million years ago.

The most widely accepted view is that having bilateral symmetry confers an advantage over radial symmetry because it enables organisms to move more efficiently. Think of the shape of a shark. It is sculpted like a submarine for good reason; it faces the same engineering challenge of moving quickly and efficiently through water. We don't build high-speed radially symmetric submarines; they all look like sharks. As life began to sense the world and move around in ever more complex ways, it was a body plan with a left and right and a top and bottom that could best house a central nervous system and provide the agility needed in the emerging world of predator and prey.

There is, however, another possibility. Jellyfish also exhibit bilateral symmetry, but it is internal. From an evolutionary perspective, this is important. It may suggest that bilateral

Having bilateral symmetry confers an advantage over radial symmetry because it enables organisms to move more efficiently.

symmetry initially evolved to improve the internal functioning of organisms; it allows, for example, for an efficient separation of the gut and respiratory systems. Furthermore, the genes responsible for the development of bilaterally symmetric animals are also found in jellyfish and sea anemones. This is taken as evidence that the common ancestor may have possessed bilateral symmetry, and the external radial symmetry we see in some complex multicellular organisms was a later evolutionary development.

This is yet another example of the wonderful pace and ever-shifting nature of science. Yesterday's textbook explanation can become tomorrow's historical curiosity, and this is precisely as it must be if our knowledge of the natural world is incomplete and continually growing. Progress in science implies that we understood less yesterday than we will tomorrow. That said, I think it is unarguable, and wonderful to consider, that we can trace our ancestry back through geological time to a period in Earth's history some half a billion years ago, when we shared a common ancestor with all the multicellular animals present on Earth today, and it would have looked something like the Kimberella.

The Universe in a snowflake

And yet, despite the underlying simplicity, each snowflake is different. As we saw for planets, galaxies and grannies, simple laws of Nature can sculpt an infinity of forms because the initial conditions and histories of formation are never precisely the same.

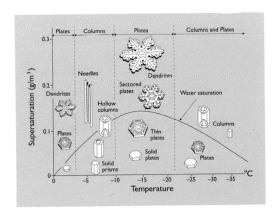

Above: The morphology diagram shows how the structure of snowflakes varies with temperature and humidity.

Let's finish where we began, bringing together everything we've discovered to answer Kepler's question about the origin of the individuality and collective symmetrical beauty of snowflakes. We will follow the formation of a snowflake from its beginnings in a high cloud to its gentle arrival on the ground. Snowflakes are formed by water vapour condensing directly into ice. They are not frozen raindrops; they are crystals that grow steadily larger as they journey through the clouds.

The structure of ice crystals at the temperatures and pressures that we find on Earth is shown in the illustration below. The 104.5-degree bond-angle of a free water molecule – a consequence of the laws of quantum theory – is the reason for a hexagonal crystalline structure, which in turn is the underlying reason for the six-fold symmetry of snowflakes. The hexagons are clearly visible in Snowflake Wilson's photographs on page 18. The snowflakes are imperfect shadows of a more 'perfect' form – the ice lattice; itself a consequence of the structure of the water molecule, which is a physical manifestation of the underlying fundamental laws of Nature that created it – the quantum theories of the strong, weak and electromagnetic forces. When you look at a snowflake, you are seeing the primal structure of our Universe.

And yet, despite the underlying simplicity, each snowflake is different. Why? Because of their individual formation histories. As we saw for planets, galaxies and grannies, simple laws of nature can sculpt an infinity of forms because the initial conditions and histories of formation are never precisely the same. The symmetries of the laws are obscured by history, and it is the job of the scientist to see through the distorting lens of history. A clue as to how this can be done for snowflakes can be found in what is known as the morphology diagram, shown in the illustration below. The morphology diagram shows how the structure of snowflakes varies with temperature and humidity.

The vertical axis of the diagram shows the humidity: the moisture content of the clouds within which the snowflakes form. The horizontal axis shows the temperature. Large, fluffy snowflakes with lots of intricate branches form at high humidity and temperatures between about -10 degrees Celsius and -20 degrees Celsius. At lower temperature and humidity snowflakes are small unbranched hexagons. Higher temperatures lead to needles and prism shapes. For complex, intricate snowflakes, humidity needs to be high. The diagram provides a clue as to how snowflakes can be similar and yet individual. By plotting the data in this way, we see that different patterns of crystal growth are favoured by different conditions and histories of formation.

To better comprehend this, we need to understand how the snowflake crystals grow. The process by which the geometry of the water molecules is transferred to the snowflake is known as faceting. A small ice crystal in a cloud grows because other water molecules bump into it and stick to it through hydrogen bonds. Faceting occurs because rough, uneven bits of the crystal have more available sites for water molecules to bind to; smooth bits, on the other hand, have fewer. This means that rough regions of the initial crystal will grow faster than smooth regions, and become smoother as the jagged spots are filled in. Faceting produces flat, hexagonal prism shapes like those labelled 'solid plates' in the morphology diagram.

The plates are flat because water molecules are more likely to bind to the rectangular thin edges, which are known as prism facets, than to the hexagonal top and bottom surfaces, which are known as basal facets. In low-humidity conditions this is the dominant method of growth, which is why snowflakes can remain broadly hexagonal with few intricate branches. If you look back to Snowflake Bentley's photographs on page 18, the snowflake in the top right-hand corner, labelled 780, is of this type.

Complexity arises from another form of crystal growth called the branching instability. If a bump forms on the crystal surface, the tip of the bump is slightly more likely to accumulate water molecules because it sticks out further into humid air. This causes the bump to grow rapidly, which is why it is referred to as an instability. Branching competes with faceting for a limited supply of water molecules, and it is this competition that leads to the complexity of snowflakes. The corners of the hexagonal prisms are subject to the branching instability – they tend to grow faster than the flat sides, causing them to become concaved. This is resisted by faceting, because there are more sites available for bonding in the centre of the concaved surface between the edges. More water molecules are available at the points, but water molecules are more likely to stick to the centre of the resulting curves. The two processes compete with each other for water molecules. If the air is humid and there is a plentiful supply of water molecules, branching dominates because the rate of growth of the instabilities outstrips the rate at which water molecules diffuse down to the faceted surface below; the corners of the hexagonal prisms therefore tend to grow rapidly, producing intricate, star-like branches. If the air is less humid, the growth rate of the branches falls below the diffusion rate and faceting dominates; the crystal evolves towards a smoother, simpler shape.

As the snowflake grows, it will pass through many different regions in a cloud and experience different conditions, passing through more humid and less humid air, and through regions of differing temperature. Each of these different regions will favour a different type of growth; sometimes faceting will dominate, and other times branching will win out. Look again at Snowflake Bentley's images. You can read the history of each snowflake from the inside out; they all begin with little hexagons; when they are small, faceting always wins. If they enter humid air, branching drives an explosion of intricacy. They may drift into a less humid region and the smooth, faceting growth reasserts itself. This is the reason why every snowflake is different. Each one follows a unique path through the clouds, and every detail of this path is written into its structure. The snowflakes retain an element of the underlying symmetry of the crystal because conditions do not vary in clouds over distances of a few centimetres, which is the size of a snowflake. Each corner therefore experiences precisely the same conditions, which lead to the same structural growth. If one side of a snowflake experiences a different history to the other – perhaps it is involved in a collision – then the symmetry of the snowflake is lost. There are, of course, many snowflakes that reach the ground in a battered, asymmetric state, but we don't take pictures of those!

As a physicist, I have to observe that snowflakes are four-dimensional objects; their structure can only be understood

The interplay between the laws of Nature, which are simple and deeply symmetric, and history, which is long and messy, produces the complex world we inhabit.

with reference to their history, and their history is encoded visibly into their structure. You can read a snowflake like a history book. Precisely the same observation can be made about living things. It is impossible to understand the structure of a manatee unless you understand its evolutionary history. Why does a manatee have finger bones embedded in its flippers? Because they evolved from the legs of a small land-dwelling ancestor. Living things are a snapshot, a temporal shadow of a much grander 4-dimensional story; they encode the entire history of life on Earth, stretching back four billion years, into their structure. No wonder they are complex and difficult to understand. Every twist and turn of history is faithfully recorded.

The interplay between the laws of Nature, which are simple and deeply symmetric, and history, which is long and messy, produces the complex world we inhabit. The triumph of modern science is that we can separate the two, and this has led to discoveries of overwhelming importance. The seeds of this approach are clearly visible in the writings of Kepler, all those years ago. 'Since it always happens, when it begins to snow, that the first particles of snow adopt the shape of small, six-cornered stars, there must be a particular cause; for if it happened by chance, why would they always fall with six corners and not with five, or seven … ?' he asks. And there it is: Nature is beautiful, deep down, and we want to glimpse that underlying beauty. Let's not guess. Let's not make something up. Let's think, observe, experiment, pay attention, look for similarities and differences across the natural world and try to understand them. Most of all, let's be comfortable, delighted, exhilarated when faced with the unknown and devote our time to exploring the infinite territory beyond. There are treasures beyond imagination in the simplest things, if we care to look closely.

Somewhere in spacetime

'Suddenly, from behind the rim of the Moon, in long, slow-motion moments of immense majesty, there emerges a sparkling blue and white jewel, a light, delicate sky-blue sphere laced with slowly swirling veils of white, rising gradually like a small pearl in a thick sea of black mystery. It takes more than a moment to fully realize this is Earth . . . home.'
— *Edgar Mitchell, Apollo 14, in orbit around the Moon, February 1971.*

'Alas I have little more than vintage wine and memories.'
— *Uncle Monty,* Withnail and I, *Camden, 1987.*

Do you remember a perfect summer's day? Not precisely where or when, but a moment of languid warmth, pepper scents, itchy grass, airborne seeds and brushing insects. Great artists are able to summon the tangled past into vivid present experience because memories are indelible. Claude Monet captured notes of a thousand childhood summers in his *Coquelicots* (Poppies). Depicting a rural landscape near the village of Argenteuil, it remains one of Monet's most loved and most recognised paintings.

Monet painted a series of similar pictures during the summer and autumn of 1873. The precise date and time of the scene are unknown, but the poppy fields around Argenteuil are in full bloom in late May and early June, and the bright sky and lack of shadow suggest that the scene was set at around noon. Let's take artistic licence of our own, though, and label the moment when a little boy ambled through the poppies with his mum, and Monet placed a carefully considered dab of red paint on his canvas. Let's say it was noon, 26 May 1873, in a field close to the village of Argenteuil, France. Almost 150 years later, that day has slipped from living memory and exists only in Monet's painting. The place is still there, but the moment is gone. Whimsical common sense, you may say, but is it correct?

In 1905, Albert Einstein published his Theory of Special Relativity, which contains the famous equation $E=mc^2$. I take great comfort in the fact that there is such a thing as a famous equation; it allows me to imagine that I glimpse a flicker of intellectual depth illuminating the all-enveloping darkness of popular culture. Special Relativity deals with moments, or more precisely events. An event is something that happens at a particular location in space and at a single instant in time. Monet's dab of paint on the canvas is an event; it has a location and there is a time that it happened. Einstein's theory tells us how we should measure the distance between events and how to think about their connection to each other. It is a theory of space and time.

What is time? Everyday experience tells us that time is something that passes, measured by the ticking of a clock. If everyone synchronises clocks, and those clocks are mechanically perfect, we might expect that everyone will agree on the time for evermore. We exist in the present, and we are comfortable defining the present moment as 'now'. Since we all agree on what time it is, therefore we must agree on what 'now' means. This implies that the past is gone, fading in memory as a canvas dims with age, and the future is yet to come.

What is space? Space feels like the arena within which things happen; a giant box containing Earth, Moon, Sun, planets and stars. Two people could measure the distance in space between Earth and Moon at an agreed time on perfectly synchronised clocks with perfectly calibrated rulers, and they would agree.

In this chapter, we will follow Einstein in discovering that the obvious statements in those last two paragraphs are wrong: we will discover that time and space are not what they seem. This will lead us to consider the startling possibility that Monet's magical summer's day may have an existence beyond his ageing canvas. As the great physicist and mathematician Hermann Weyl wrote, 'The objective world simply is, it does not happen. Only to the gaze of my consciousness, crawling along the lifeline of my body, does a section of this world come to life as a fleeting image in space which continuously changes in time.'

But we must start at the beginning, and think carefully about how concepts such as distances in space and intervals in time are treated in physics. The first steps towards the modern understanding of space and time were arguably the first steps along the road to modern science itself. Our story begins in the seventeenth century with Galileo, Newton, and the systematic study of the motions of the planets and Earth's place in the Solar System.

Left: Our story of the modern understanding of space and time begins with the early astronomers, shown in this 1692 engraving: from left to right, Galileo, Hevelius, Aristotle, Brahe, Copernicus and Ptolemy.

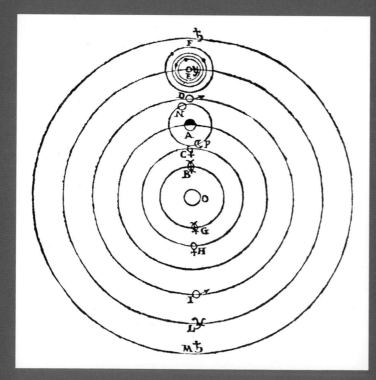

Left: Galileo's diagram of the Copernican (heliocentric) system of the Universe. It also shows his own discovery, the four moons of Jupiter.

Right: The frontispiece of Isaac Newton's seminal work, *The Principia Mathematica,* published in 1687, which expressed his principle of inertia.

Life on a spinning, orbiting planet

The study of motion has a long and controversial history that stretches back many thousands of years. At first sight it is hard to imagine how the study of motion could ever be controversial; it seems like such a basic thing. The origin of the controversy was, in part, due to the fact that we live on a spinning planet that is hurtling around the Sun. That statement was still problematic in Newton's time, partly for well-known theological reasons but also because it really doesn't feel as if we are moving. Common sense informs us that we are standing still, and common sense of the 'I might not know much about science but I know what I think and feel' variety has a profoundly negative effect on public discourse in the twenty-first century – never mind in the seventeenth. If the feeling that we are standing still at the centre of the Universe on an immovable planet really were reliable, Galileo and many others would have been saved a lot of bother.

It is sometimes the case that remarkable ideas become so embedded in culture that they cease to feel remarkable simply because they are familiar. The motion of the Earth around the Sun and the sheer hidden violence of the celestial dynamics that Nature conspires to conceal from us is an excellent example of this conundrum. Most of us give very little thought to what's actually happening to the ground beneath our feet because we've been taught to hold difficult concepts in our heads with reckless intellectual abandon. An educated person probably knows that we're all walking around on the surface of a sphere of equatorial circumference of 40,000 km and mass 6 thousand million million million tonnes, spinning around an extravagantly tilted axis once every 24 hours, and that the whole vast spinning thing is barrelling around the Sun at close to 30 kilometres per second in order to make it around the 940-million-kilometre orbit every year. Such a person probably doesn't find it amazing that we don't notice this on a day-to-day basis. It's dizzying.

The reason why we don't notice is a deep one, and to appreciate it we need to explore precisely what we mean by motion. Before the seventeenth century it was widely believed that things move when they are pushed and stand still when they are left alone. Aristotle is usually credited with the expression of this intuitive view, based on the idea that everything that happens must have a cause. Since motion is something that happens, involving a change in the position of an object over some interval of time, it must have a cause. If the cause is removed, the motion should stop. Intuitively reasonable perhaps, but not correct.

It is true that if you push an object along a table, it moves, and if you stop pushing it, it stops. That is because friction between the object and the table slows it down. If there is no friction and you give the object a push, it will carry on moving until you give it another push. This is known as the principle of inertia, and it is a remarkable thing when you think about it.

The incomparable Nobel Prize-winning physicist Richard Feynman described how his father introduced him to the concept of inertia when he noticed something whilst playing with a toy wagon and a ball.

> "'Say, Pop, I noticed something. When I pull the wagon, the ball rolls to the back of the wagon, and when I'm pulling it along and I suddenly stop, the ball rolls to the front of the wagon. Why is that?"
>
> "'That, nobody knows,' he said. 'The general principle is that things which are moving tend to keep on moving and things which are standing still tend to keep standing still, unless you push them hard. This tendency is called inertia, but nobody knows why it's true.'
>
> 'Now, that's a deep understanding. He didn't just give me the name.'

I like this because it illustrates something important. There are some questions about Nature that have the answer 'because that's the way our Universe is'. There have to be answers like this, because even if we knew how to derive all of the laws of Nature from first principles, we'd still need to know what those principles are. The law of inertia, as expressed by Feynman's dad, is one such principle as far as we know. One of the most difficult things in modern physics is to find out which properties of the Universe are truly fundamental and which follow from a deeper principle or law. This book is all about asking 'Why?' Sometimes, the answer is 'because it is'. This may be wrong – there may be a deeper reason for something that we haven't yet discovered, but it isn't a superficial answer.

Isaac Newton expressed the principle of inertia in the first of his three laws of motion, which he published in 1687 in *The Principia Mathematica*. Virtually everyone today can recite it word for word, or at least remembers a time at school when they could:

'Every object continues in a state of rest or uniform motion in a straight line unless acted upon by a force.'

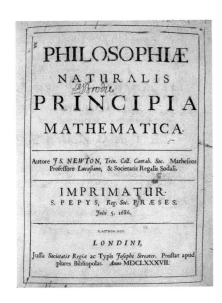

'Absolute, true and mathematical time, of itself, and from its own nature flows equably without regard to anything external …'
— *Isaac Newton.*

EVERY OBJECT CONTINUES IN A STATE OF REST OR UNIFORM MOTION IN A STRAIGHT LINE UNLESS ACTED UPON BY A FORCE.

There is a subtlety here. If we are to say that an object is moving, then we have to answer the question 'relative to what is the object moving?' Newton certainly thought about this question, and almost got the answer right. His writings on the subject are illuminating, and go to the heart of questions about the nature of space and time, and how they are linked to motion. Newton stated the assumptions behind his laws clearly.

Absolute, true and mathematical time, of itself, and from its own nature flows equably without regard to anything external ...'
That's the intuitive view that time ticks along, and everyone agrees on the rate at which it ticks.
Absolute space, in its own nature, without regard to anything external, remains always similar and immovable ... Absolute motion is the translation of a body from one absolute place into another.'

Truly deep concepts often sound like utter pedantry. This is one of the few similarities between physics and philosophy.

Below: A 360-degree panoramic view of the Milky Way over the ALMA radio telescopes in the Atacama desert of northern Chile.

This is Newton's assertion that there is some sort of giant box within which everything happens. We can go a little further and imagine a series of grid lines crisscrossing the box, against which we can mark the position of anything in the Universe. We could then define absolute motion as being motion relative to this universal grid, which we assert to be standing absolutely still in absolute space. This giant grid is an example of what we'll call a frame of reference. In order to define absolute motion, Newton is assuming that there is a very special frame of reference: the frame corresponding to the universal grid, at rest with respect to absolute space, against which all motion is measured.

Then, wonderfully, Newton makes a further observation;

'…. *but motion and rest, in the popular sense of the term, are distinguished from each other only by point of view, and bodies commonly regarded as being at rest are not always truly at rest.*'

Newton is saying that it is impossible to determine whether or not an object is 'actually' in motion in a straight line, or 'actually' standing still. We might not be 'truly at rest', as he puts it, but we can't tell. This is the reason why we don't feel as if we're moving around the Sun while we are standing on the surface of the Earth; on minute-to-minute timescales, we are almost travelling at constant speed and approximately in a straight line. Newton was correct in noticing that if this is the case we won't feel as if we are moving; indeed, we are at liberty to claim that we are at rest, even though we might not be, in his language, 'truly at rest'.

Let us make an apparently philosophical aside that has extremely important consequences for the development of Einstein's theory of relativity. If it's impossible to decide whether or not we are moving, even in principle, then what use is the concept of absolute space? Is there, in reality, no special frame of reference against which all motion can be judged? Shouldn't we just jettison the idea? Yes, that is correct, we should, but Newton never did. The wonderful thing is that his laws of motion do only deal with relative motion, and do not rely on his assumption about the existence of a special frame of reference against which all motion should be calibrated. He got the equations right, but then saddled their interpretation with the unnecessary philosophical baggage of absolute space. All of this might seem like pedantry without relevance, but it isn't. The redundant but comforting idea that space is the fixed arena within which 'stuff happens' is positively harmful to our understanding of nature. Jettisoning it allowed Einstein to construct an entirely new theory of space and time, which delivers a more accurate description of the natural world than Newton's laws.

This does not mean that we want to jettison the concept of a frame of reference – far from it! I've realised something about physics during my years of trying to understand it for myself and explain it to others. Truly deep concepts often sound like utter pedantry. This is one of the few similarities between physics and philosophy. Our careful introduction to the idea of frames of reference is a good example; it may seem that we've been almost too careful, but we'll need to take care if we are to understand the somewhat cryptic comments we've made so far about the implications of Einstein's Theory of Special Relativity. With that in mind, let's take a brief diversion to explore frames of reference in more detail. The effort will be worth it.

Let's consider a particular event: a firework exploding. The time of the explosion event is the time recorded on a clock sitting next to the firework when it explodes. This is different to the time measured by someone watching from a safe distance away, because the flash of light from the firework will take a small amount of time to reach the person watching.

An important aside: frames of reference

We can imagine erecting a set of grid lines that span the Universe, just as Newton did. The positions of objects can then be measured with reference to the grid. This grid represents a frame of reference.

Reference frames are more than an interlocking set of rulers, however. We also need to measure time. Let's also imagine an array of identical clocks scattered across the Universe. All of the clocks sit at fixed positions with respect to the grid. We can now go ahead and measure where and when an event happened; it happened at some position in space (we can use the grid to record precisely where) and at some particular time (we can use the clock adjacent to the event to record precisely when).

It isn't overstating things to say that the whole of physics can be reduced to understanding the relationships between events. This is why we are taking care to set up the framework (quite literally) that we will use to record the positions in space and time of events. Care is necessary: we need to be very clear on how to measure the time of an event.

To illustrate why, let's consider a particular event: a firework exploding. The time of the explosion event is the time recorded on a clock sitting next to the firework when it explodes. This is different to the time measured by someone watching from a safe distance away, because the flash of light from the firework will take a small amount of time to reach the person watching. Light travels at approximately one foot per nanosecond, or 30.48cm in a billionth of a second, if you're of metric persuasion. I always think that, if there is a creator, this is evidence that She worked in imperial units. Another way of appreciating why we need to be careful is that we must make no assumptions regarding the rate at which all the clocks tick. We said that they are identical clocks, so you might think they all merrily tick together. But that would be an assumption, and as we will discover later on, that is wrong. This is why we have to be very clear in defining precisely how we should measure the time.

A reference frame is also a way of establishing our point of view; our perspective on the Universe. We are free to erect our imaginary frame of reference, and somebody else is free to erect their own imaginary frame. Generally speaking, any two frames of reference might be moving with respect to each other (imagine one array of clocks and rulers sliding past a second array of clocks and rulers). The range of possible reference frames is limitless, but in his Theory of Special Relativity Einstein singled out a special set of reference frames. Specifically, he introduced the idea of an 'inertial reference frame'.

You are at rest in an inertial frame if you observe that an isolated object is either sitting at rest or moving in a straight line at fixed speed. Frames that are spinning, such as the frame you are currently sitting in on the rotating Earth, are not inertial. Many of the things we take for granted in our lives, from the behaviour of storm systems to the ebb and flow of the tides, are the result of the fact that we are spinning, and therefore not in an inertial frame of reference, even though we don't feel it. We will see how this works when we explore the ocean tides and the behaviour of storm systems.

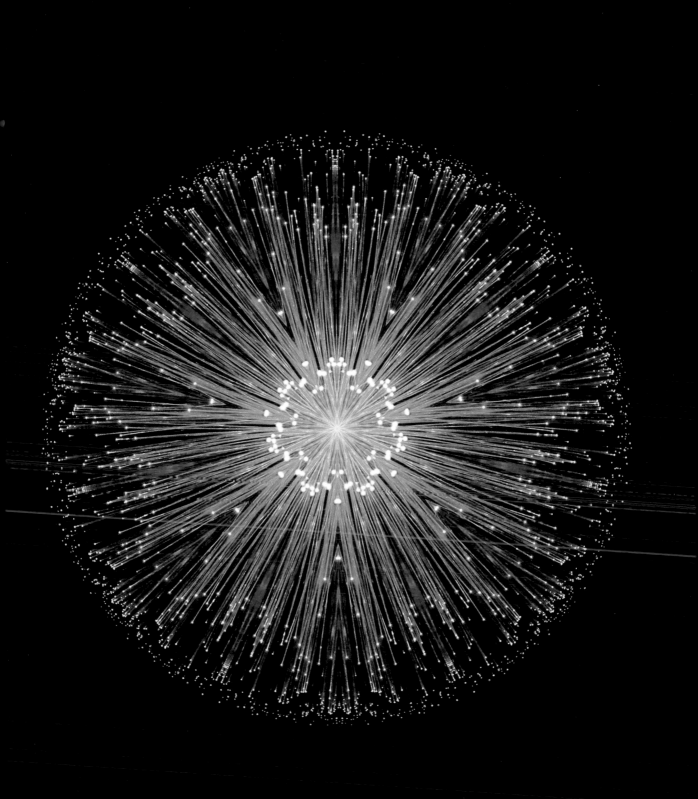

As we've already mentioned, there isn't a 'special' inertial reference frame; all inertial reference frames are as good as each other. If you're in an inertial reference frame, you are allowed to say that you are standing still, and there is absolutely no measurement you can make that will tell you otherwise. It is because we are approximately sitting in an inertial reference frame on the surface of the Earth that we don't feel as if we are moving from moment to moment.

Einstein elevated the requirement that all inertial frames are equivalent to a fundamental principle. This means that identical experiments carried out in different inertial frames will always lead to the same results. To put it another way, the laws of Nature do not change as we switch our point of view between inertial reference frames; if they did, we could tell the difference between the reference frames! I don't want to give the game away early in the chapter, but this ultimate democracy between inertial frames turns out to be such a severe constraint on the laws of Nature that Newton's laws and the laws of electricity and magnetism cannot both be right. This may not sound too serious, but we will see in Chapter Four that the laws of electricity and magnetism are one of the great pillars of physics alongside Newton's laws. They describe so many things we take for granted in our everyday lives; the action of electrical generators and motors, the formation of a rainbow, the action of lenses, the optical fibres that bring the internet into your home, and, when merged with quantum theory, the structure of atoms and molecules; the list is virtually endless. It is inconceivable that the framework we use to describe one of the four fundamental forces of nature could be incompatible with the theoretical framework we use to describe motion. This conflict is what motivated Einstein to develop a new theory of space and time. We'll get to that. For now, let's explore the idea of describing the world from different points of view, which is to say using different reference frames, within a Newtonian framework. This will lead us to an understanding of the passing of the seasons, the rotation of storm systems and the ocean tides.

Life on an orbiting planet

The Seasons

The passage of the seasons is a gentle experience with powerful resonance. I can recite the words of hymns memorised decades ago that celebrate the great cycles of life in the North; 'In the bleak midwinter, frosty wind made moan. Earth stood hard as iron, water like a stone'. A handful of out-of-time voices drifts in the dark depths of a winter snow painted by yellowed light that falls through stained glass. 'We plough the fields and scatter the good seed on the land.' The quiet of autumn woodland in September, faded green splashed with berry red. The daily transitions are gentle, the reddening leaves and cooling of the streams subtle, but the seasonal shifts mask jarring celestial violence.

I love simple questions; they provide the opportunity to learn a lot, if not dismissed too lightly. They are also traps for the overconfident. Scientists are sometimes described as possessing a childlike quality when contemplating Nature, which I take to mean that scientists don't simply wave away questions that appear to have obvious answers without checking whether the obvious answer has content and meaning. Perhaps children have a better-developed sense of intellectual honesty. The answer to the question 'Why do the seasons pass?' has a superficial answer: 'because the Earth goes round the Sun'. But what keeps the Earth in orbit around the Sun? That also has a deceptively simple answer: gravity. But gravity is a force that acts between the Earth and the Sun, pulling them together, so why does the Earth keep orbiting and not just simply fall in? That's a deeper question.

The seasons are obviously something to do with the Earth's orbit around the Sun, which has something to do with gravity. Newton was the first to write down a mathematical model for the force of gravity. He published it in 1687 in *The Principia Mathematica*, alongside his laws of motion. Newton's law of universal gravitation states that there is a force of attraction between all massive objects which is inversely proportional to the square of the distance between them.

$$F = G\frac{m_1 m_2}{r^2}$$

The first thing to notice is that the force of gravity acts directly along a line drawn between the centres of the Earth and the Sun, pulling them together. You may remember Newton's second law of motion from school. It is usually written as an equation:

$$F = ma$$

This says that an object will accelerate in the direction in which the force acts, and the acceleration is proportional to the strength of the force and the mass of the object. This is intuitively obvious; if you want a bus to accelerate you have to push harder than if you wanted a feather to accelerate. The force of gravity therefore accelerates the Earth directly towards the Sun. This would seem to suggest that the Sun and Earth should get closer together over time, but this doesn't happen. Why? The Earth must also obey Newton's first law of motion – the law of inertia; if no force acts on it, it will continue to move in a straight line forever. If the Sun is nearby, the force of gravity acts along a line between the centre of the Sun and the centre of the Earth. Since F = ma, this will cause the Earth to

The quiet of autumn woodland in September, faded green splashed with berry red. The daily transitions are gentle, the reddening leaves and cooling of the streams subtle, but the seasonal shifts mask jarring celestial violence.

Below: The annual migration of caribou herds in the Arctic is a key marker in the changing of the seasons. The animals will travel around 200 kilometres to avoid the harsh windy conditions of their grazing area as winter approaches.

Right: The Earth's orbit around the Sun is an ellipse, with the Sun at one focus. The Earth's spin axis is tilted at an angle of 23.5 degrees to the plane of its orbit, and it is this tilt that gives us our seasons.

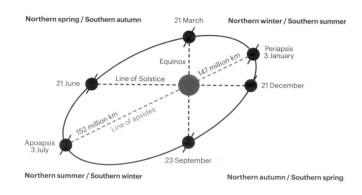

Northern spring / Southern autumn

21 March

Northern winter / Southern summer

Equinox

Periapsis
3 January

147 million km

21 June

Line of Solstice

152 million km

Line of apsides

21 December

Apoapsis
3 July

23 September

Northern summer / Southern winter

Northern autumn / Southern spring

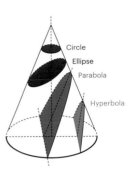

Right: A conic is a curve that is created as the intersection between a plane and right circular conic surface. The four basic conics are the circle, ellipse, parabola and hyperbola, depending on the angle of intersection.

Circle
Ellipse
Parabola
Hyperbola

be deflected from its straight line so that it accelerates towards the Sun in the direction of the force. It will still continue happily on its way in the direction of the 'straight line', though, because no forces are acting in this direction. The Earth is therefore accelerating towards the Sun, but also flying along in a direction at right angles to the acceleration, and the net effect is that it orbits around the Sun forever. Think of the Earth falling towards the Sun but continually missing because it's also got some speed at right angles to the force that's making it fall.

There is a great deal of beautiful subtlety in the analysis of orbits. Newton discovered the family of all paths that objects will take if they move under the influence of a force proportional to the square of the distance between them. These curves are known as the conic sections, because they are the shapes you get if you cut through a cone at different angles (see illustration, left).

Isn't that a beautiful thing? Perhaps you can see that a circular orbit is a very special case – it only happens when the cone is sliced parallel to its base. At shallow angles the orbits are elliptical, and at steeper angles the orbits are known as parabolic or hyperbolic.

The Earth's orbit around the Sun is an ellipse. The closest approach, known as perihelion, occurs near the beginning of the calendar year around 3 January, when Earth passes within 147 million kilometres of the Sun. Six months later, our orbit carries us 5 million kilometres further out. The most distant point, known as aphelion, occurs around 3 July. The particular details of the orbit – the angle of the slice through the cone – are determined by what physicists call the initial conditions. In our description of the Earth's motion we broke things down into two parts; the Earth's straight-line motion without the Sun, and the deflection caused by the gravitational force if we put the Sun down somewhere near it. This isn't how it happened! But in this imaginary case, the initial conditions would be the initial speed of the Earth relative to the Sun, the relative positions of the Earth and Sun when we dropped the Sun in, and the mass of the Sun.

Can you see why the details of the orbit don't involve the mass of the Earth? That's an exercise for the interested reader. All the planets move in elliptical orbits. Some comets move in parabolic or hyperbolic orbits, which means that they will only visit the inner Solar System once before escaping off into space. Halley's Comet is in an elliptical orbit, otherwise it wouldn't return every 76 years. We've built five spacecraft that are travelling on hyperbolic trajectories away from the Sun, which means that they will journey into interstellar space, never to return. They are Pioneers 10 and 11, Voyagers 1 and 2, and New Horizons. All these different paths are a consequence of Newton's law of gravitation and his laws of motion, and the particular initial conditions that started the whole thing off.

The Earth's orbit is half the explanation for the gentle passage of the seasons. To see why it isn't the whole story, consider the climate in Tasiilaq, southeastern Greenland, one of the locations we filmed in for *Forces of Nature*. Tasiilaq is a remote settlement sitting approximately 100 kilometres south of the Arctic Circle. The two thousand residents of the town experience extreme seasonal fluctuations. It's rarely what one might call warm, with summer temperatures rising to around 10 degrees Celsius on the average July afternoon. Winters, on the other hand, are brutal. The average high temperature in December is -4 degrees Celsius, and temperatures regularly approach -30 degrees Celsius. That's mild compared to northern Greenland, where a temperature of -70 degrees Celsius has been recorded. Compare that to the coldest temperature ever recorded on Earth, in Antarctica on 10 August 2010, which was -93 degrees Celsius. That's chilly.

Notice that winter is at its harshest in Tasiilaq in January when the Earth is closest to the Sun, and warmest when the Earth is furthest away. That is, of course, because the timing of winter in the northern hemisphere has nothing to do with the distance between the Earth and the Sun; it's because the Earth's spin axis is tilted at an angle of 23.5 degrees to the plane of its orbit around the Sun, as shown in the illustration on page 94. In January, the North Pole and virtually all of Greenland are pointing away from the Sun and experiencing near-perpetual night. This is why it's cold. Why is the Earth's axis tilted? That's a good question.

Opposite top: The Voyager probes were launched in 1977, destined never to return from their mission to explore the outer reaches of the Solar System. In their travels around interstellar space they have sent back images of Jupiter and Saturn.

Opposite bottom: Pioneer 10, launched on 3 March 1972, completed the first mission to the planet Jupiter and became the first spacecraft to travel through the asteroid belt.

Below: This illustration shows the current positions of four spacecraft which are leaving the Solar System on escape trajectories – our first emissaries to the stars. On this scale, the nearest star to the Sun would be approximately 100 metres away, and it would take Voyager 1 about 70,000 years to cover that distance (view from 10 degrees above ecliptic plane).

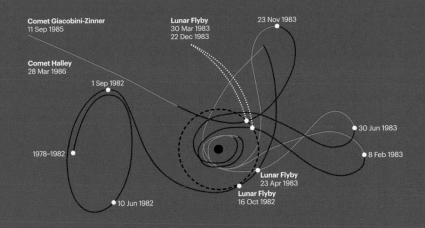

Comet Giacobini-Zinner
11 Sep 1985

Comet Halley
28 Mar 1986

Lunar Flyby
30 Mar 1983
22 Dec 1983

23 Nov 1983

1 Sep 1982

1978–1982

30 Jun 1983

8 Feb 1983

Lunar Flyby
23 Apr 1983

Lunar Flyby
16 Oct 1982

10 Jun 1982

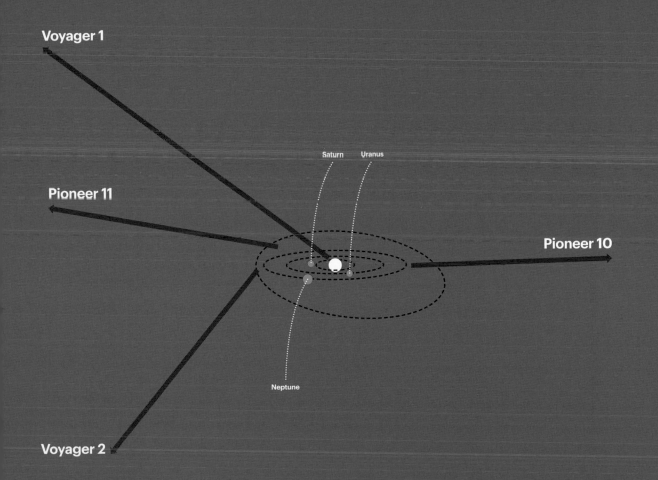

Voyager 1

Pioneer 11

Saturn   Uranus

Pioneer 10

Neptune

Voyager 2

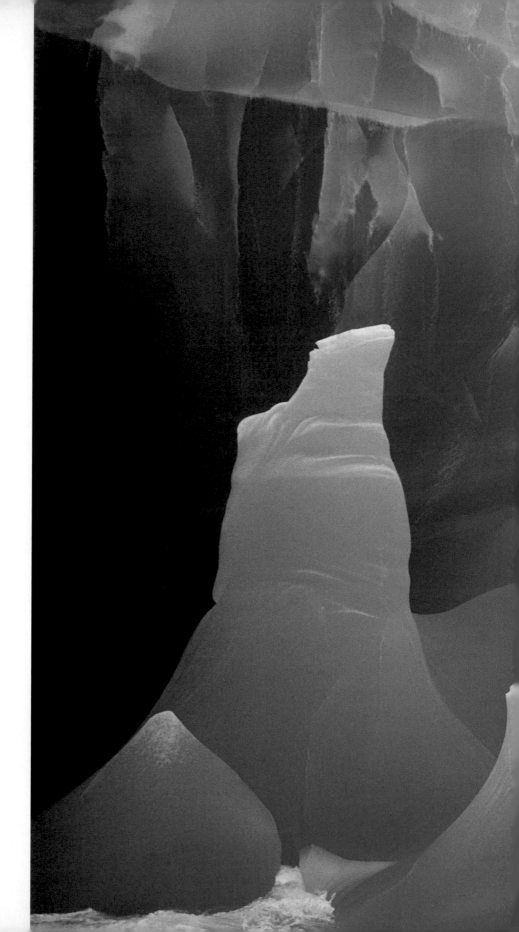

Right: Antarctica is the coldest place on Earth, with an average temperature of -34.4C, beating Tasiilaq by a long way! The tilt of the Earth's axis at its southernmost point means Antarctica has just two seasons: summer and winter.

The timing of winter in the northern hemisphere has nothing to do with the distance between the Earth and the Sun; it's because the Earth's spin axis is tilted at an angle of 23.5 degrees to the plane of its orbit around the Sun.

Below and opposite: Tasiilaq, Greenland, one of our filming locations for *Forces of Nature*. This remote settlement sits about 100 kilometres south of the Arctic Circle. Summer temperatures peak at around 10 degrees Celsius, and winters are brutal – with temperatures ranging from -4 to -30 degrees Celsius. Dog sleds or snowmobiles are the only ways to traverse the frozen waterways and snow-covered trails.

The formation of the Earth and Moon

Four and a half billion years ago, when the Earth formed, there was no Moon. Our planet was a hostile, molten ball of rock travelling around the Sun. The young Solar System was a chaotic place, with crowded orbits and frequent collisions.

Today the Earth orbits in an astronomical highway that is mainly clear of debris, which is good if you are travelling at 30 kilometres per second. A cleared orbit is one of the three definitions that the International Astronomical Union (IAU) uses to classify a planet. To clear its orbit the Earth had to go through a violent period of collisions and near-misses as smaller bodies were either thrown out of the orbit or added to the mass of the planet itself in collisions.

Not all of the objects the Earth encountered as a young planet were small. It is thought that there were dozens of

The Giant Impact Hypothesis suggests that there was a glancing collision between the newly formed Earth and a Mars-sized planet around 4.5 billion years ago, resulting in a planetary merger.

proto-planets orbiting the Sun in those days, swirling around in crowded orbits, and Earth would have experienced a number of significant collisions. Direct evidence of these planetary collisions has long been erased from Earth's surface, but one particular collision left an indelible mark.

The Giant Impact Hypothesis suggests that there was a glancing collision between the newly formed Earth and a Mars-sized planet around 4.5 billion years ago, resulting in a planetary merger. The colliding planet has been named Theia, after the Greek goddess who gave birth to Selene, the goddess of the Moon. Scientists love their Greek mythology, and there is a good reason for the choice of goddess in this case. Computer simulations suggest that the collision resulted in large amounts of material from both Theia and Earth entering orbit around the battered larger planet, and over time the debris combined under the action of gravity to form the Moon. The supporting evidence for this hypothesis is strong, although, as always in science, healthy scepticism remains. Without scepticism there can be no progress. Computer simulations certainly match the details of the spins and orbit of the Earth–Moon system, but there is also physical evidence of a common origin for the system from the lunar rock samples returned by the Apollo astronauts. In particular, the abundances of oxygen isotopes ^{16}O, ^{17}O and ^{18}O in lunar rocks are near identical to those on Earth. For those who need a bit of chemistry revision, isotopes are atoms of the same chemical element but which have different numbers of neutrons in the nucleus. The most plausible reason for this similarity is that the rocks have a common origin – namely the collision 4.5 billion years ago. The Moon also has significantly less iron in its core than Earth. This is also consistent with the computer models describing such an impact. To get the spins and orbit right a glancing collision is required, and in such collisions the iron-rich cores of the colliding planets tend to merge together, leaving the iron-depleted rocks from the outer layers to form the Moon.

The Giant Impact Hypothesis is able to explain the composition of the Earth and Moon and the details of their orbits and spins. This includes the origin of Earth's tilted spin axis, angled at 23.5 degrees to the plane of the Solar System, which gives us our seasons (see page 94). I find this a wonderful thing; there are few certainties in science, but I would contend that we wouldn't be here today if our spin axis wasn't tilted. The Moon was likely formed in the event that tilted our spin axis, but in any case her presence acts to stabilise the orientation of Earth's axis, and a reasonable level of stability over geological timescales is a prerequisite for the evolution of complex life. Humans wouldn't be here without the Moon; at the very least, evolution would have taken a different path, and it is a major understatement to say that the road to humanity was convoluted. In one sense that's a superficial observation. There are a vast number of chance events in our past that could have happened differently, and changing any one of them would have meant that we wouldn't be. We shouldn't fall into the trap of attaching particular importance to a single event; we'll leave that to the sonorous voice-overs of badly made television documentaries. The deeper unarguable point, which does bear at least a thought, is that we are very lucky indeed to be here. There cannot be any cosmic significance to our existence, because our existence is far too contingent on a series of chance events stretching back to the formation of the Solar System and beyond. Does the fact that you're lucky to be alive make you feel irrelevant or valuable? I'll leave that to you. In his essay 'Some Thoughts on the Common Toad', George Orwell reflects on the simple and available delight of noticing things like the passage of the seasons, and that is really what this book is about: 'The point is that the pleasures of spring are available to everyone and cost nothing', he writes. 'How many a time have I stood watching the toads mating, or a pair of hares having a boxing match in the young

Humans wouldn't be here without the Moon; at the very least, evolution would have taken a different path, and it is a major understatement to say that the road to humanity was convoluted.

Below: Humans wouldn't be on Earth without the Moon, a fact we are always reminded of as we look up and see its ever-changing face in the night sky as it orbits the Earth, moving through its eight distinct phases.

corn, and thought of all the important persons who would stop me enjoying this if they could. But luckily they can't.

'The atom bombs are piling up in the factories, the police are prowling through the cities, the lies are streaming from the loudspeakers, but the Earth is still going around the Sun, and neither the dictators nor the bureaucrats, deeply as they disapprove of the process, are able to prevent it.'

You don't need permission to do science, to think carefully and without preconception about what Nature is telling you. After all, Nature is a more reliable guide to the truth than the opinions of those incalculably lucky humans.

Life on an orbiting planet

Storms

The passage of the seasons is a gentle reminder that we live on a planet in orbit around the Sun. Although we're moving at close to 30km/second in orbit, we can't tell that from moment to moment because we're moving in a straight line at constant speed to a good approximation, so it feels as if we're standing still. This is why we don't feel as if we are flying through space very quickly on a ball of rock. But there is a very important caveat; we are also spinning around as the Earth rotates once a day on its axis, and this does have definite physical consequences that we experience on timescales of hours rather than months.

How do we know we're spinning?

You don't have to be particularly observant to notice that something is spinning. The Sun rises in the east and sets in the west, arching across the sky. When it sets, the stars follow suit. There is obviously something circular going on.

From the evidence available to us, we might offer two possible explanations. The first and perhaps most natural is that the Earth is stationary and the Sun and stars circle around us once a day. The other possibility is that it is we who are doing the rotating rather than the Sun and stars. Copernicus

Below: This eight-hour wide-angle star trail photo, taken in New Hampshire, USA in October, shows an Iridium flare streaking down near the horizon.

Right: This depiction of Copernicus' heliocentric system of the Universe shows the Sun, the orbits of the planets and the firmament of the fixed stars.

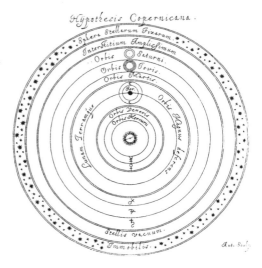

We don't need to resort to the laboratory to observe a direct physical effect of the Earth's rotation because we have spacecraft and weather.

described a spinning Earth moving in orbit around a fixed Sun in *De revolutionibus*, published in 1543. He was motivated primarily by his distaste for the inelegant explanation of the observed motions of the planets against the stars laid down by the Greek astronomer Ptolemy in the second century. Observed over the course of months, the planets do not follow neat circular arcs across the sky. They perform occasional loops, reversing their motion against the starry background. We now know this happens when the Earth overtakes a planet as it orbits the Sun. If you don't accept that the Earth is in orbit you have to come up with some other mechanism for the planetary loops, and Ptolemy's Earth-centred model, whilst delivering accurate predictions for the motions of the planets, is a terrifically messy affair. If you accept that the Earth goes around the Sun, on the other hand, you also have to come up with an explanation for day and night, which is separate from the yearly orbital motion. This is why Copernicus proposed that the Earth spins around on its axis once every 24 hours.

Copernicus's model wasn't convincing to many astronomers and natural philosophers of the day. It's revealing to read a criticism from the greatest observational astronomer of the age, Tycho Brahe: '... such a fast motion could not belong to the Earth, a body very heavy and dense and opaque, but rather belongs to the sky itself whose form and subtle and constant matter are better suited to a perpetual motion, however fast.'

Here again we see how difficult it is to accept that we live on a moving planet when we feel so powerfully that we are standing still.

Almost 150 years after Copernicus, the Italian priest and astronomer Giovanni Riccioli offered a more scientific objection to Copernicus's spinning Earth than the rather philosophical statement that it just doesn't feel right. He carried out a rather beautiful analysis of the motion of projectiles on a spinning planet in *Almagestum Novum* (New Almagest), published in 1651, when the young Isaac Newton was just 9 years old. Riccioli was concerned with laying out the evidence for and against the motion of the Earth, which he did in 77 carefully constructed arguments. Argument number 18 is an analysis of the motion of a cannonball on a spinning planet. Riccioli argued that a cannon ball fired northwards (in the northern hemisphere) should follow a flight path that is distorted by the spin of the Earth. Here is what he said:

'If a ball is fired along a Meridian toward the pole (rather than toward the East or West), diurnal motion will cause the ball to be carried off [that is, the trajectory of the ball will be deflected], all things being equal: for on parallels of latitude nearer the poles, the ground moves more slowly, whereas on parallels nearer the equator, the ground moves more rapidly.'

Riccioli could find no experimental evidence to show that cannonballs are deflected as they fly north, so he concluded that the Earth is not spinning. It's probably more correct to say that he reinforced his own prejudice that the Earth isn't spinning. But that's not the point. Riccioli didn't have access to good enough data to see the effect of Earth's spin on a flying cannonball, which *is* deflected in flight because of the Earth's spin. Riccioli didn't stop there, though. He also proposed that the same effect should be seen for objects falling vertically to the ground, a point he made poetically in argument number 10 of New Almagest:

This grainy black-and-white image occupies an historic place in the archives of meteorology. Taken by NASA's TIROS-3 satellite, it is the first time a hurricane was discovered using satellite imagery and is one of the first photographs of a tropical cyclone from space.

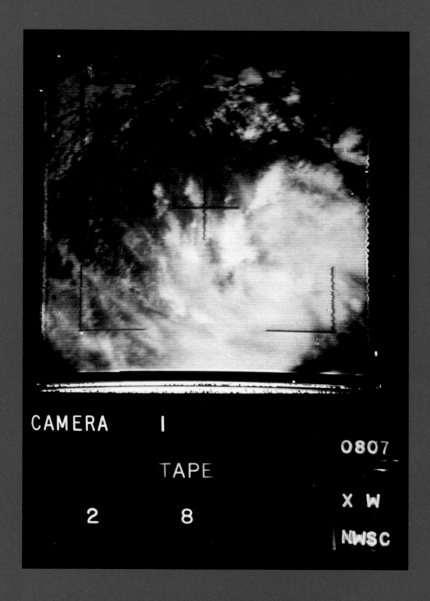

CAMERA I

0807

TAPE

2 8

X W

NWSC

Right: A seventeenth-century illustration of a compound microscope as used by English natural philosopher Robert Hooke (1635–1703).

Bottom right: Illustration from Riccioli's 1651 *New Almagest* showing the effect a rotating Earth should have on projectiles. Riccioli's explanation for expecting a curved path is as follows: The more southerly cannon is moving faster relative to the more northerly target (E). Because the ground is moving more slowly at the target (E), it will follow a curved path and land to the right of the target at (G) instead. No such effect should be seen if the cannon is fired in the direction of the Earth's spin at an easterly target (C). This is because in this case the cannon and the target are both travelling at the same speed relative to each other and so the cannonball will fly as if the Earth is completely still. This last part of Riccioli's argument is incorrect, but he was on the right track.

'If an angel were to let fall a metal sphere of great weight hung to a chain, while holding the other end of the chain immobile, that chain by the force of the sphere might be extended to its full length perpendicularly toward the Earth. But following the Copernicans, it ought to curve obliquely toward the east.'

Right again, and with plenty of towers to choose from in northern Italy, Riccioli climbed to the top of the Torre degli Asinelli in Bologna and dropped some weights. He searched for a deflection in vain, which again confirmed his belief that the Earth is not spinning. His problem, again, was not his theoretical prediction (which is spot on), but the quality of his experimental data.

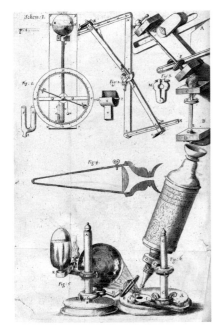

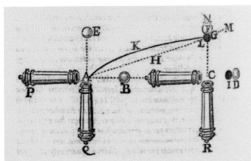

[1] For a height of 97 metres (the height of the Asinelli tower) at a latitude of 44.5 degrees north (Bologna) and with $\omega = 7.3 \times 10^{-5}$ /s (the angular speed of Earth), the deflection is equal to 1.8 centimetres. The details of this calculation can be found, for example, in Forshaw and Smith, *Dynamics and Relativity* (Wiley).

For those attempting to find Earthly experimental proof for the Copernican view of a Sun-centred Solar System, Riccioli's experiment was a prime target. Writing in 1679, Newton shared 'a fansy of my own about discovering the Earth's diurnal motion' with his contemporary and rival physicist, Robert Hooke. Hooke decided to attempt the experiment, culminating in a demonstration at the Royal Society on 22 January 1680. With such slight margins – a modern calculation of the deflection for an 8-metre drop is 0.3mm – the experiment failed and the records of the Royal Society give no indication that Hooke ever attempted it again.

To this day, drop-experiments such as the Torre degli Asinelli experiment proposed by Riccioli are reasonably difficult to perform, although certainly not impossible[1], but we don't need to resort to the laboratory to observe a direct physical effect of the Earth's rotation because we have spacecraft and weather.

The grainy black-and-white image shown opposite occupies an historic place in the archives of meteorology. The TIROS satellites were little spinning drums, just over a metre in diameter, and carried two wide-angled television cameras, a tape recorder for the images and a 2-watt transmitter. On 10 September 1961, TIROS-3 peered down onto the Atlantic Ocean from low Earth orbit and observed the birth of Hurricane Esther hours before its formation was spotted back on Earth.

Half a century later, the quality of space-based weather imagery is extraordinary. High-definition images allow us to keep track of the surface of the Earth and the formation of major weather systems in real time. They are ubiquitous, and because of this we know what storm systems look like. The most obvious feature is that they rotate, and the reason for this is the rotation of the Earth, as Riccioli predicted. The force that acts on weather systems causing them to rotate is the Coriolis Force, named after the French mathematician Gaspard-Gustave de Coriolis, who first published a full mathematical treatment as part of an analysis of the physics of water wheels in 1835.

The Coriolis Force is known as a 'fictitious force', although its effects on weather systems are very real. It's called a fictitious force because it's not a fundamental force of Nature. It's not gravity, it's not electromagnetism, and it's not the strong or weak nuclear force. Rather, its origin lies in the fact that the Earth's surface is NOT an inertial reference frame. Why is the Earth not an inertial frame? Because if we stand on the surface of the Earth we are constantly changing direction as we spin around in a circle once every day. We are certainly not moving in a straight line and we are therefore not in an inertial reference frame.

How might this lead to a force 'magically' appearing? Imagine that you're sitting on a train moving at constant speed and you decide to put a cricket ball on the table in front of you. It will stay exactly where you put it. This is as it should be, because the train is an inertial reference frame and there is no experiment we can do to tell whether or not we are moving. We must all have had the experience of sitting peacefully in a train carriage, rolling gently through a station at constant speed and getting the slightly dizzying feeling that the station is drifting by. This isn't an error of perception; you are absolutely entitled to claim that you aren't moving and the platform is. If the train accelerates quickly out of the station, however, the ball will roll towards you. How should you interpret what is happening?

Newton's second law of motion states that $F = ma$. From your perspective on the train, you'll see the ball accelerate towards you on the table, and you will describe the acceleration as being due to a force acting on the ball. This force is a fictitious force. It appears *because you are no longer in an inertial frame of reference because the train is accelerating.* This might appear to be a subtle point, but it provides a way of determining experimentally whether or not you are in an inertial frame. If things in your world deviate from their state of rest or uniform motion in a straight line and the cause isn't one of the fundamental forces of nature, then you can deduce that you are not in an inertial frame, and here is where the abstract becomes concrete. This fictitious force is very real from the point of view of the person sitting in the accelerating

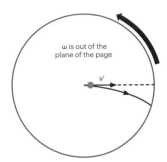

frame. If you were resting your face on the table when the
train started accelerating, the cricket ball would hit you in
the head, and there is nothing fictitious about a broken nose.
The Coriolis Force that drives the great storm systems on
the surface of our planet is another very powerful example of
a fictitious force.

The origin of the Coriolis Force is not as simple as the
accelerating train, or for that matter as simple as Riccioli's
description in his cannonball experiment; this is why it isn't
called the Riccioli Force. Here is the explanation.

The Earth is a three-dimensional spherical object, which
complicates things, so let's consider what happens to an object
that moves around on a flat spinning disc. The arguments
will be the same and easier to visualise. Imagine the rotating
disc from two different perspectives. One will be that of an
observer watching everything from afar – dare we say it, in
an inertial frame of reference. (There is a drinking game here
somewhere.) The other will be that of an observer sitting at
the edge of the rotating disc, whizzing around with it. This
is our situation as we sit on the surface of our spinning planet.

Now imagine that the rotating observer decides to throw
a ball directly towards the centre of the disc. From their
perspective, the ball sets off happily in the direction in which it
is thrown but immediately starts to curve away in the direction
of rotation. What is happening? It's easiest to see from the
perspective of the observer watching from afar (see above).

From the distant perspective, the ball is flying around in
a circle with the disc, before it is thrown inwards. When it's
thrown, it hangs on to the initial speed it had in the direction
of rotation. This is the law of inertia again. Nobody pushed
on the ball in the direction of the spin of the disc, which is
known as the tangential direction, so it simply keeps on going.
As it rolls inwards, however, it finds itself travelling too fast
in the tangential direction for the inner parts of the disc. This
is because the points closer to the centre have less far to travel
to circle once around, so they must be travelling more slowly
than the points further out. As a result, the ball gets ahead
of the disc and curves away in the direction of rotation. From
the distant observer's perspective, there is no force acting on
the ball. The curved path is explained purely in terms of the
rotation of the disc.

From the rotating observer's perspective, however, there
appears to be a force acting on the ball in accord with Newton's
first law, because it doesn't travel in a straight line relative to
them. This is the Coriolis Force. It acts at right angles to the
direction of motion of the ball, deflecting it onto a curved
path. On the surface of the Earth, the Coriolis Force always
pushes objects moving in the northern hemisphere to the right,
and objects in the southern hemisphere to the left, if we view
the Earth as being orientated with the North Pole at the top.
At the Equator, the Coriolis Force pushes neither to the right
nor the left, although it does try to lift an object gently off the
surface! Such is the complexity of a rotating three-dimensional
sphere rather than a disc, but the principle is the same.

We can now see why storm systems rotate the way they do
on the surface of the Earth. Large bodies of air do not move
in straight lines because of the action of the Coriolis Force.
A cyclone is a region of low pressure. The higher-pressure air
around it will fall inwards to try to equalise the pressure. In the

northern hemisphere, the moving air will experience a Coriolis Force to the right as viewed from above, and therefore will rotate in an anti-clockwise direction around the low-pressure area. In the southern hemisphere, a cyclone will rotate in a clockwise direction because the inward-falling air is deflected to the left. This is why the hurricanes that form every year in the Atlantic which threaten the Caribbean Islands and the southeastern states of America always rotate anti-clockwise, whereas the tropical cyclones (the name for a hurricane that forms in the southern hemisphere) that batter the Pacific Islands are always rotating in the opposite direction.

For anti-cyclones, the opposite is true. The air flows outwards from a high-pressure central region, and the deflection to the right by the Coriolis Force in the northern hemisphere induces a clockwise rotation.

As well as creating the distinctive spirals of storm systems as seen from space, the Coriolis Force also increases the strength of the storms. The stronger the deflection of the air current around a high-pressure system, the faster it will rotate. This is one reason why the most powerful storms in the Solar System occur on faster-spinning planets. Jupiter is not only the most massive planet, it is also the fastest rotating, spinning once on its axis approximately every 9.8 hours. The most recognisable storm system in the Solar System is the Great Red Spot, a spiralling storm that has raged on the gas giant for at least two hundred years, but probably far longer.

The most recognisable storm system in the Solar System is the Great Red Spot, a spiralling storm that has raged on the gas giant for at least two hundred years, but probably far longer. Famously large enough to swallow the Earth whole, it is 20,000 kilometres long, 12,000 kilometres wide and boasts wind speeds of up to 700km/hr.

Famously large enough to swallow the Earth whole, it is 20,000 kilometres long, 12,000 kilometres wide and boasts wind speeds of up to 700km/hr. The Coriolis Force generated by the size and rotation speed of Jupiter is a significant contributing factor to the power and size of the Great Red Spot and the many other storm systems that rage through Jupiter's swirling clouds. The Great Red Spot is an anti-cyclonic (high-pressure) storm in Jupiter's southern hemisphere and, just as here on Earth, it therefore rotates in an anti-clockwise direction. The laws of Nature are universal.

The reason for the rotating storms on Earth and across the Solar System is interesting in itself, but there is a deeper reason why we've spent time studying the Coriolis Force. It appears in our description of the physics when we try to explain a real-world natural phenomenon from different perspectives – that is to say from different frames of reference. Hold that thought, because we'll come back to it.

Recall that we began this chapter musing about the nature of space and time, and hinting at the rather wonderful suggestion that events in our past may have an existence beyond our memories. This chapter is a wandering adventure in a sense; our explanations of natural phenomena will serve to illustrate something we need to know on the road to relativity. Let us explain one more everyday physical phenomenon that requires us to jump between different frames of reference to understand: a classic problem in physics – the ocean tides.

Life on an orbiting, spinning planet
The tides

The ebb and flow of the tides creates a dramatic, recurring and rapid transformation of Earth's coastline. With a little patience and a comfortable deckchair you can watch the landscape change before your eyes. Geological in timescale it isn't. The Bay of Fundy on Canada's east coast holds the record for the greatest tidal range: 56 feet, as measured by the Canadian Hydrographic Service at Burntcoat Head. I am delighted to leave this measurement in feet as a celebration of cultural diversity.

The origin of the tides is an ancient puzzle. The connection between the tides and the lunar cycle has been known for well over 2000 years, but the recognition of patterns and the prediction of high, low and spring tides does not require an understanding of the underlying mechanism. If all you want to do is sail, you don't need to know why; you just need to know when. With the emergence of a heliocentric model of the Solar System in the sixteenth century, the understanding of the origin of the tides received a great deal of attention from the astronomers of the day because it presented an Earth-bound phenomenon that appeared to be connected to the motion of Earth, Moon and Sun. Johannes Kepler asserted that the tides were created by a force of attraction exerted by the Moon on the Earth's oceans, but was unable to provide a mechanism to explain the force. Galileo disagreed, and in an increasingly fractious dialogue proposed the counter-argument that the tides are a result of the Earth's rotation and revolution around the Sun: 'Among all the great men who have philosophised about this remarkable effect, I am more astonished at Kepler than at any other. Despite his open and acute mind, and though he has

Below: Although seemingly calm and serene at low tide, the Bay of Fundy, in Canada, holds the record for the greatest tidal range – the vertical difference between the high tide and low tide – of 56 feet.

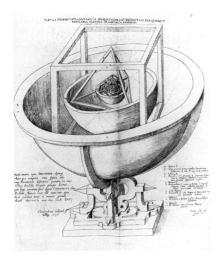

at his fingertips the motions attributed to the Earth, he
nevertheless lent his ear and his assent to the Moon's dominion
over the waters, to occult properties, and to such puerilities.'

'Puerilities' is a word I intend to use more often. In an essay
written in 1616 entitled 'Discourse on the Tides', Galileo
likened the movement of the Earth's oceans to the movement
of water in a vase. He reasoned that because the water is
distorted by changes in the orientation and acceleration of
the vase, so the oceans are distorted in their movement by
the orientation and acceleration of the Earth. He posited
a mechanism of positive and negative acceleration to explain
the back-and-forth motion of the tides, a theory that has
often been labelled his 'great mistake'. The irony is, both
Galileo and Kepler were partly right. Here is the explanation
for the origin of the tides.

Kepler was correct in the sense that the tides are caused
by the Moon's gravitational effect on the Earth. He didn't
put it in those terms, of course, because Newton had yet to
publish his theory of Universal Gravitation. Galileo was
correct because the Earth is accelerating. He just didn't
appreciate towards what.

Let's accept that the tides have something to do with the
Moon; its orbit can be described in precisely the same way
that we described the Earth's orbit around the Sun. The Moon
is being pulled towards the Earth by the force of gravity but
is continually missing it because it continues to try to move
in a straight line, in accord with the principle of inertia.

We now need to introduce Newton's third and last law of
motion. It states:

TO EVERY ACTION, THERE IS AN EQUAL AND OPPOSITE REACTION.

From the point of view of the observer sitting at the centre of the Earth, the force of gravity is trying to accelerate the Earth towards the centre of the Moon in a straight line, in accord with Newton's law of universal gravitation.

This means that forces always come in pairs. If the Earth exerts a gravitational pull on the Moon, the Moon exerts an equal and opposite gravitational pull on the Earth. This means that the Earth has to fall towards the Moon, accelerated by the force of gravity along a line connecting their centres. Why doesn't the Earth career towards the Moon? For the same reason that the Moon doesn't career towards the Earth – because it falls and misses. The Earth must also be in orbit! But around what? The answer is that we were a little lax in our language when we said that the Moon orbits around the Earth. It does to a good approximation, but in fact it orbits around a point slightly displaced from the centre of the Earth known as the centre of mass of the Earth-Moon system. To get an instinct for what's happening, imagine two moons of equal mass orbiting around each other in circular orbits. Everything is perfectly symmetric, and they both orbit around a point that is equidistant between their centres. This is called the centre of mass of the system. If one of the moons is more massive than the other, the centre of mass will be closer to the massive moon, and they will both orbit around this offset point. The Earth is 81 times more massive than the Moon, so the centre of mass point about which they orbit is very close to the centre of the Earth, but not quite at the centre; it is displaced by 4,700 kilometres, which is about 1/81 of the distance between the Earth and the Moon. This is why it's superficially reasonable, but not accurate, to say that the Moon orbits around the Earth. It's only reasonable in a superficial sense because it dodges the problem of how the Earth can accelerate towards the Moon – as it must – and keep missing!

The fact that the Earth is in orbit around the centre of mass of the Earth-Moon system is critical to an understanding of the tides. The key is to switch perspective, or frame of reference, just as we did when we explored the Coriolis Force and its effect on storm systems. We're hopping between reference frames again, searching for fictitious forces – physicists are always doing this because it's bloody useful, and we know how to do it! (See illustration opposite.)

Let's picture what's happening from the point of view of an observer sitting at the centre of the Earth. This is the point that is orbiting around the centre of mass of the Earth-Moon system. We can assume that the centre of the Earth is going round in a perfect circle, which it very nearly is. This reference frame is not inertial, because it's rotating, and we will therefore expect fictitious forces to be present. But which? This time it's not the Coreolis Force, which appears when things roll around in rotating reference frames, but the Centrifugal Force. What does this one do? From the point of view of the observer sitting at the centre of the Earth, the force of gravity is accelerating the Earth towards the centre of the Moon in a straight line, in accord with Newton's law of universal gravitation. And yet, the Earth doesn't approach the Moon – it stays a fixed distance away from the centre of mass of the Earth–Moon system if the orbit is circular. This must mean that the observer at the centre of the Earth experiences a force acting with the same strength as the Moon's gravitational pull, but in the opposite direction, to precisely cancel it out. This force, equal and opposite to the gravitational force, is called the Centrifugal Force. It's none other than the familiar force we experience if we sit on a fast-rotating fairground ride. We are thrown outwards, and if it's

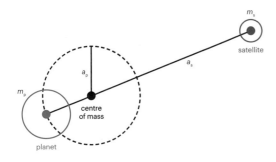

Above: The centre of mass.

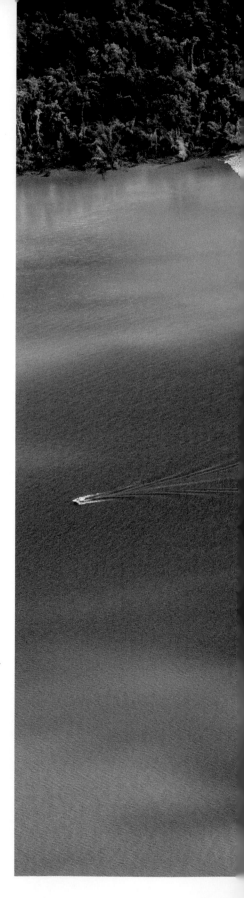

the right sort of ride, the little cars we sit in will rise up and outwards as the speed increases. The force that does this is the Centrifugal Force.

Great. But what's that got to do with the tides? We're about halfway through, so perhaps you should have a break for a cup of tea and come back refreshed. As an aside, I find something amusing about this explanation for the tides, which is quite a wonderful explanation if you have the patience to follow it. Let me tell you what I find amusing. Imagine, as I tell you, that there is a hint of Joe Pesci in *Goodfellas* in my voice. I have a love–hate relationship with television. I love most of it, to be honest, but I sometimes find it a superficial medium. The trick is to find a way of exploring ideas in sufficient depth within a television programme that is the length of a single undergraduate lecture, in a visual and entertaining way. I get into a lot of 'creative debates' about the definition of 'sufficient depth', as you might imagine. Usually we are exploring grand ideas about the origin of the Universe or the beginning of life on Earth, and because the answers to these ideas are speculative, there is room for a bit of hand-waving. In a programme about tides, however, there can be no hand-waving because the reason for the tides is known. I think the tides are a good thing to explain. But I offer a wry smile. 'Sufficient depth' is a well-defined concept in this instance. It is defined as being *the* explanation. Such is the trap, lying in wait for the unwary television executive, in wanting to make a television series about simple questions that actually have answers, rather than complicated questions that don't.

Here is the rest of the explanation for the tides. Recall that the Earth is in a little orbit around the centre of mass of the Earth-Moon system. At the centre of the Earth, the Moon's gravitational pull is perfectly balanced by a fictitious

Left and right: The effect of the variance of gravitational pull and the Centrifugal Force of the Moon can be witnessed all over the globe in our tides. These tides change the appearance of our coastal landscapes every day, and we now have the technology to monitor them and predict them to be able to use that information for maritime purposes – as well as leisure pursuits such as surfing!

Usually we are exploring grand ideas about the origin of the Universe or the beginning of life on Earth, and because the answers to these ideas are speculative, there is room for a bit of hand-waving.

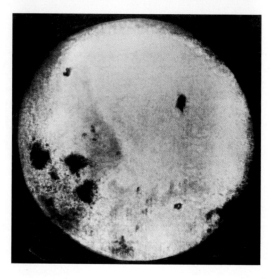

Top: It is the Moon that dictates the tidal forces on Earth, caused as a result of the imbalance between the Moon's gravitational pull and the Centrifugal Force.

Above: The far side of the Moon, in an image taken by the Luna 3 space probe, 28 October 1959.

Below: The tides.

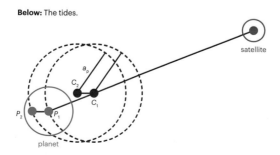

force called the Centrifugal Force. Now consider a point on the surface of the Earth directly beneath the Moon. That too will be in a little orbit, and it will have to go around in a circle of precisely the same radius as the point at the centre of the Earth, because the Earth is a solid ball of rock and a point on the surface can't move in a different way to the centre. This means that the Centrifugal Force experienced at a point on the surface beneath the Moon must be exactly the same as that experienced by the centre of the Earth. But – and this is the crucial point – the Moon's gravitational pull at the Earth's surface directly beneath it is stronger than it is at the centre of the Earth, because the surface of the Earth is closer to the Moon than the centre. The two forces won't precisely balance! There will be a little too much gravitational pull at the surface directly beneath the Moon, and it is this little extra pull that deforms the oceans and raises a tide beneath the Moon.

Now consider the situation on the other side of the Earth. Again, the Centrifugal Force must be the same, because every point on the Earth's surface has to orbit in a circle of precisely the same radius as every other point, but now we are further away from the Moon than the centre of the Earth is, so we'll experience a weaker gravitational pull from the Moon. This means that the Centrifugal Force, which always points away from the Moon, will be slightly too large, and this will also result in oceans being deformed away from the surface, raising a tide. This is why there are two tides on Earth every day – one beneath the Moon and one on the opposite side of the planet.

The tidal forces are the result of the imbalance between the Moon's gravitational pull and the Centrifugal Force, which is present because the Earth is orbiting around the centre of mass of the Earth-Moon system. Although we usually perceive them because of the large deformation of the surface of the oceans, they are sufficiently large that the Earth's crust is deformed by a measurable amount, shifting the rocks every day by as much as half a metre. This is not a great shift, but GPS systems are adjusted to take account of the changes in the Earth's gravitational field caused by the rock tides, and geologists monitor the impact of these tides on the Earth's fault lines and the potential they have to trigger earthquakes and volcanic eruptions.

Our explanations of rotating storm systems and tides are quite beautiful in my view, because they embody one of the central themes of this book – that apparently complex and disconnected naturally occurring phenomena can be explained using a simple, underlying framework – in this case Newton's laws of gravitation and motion. I don't believe we need a reason to seek an explain for these things beyond the fact that it's interesting and fun. But the explanations of the tides and the rotation of storm systems both benefitted from us jumping between different frames of reference, which is to say looking at physical phenomena from different points of view. This idea is the launch-pad for something deeper. As we discussed at the beginning of this chapter, Albert Einstein elevated the idea that the laws of Nature *must* take the same form in all frames of reference to a fundamental principle. Our Universe is built this way. Implementing this requirement forced him to discard Newton's laws and redraw our intuitive picture of space and time, the grand arena that is so very tempting to take for granted.

Tangential speed of Earth's surface due to rotational motion

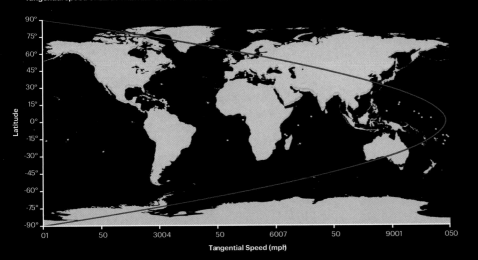

Latitude axis: 90°, 75°, 60°, 45°, 30°, 15°, 0°, -15°, -30°, -45°, -60°, -75°, -90°

Tangential Speed (mph) axis: 01, 50, 3004, 50, 6007, 50, 9001, 050

Tangential Speed (mph)

Calculate your own speed of rotation

At the Equator, the circumference of the Earth is 40,070 kilometres and the day is 24 hours long, so the speed is 1670 kilometres/hour (1037 miles/hour). This decreases by the cosine of your latitude so that at a latitude of 45 degrees, $\cos(45)$ = .707 and the speed is .707 x 1670 = 1180 kilometres/hour. You can use this formula to find the speed of rotation at any latitude.

Einstein's Theory of Special Relativity

That Newton felt it necessary to state that absolute time exists as an assumption is, to my mind, a clear example of his brilliance as a physicist. Newton treated this assumption as we now treat the law of inertia; as an axiom, in agreement with observations at the time, but not provable from first principles.

The subject of motion is unexpectedly rich. Subtleties are evident even in Newton's *Principia*. After dealing with the motion of objects in general, and developing many of the tools that modern-day physicists take for granted, Newton's focus turned to the motion of the planets around the Sun in order to address age-old questions about the tides and the passing of the days, months and years. He was also keenly aware that an understanding of space and time is necessary, and he carefully stated his assumptions about the existence of absolute space and absolute time. That Newton felt it necessary to state that absolute time exists *as an assumption* is, to my mind, a clear example of his brilliance as a physicist. Newton treated this assumption as we now treat the law of inertia; as an axiom, in agreement with observations at the time, but not provable from first principles. It is a remarkable thing that he identified such an assumption and considered it worthy of note, even though in the seventeenth century, and surely today in most people's minds, it must 'go without saying' that there is not much to say about time other than that it is absolute and that it ticks. And so we return to our musings at the beginning of the chapter about Monet's field of poppies, vanished forever – perhaps – with the passing of the years. We are now in a position to explore the tantalising 'perhaps'.

Why did Einstein replace Newton's Laws of Motion?

Central to our exploration of motion has been the idea of an inertial frame of reference. If you've grown weary of the term, if you recall I suggested a drinking game. If you go down this route, you are about to discover a link between vintage wine and memories.

To recap, the idea is that it isn't possible to work out which inertial reference frame you are in; they are all absolutely equivalent to each other and the notion of 'at rest' is always a relative one. In simpler language, this means that you can't tell whether or not you are moving. If you accelerate, the story is different, and fictitious forces appear. Albert Einstein thought very deeply about these ideas – more deeply, in my opinion, than anyone else. Einstein is the archetypal wild-haired, sockless genius. In later life he looked otherworldly, appearing to inhabit an abstract space beyond Earthly trivia alongside his theories. This is, of course, a cliché; Einstein was a great physicist, but he discovered no Royal Road to understanding because no such road exists. He worked hard, thought deeply and learnt how to do sums. That said, his theories of relativity are certainly amongst the greatest of human achievements. Over a century after their publication, they are still part of the essential foundations of modern physics.

Einstein discovered his Theory of Special Relativity by elevating the idea that all inertial reference frames are equivalent to a great principle; an axiom; a fundamental property of our universe. It was his guiding light. To understand why this was so important to Einstein, we need to revisit a concept we explored in Chapter One, symmetry.

The statement that all inertial frames are equivalent is a statement of symmetry. If you recall, symmetry in mathematics and physics means doing something with the result that nothing changes. A square has a particular symmetry in the sense that we can change our point of view by rotating around the square by 90 degrees and everything will look the same. We can ask a similar question about physical laws such as Newton's laws of motion. Do the laws remain the same if we change our perspective? One such symmetry relates to the question: do the laws of Nature look the same in all inertial frames?

Here's another way of looking at it. The laws of physics describe real things and how they behave. Newton's laws, as we've seen, say that a rolling ball will continue to roll in a straight line unless acted upon by a force. If there is a force, the equation that describes what will happen to the ball is F = ma. Let's imagine that we are watching a rolling ball, and we decide to change our perspective by hopping into a different inertial reference frame. We will choose a frame of reference that is flying towards the rolling ball and see how our description of what's happening changes. Note well that 'our description of what's happening' is another way of saying 'the laws of Nature', so what we're really saying is that we want to know how the laws of Nature change. The ball will

Right: Albert Einstein was awarded the Nobel Prize in Physics in 1921. As for other Nobel winners, the idea of symmetry in the laws of Nature was also of great importance.

What do we mean when we speak of symmetries of the laws of Nature, and why do Nobel Prize-winning physicists consider those symmetries so fundamental?

still appear to move in a straight line because there are no forces acting, but its speed will look different. If we fly towards the ball at 20 m/s, and the ball was rolling towards us at 10 m/s, then common sense informs us that we'll see the ball rolling towards us at 30 m/s. As long as we account for the change in speed by adding the speed up in this way, we can use Newton's laws and we'll get all of our predictions correct. Our description of the physics of the situation is left unchanged by our shift in perspective. This is a symmetry of Newton's laws; they remain the same if we jump between inertial frames of reference and keep track of the change in the speeds of all the objects in a simple and intuitive way.

A little piece of jargon: accounting for the change in speed in this way is known as a Galilean Transformation, in honour of Galileo. In full physics mode, we can say that Newton's laws are invariant under Galilean Transformations – this is a symmetry of Newton's laws.

Now let's think about our explanations of storms and tides. These involve situations in which Newton's laws are not the same when we hop into a different frame of reference. In a rotating frame, a rolling ball curves and doesn't continue in a straight line due to the appearance of the Coriolis Force. We account for this by changing Newton's second law in the rotating reference frame. It doesn't look like $F = ma$ any more. It changes into $F + F_{cor} = ma$, where F_{cor} is the Coriolis Force. Similarly, when we think about the origin of the tides, we jumped into the rotating reference frame of the Earth orbiting around the centre of mass of the Earth-Moon system, and saw that $F = ma$ changes into $F + F_{cen} = ma$, where F_{cen} is the Centrifugal Force. In both cases, Newton's laws do *not* look the same in the rotating frames because extra 'fictitious forces' appear. We can say that Newton's laws are not invariant when we transform from an inertial reference frame into a rotating reference frame. Incidentally, the Centrifugal Force and the Coriolis Force are always both present, but for the tides the Coriolis Force isn't important, whilst for cyclones and anti-cyclones, the Centrifugal Force isn't important.

We've taken quite a bit of time to discuss these ideas because they are absolutely central to modern physics – and to understanding why Einstein wrote down his theory of relativity.

Einstein was the first to take a very important and, at first sight, rather odd fact seriously. Unlike Newton's laws, the laws of electricity and magnetism are not invariant under Galilean Transformations. They do not look the same in all inertial frames of reference if you change all the speeds in the way you do for Newton's laws to account for the shift in perspective. This means that Newton's laws and the laws of electricity and magnetism are not consistent with each other! This was the situation that Einstein faced in 1905.

Left: A strike at goal illustrates what these clever physicists were trying to impart – a rolling ball will continue to roll in a straight line unless acted upon by a force.

MAGNETISM, LIGHT, AND MOLECULAR SPINNING TOPS.

Page 122.

The reason why the laws of electricity and magnetism cause a problem is a simple one, but a little bit of history is in order first. During the nineteenth century, the exploration of electricity and magnetism was at the cutting edge of physics. The names of many of the scientists are remembered in the language we use to speak about electricity today: André-Marie Ampère gives his name to the Amp, the unit of electric current, and the Volt is named after Alessandro Volta. The greatest experimental breakthrough came during 1831 and 1832 when, in a series of experiments at the Royal Institution and Royal Society in London, Michael Faraday discovered electromagnetic induction, and in doing so invented the electric generator and laid the foundations for the modern world.

During the 1860s, the Scottish physicist James Clerk Maxwell discovered a unified theoretical description of all electrical and magnetic phenomena. Maxwell's equations are one of the great achievements of the human mind. Einstein later described Maxwell's work as 'the most profound and the most fruitful that physics has experienced since the time of Newton.' The equations are so beautiful that I can't resist showing them to you. To hell with those who think equations reduce the number of sales of popular science books. Here they are:

$$\nabla \cdot E = 0 \qquad \nabla \times E = -\frac{\partial B}{\partial t},$$

$$\nabla \cdot B = 0 \qquad \nabla \times B = \frac{1}{c^2}\frac{\partial E}{\partial t}.$$

The Es and Bs stand for electric and magnetic fields, the basic building blocks of Maxwell's description of electric and magnetic phenomena. Written in this notation, there are only two other letters in the equations: t stands for time and c stands for the speed of light. This is the key that unlocked the door for Einstein. The speed of light enters Maxwell's equations as a constant – a fundamental number that does not change. It is one of the axioms – the building blocks of our universe. It is a speed upon which everyone agrees, irrespective of which frame of reference they are in. This is shocking, and looks like a disaster for physics. How can it make any sense that everyone agrees on the speed of light, irrespective of what frame of reference they are in? Recall our example of jumping between different reference frames and observing a rolling ball. All we had to do was add all the speeds together in the intuitive way encoded into the Galilean Transformations and all is well. Maxwell demolishes this idea.

Imagine someone holding a torch. Light streams out of the torch at the speed of light: 299,792,458 metres per second. Now imagine someone else looks at the situation from a different inertial frame of reference, flying towards the torch at half the speed of light. We might expect that we will be able to describe everything in either frame as long as we add the speeds, in accord with the Galilean Transformations. The person flying towards the torch would conclude that the light whizzes past them at 450,000,000 metres per second – which is c + ½ c. Maxwell's equations demand that this is not the case. They say that both observers measure the speed of light to be precisely equal to 299,792,458 metres per second. The speed of light doesn't change, irrespective of how you look at it. It is a constant – a fundamental property of Nature.

If this sounds weird, it is. I have no way of explaining why, other than to say that our universe is constructed like this. Maxwell's equations are correct. The statement that the speed of light is a constant in *all inertial frames of reference* is on the same footing as the principle of inertia. It is because it is.

Einstein's brilliance – let us call it genius – was to take Maxwell's equations at face value and insist that when we hop between inertial frames of reference we keep the speed of light the same. We are not allowed to add velocities in the way that we have been doing; it is simply wrong. The Galilean Transformations are wrong, and therefore Newton's laws, which possess the symmetry represented by the Galilean Transformations, are also wrong.

Left: This engraving shows a scientist, thought to be James Clerk Maxwell, investigating magnetism, light, and molecular spinning tops.

Maxwell's equations are one of the great achievements of the human mind. Einstein later described Maxwell's work as 'the most profound and the most fruitful that physics has experienced since the time of Newton.'

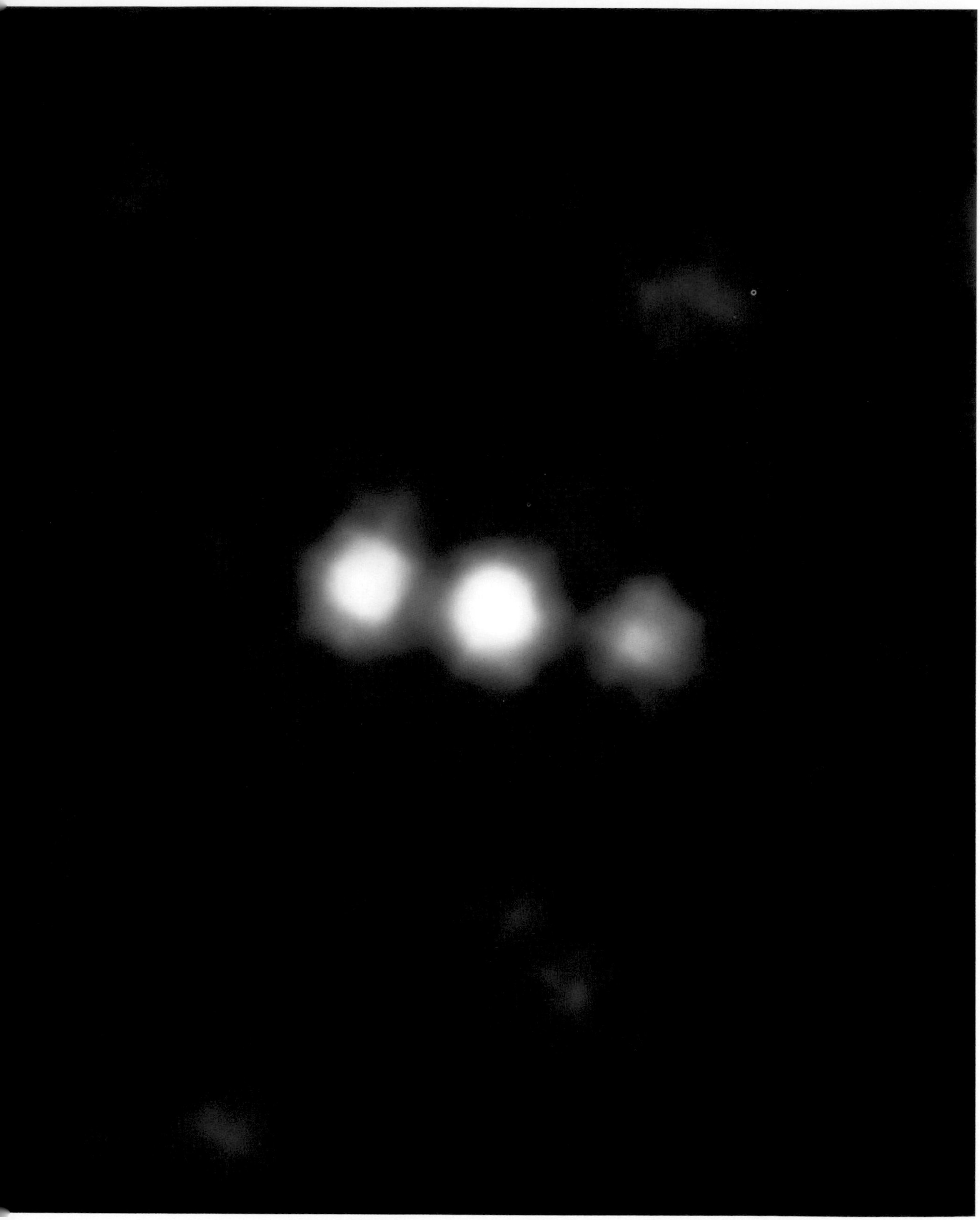

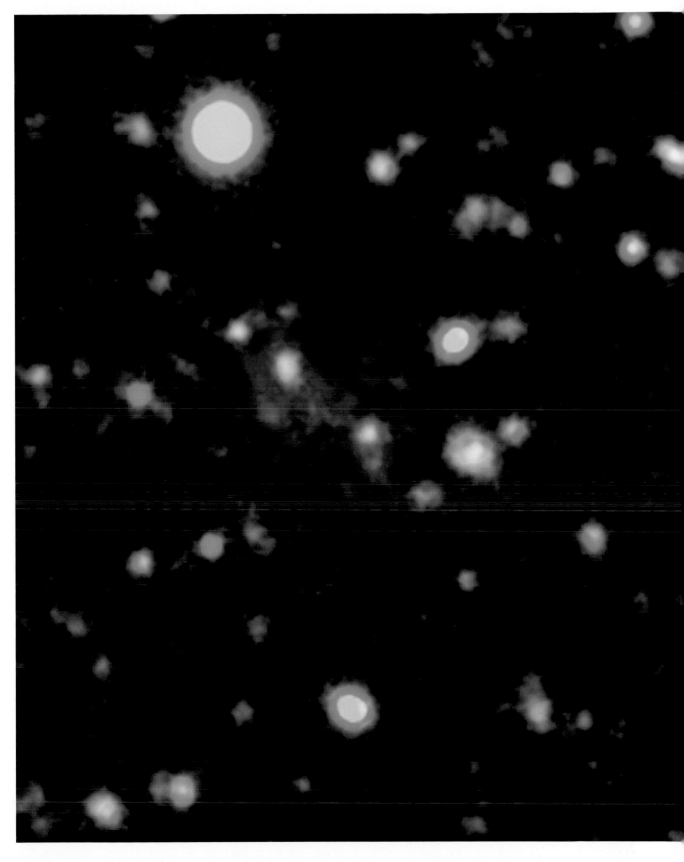

Somewhere in spacetime

We can now bring all these ideas together. Einstein rebuilt physics from the ground up by insisting on two axioms, which are known as Einstein's postulates. The first is one with which we are very familiar indeed.

The laws of physics are the same in all inertial frames of reference.

The second postulate is the one that comes from taking Maxwell's equations at face value:

The speed of light in a vacuum is the same in all inertial frames of reference.

If we were writing a physics textbook, we'd now proceed to derive all the consequences of these two postulates, and in the process discover treasures such as $E = mc^2$ – the statement that mass and energy are interchangeable. This isn't a textbook. Here, we want to explore a very particular consequence of Einstein's two postulates: the idea that space and time are not what they seem.

Previous page: The High Redshift Galaxy Cluster has been a source of some confusion for astronomers. It is one of a number of objects termed 'giant galactic blobs'.

Below: Claude Monet's *Poppy Field* (Giverny). This painting reveals a moment in time – an event – which can help us explore Einstein's theory that space and time are not what they seem.

As the light fades, Monet slips the half-finished canvas under his arm, walks back to his room in the village and closes his door. The click of the lock marks another event, with a different latitude, longitude and height above sea level and a different time; by his watch.

Let's return to the beginning; the moment at which Monet sat down in a field of poppies just outside Argenteuil and, lungs filled with the scents of a late-spring afternoon, dabbed a delicate spot of red paint onto his canvas. The position in space and time of the dab of red paint is known in the language of relativity as an *event*. Because we live in three-dimensional space, we need three numbers to describe the position of the painted poppy on the canvas. These numbers could be the latitude and longitude of the easel in the poppy field and the height of the canvas above sea level. These three numbers specify *where* the event happened. We also need a time and date to specify *when* it happened; noon on 26 May 1873. An event in space and time has four coordinates; three to specify its position in space, and one to specify its position in time.

Now consider another event. As the light fades, Monet slips the half-finished canvas under his arm, walks back to his room in the village and closes his door. The click of the lock marks another event, with a different latitude, longitude and height above sea level and a different time, by his watch. It's now 8pm on 26 May 1873.

Let's imagine that Monet decided to measure the distance between his easel and his door and found it to be precisely 2 kilometres, and that they are at the same height above sea level. This is the distance in space between the two events. The difference in time is 8 hours, by Monet's watch.

Newton, and everyone else before Einstein came along, would agree with the common-sense notion that any observer who decided to measure the distance between Monet's easel and door and the time between the dab of paint and the click of the lock would be in complete agreement with Monet, assuming that their rulers and watches were accurate and synchronised. Einstein discovered that, if he imposed his two postulates, this is not the case. Different observers do not agree on the spatial distance and temporal difference between events. Let's be specific. Imagine that an enterprising French lady with access to a futuristic aircraft was flying past Monet on 26 May 1873 at half the speed of light. She would measure the time difference between Monet's dot on the canvas and the click of his lock to be 9 hours and 14 minutes and the distance between the easel in the poppy field and his door to be 1.73 kilometres. This discrepancy has nothing to do with the way time and distance are measured, or the measuring devices used. Furthermore, neither Monet nor the aviator is wrong; each is absolutely entitled to claim that their measurements are correct. Rather, Einstein discovered that in reality there is no such thing as absolute time and no such thing as absolute space. Let's repeat this, because it's very odd. From the point of view of the aviator, Monet's time passes more slowly than hers, which means that Monet ages more slowly than she does, and Monet really does walk 1.73 kilometres on his way home. The converse is also true. If Monet glanced up and saw the aircraft fly by, he would see the aviator's clock ticking more slowly than his, and he would conclude that she was ageing more slowly than he. He would also conclude that her aircraft is 0.866 times shorter than it appears to her. Arguably he wouldn't have continued to paint a poppy field had this really happened, but the point is that this is not theoretical; the effect is real. Nature really is constructed this way. The slowing down of moving clocks is known as time dilation, and the shrinking of moving objects is called Lorentz Contraction.

If you are comfortable with a bit of mathematics, you'll find a derivation of the result that Monet's clock runs slow as viewed by the aviator, and by how much, on page 146. The conclusion follows directly from Einstein's two postulates, and the argument is quite simple and requires no mathematics beyond Pythagoras's theorem. If you're happy to take our word for it without reference to page 146, then accept it and read on!

The reason why Einstein's theory predicts that distances in space and intervals of time are not the same in different frames of reference are his two postulates – the requirement that the laws of Nature take the same form in all inertial frames of reference and that the speed of light is constant in all inertial frames of reference. These two postulates imply that moving clocks run slow, as proved on page 146. In more precise language, Einstein had to replace the Galilean Transformations, which tell us how to switch between different inertial frames, with a new set of equations called the Lorentz Transformations. Lorentz Transformations leave the speed of light the same, as required by the second postulate, but there is an apparently terrible price to pay: Distances in space and intervals in time do change under Lorentz Transformations: moving rulers shrink and moving clocks run slow!

So where does this leave us? We've discovered that space and time are not as they seem, if we accept that the speed of light must remain constant for all observers. There is no such thing as absolute space, because observers moving at different speeds relative to each other disagree on the distance between events. The comfortable picture of the Universe as a big box, where every star, planet and galaxy has a well-defined place, cannot be right, because the distances between the stars, planets and galaxies cannot be defined in a unique way. Similarly, there is no such thing as absolute time, because it is not possible to define the time between events in a unique way.

This is fun, and strange, but it also presents a serious problem for physics. The problem lies in Einstein's first postulate: *the laws of physics are the same in all inertial frames of reference.* The laws of physics are the tools that we use to predict the outcome of real-world experiments; they are descriptions of Nature. If they are to be the same in all inertial frames, then it follows that they should be constructed out of quantities that are the same in all inertial frames. But the laws of physics we learn at school concern distances measured by rulers and times measured on clocks. Think about Newton's second law of motion, $F = ma$, which describes how fast an object of mass, m, accelerates in response to a force, F. Acceleration is measured in metres per second squared – a quantity that involves changes in distance over some time interval. But since we've discovered that distance intervals and time intervals are not the same in all reference frames, it follows that Newton's laws are not the same either! This looks like a disaster.

It isn't, fortunately, because Einstein found a way out. He discovered that, whilst the distance in space between two events and the difference in time between two events each change, there is a quantity that does *not* change if we switch perspective between inertial frames: the distance in space *and* time, taken together in a very special way.

If we call the distance between Monet's easel and door Δx and the time difference between the dab of red paint and the click of the lock Δt, then the 'distance' $\Delta s^2 = c^2 \Delta t^2 - \Delta x^2$ does not

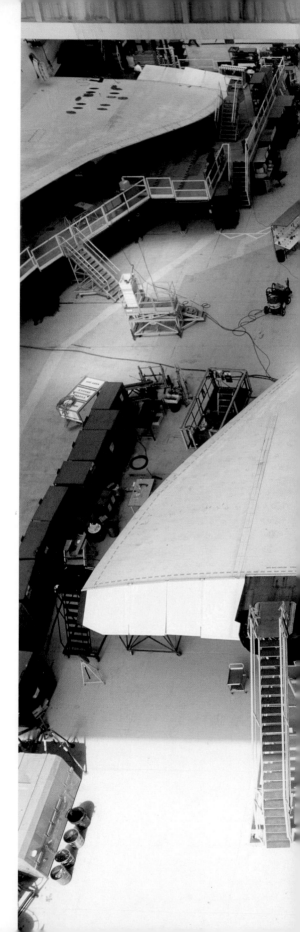

Left: The world's only supersonic passenger airliner, the Concorde, is shown here in the maintenance hangar at Heathrow Airport. The swept-back delta wings are designed to maximise lift generation during take-off and to minimise drag at high speeds. The wing design also provides sufficient stability that horizontal stabilisers are not needed on the tail, unlike conventional passenger aircraft. Concorde made its first commercial flight in 1976 and retired from service in 2003.

change. Both the aviator and Monet agree on Δs, even though they disagree on Δt and Δx. The quantity Δs is known as the distance in spacetime between the two events. The speed of light, c, has entered the equation in a rather subtle way, multiplying the time difference Δt. Why? One thing we can say immediately is that some speed or other had to be there to make the definition of the distance in spacetime sensible. Let's say we chose to measure time differences Δt in seconds and distances between events Δx in metres. We can't simply subtract something in seconds from something in metres – that's like subtracting five apples from ten oranges. But if we multiply the time difference in seconds by a speed, which is measured in metres divided by seconds, then we get the object c Δt, which is measured in metres, and we can happily go ahead and subtract Δx from it. That argument doesn't inform us what value c should take, but it does tell us that it has to be some speed or other.

In an undergraduate lecture course on physics, we would now proceed to consider how energy and momentum are treated in special relativity and show that this special speed can

The fact that distances between events in spacetime are agreed upon by everyone suggests that we should rebuild our laws of Nature out of quantities like Δs, and this is precisely what Einstein did, replacing Newton's laws and quantities familiar to physicists such as energy and momentum with spacetime versions.

be interpreted as the speed of massless particles. Coincidently, as far as we know, photons happen to be massless and therefore travel at the special speed c – and this is why we call it the speed of light.

The fact that distances between events in spacetime are agreed upon by everyone suggests that we should rebuild our laws of Nature out of quantities like Δs, and this is precisely what Einstein did, replacing Newton's laws and quantities familiar to physicists such as energy and momentum with spacetime versions. This is where $E = mc^2$ comes from. I think it's quite satisfying that Nature is constructed in this way. Events, after all, form the narrative of our lives. We don't separate our memories into separate spatial and temporal components. I remember a perfect summer's day in August 1972 when a yellow sun lifted the scents of the lawn and Doppler-shifted bees drowned out the hum of the town. We set up a paddling pool in my parents' garden and played in the water so long we chafed our thighs. I remember this as an event, not a moment with a separate latitude, longitude and time stamp.

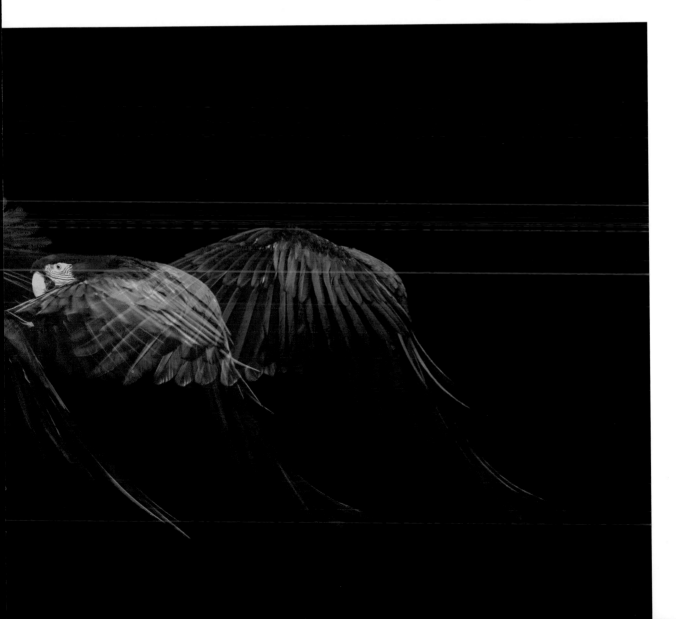

There is a vivid way of visualising these ideas known as a spacetime diagram. In order to draw it, we can represent the position of events in space along the horizontal axis and the position of events in time on the vertical axis, as shown in the diagram opposite. We've neglected two spatial dimensions here for clarity because they don't matter for our argument, and it's hard to draw a four-dimensional diagram on a piece of paper. Let's draw my life as a spacetime diagram. It's important to define precisely what frame of reference we're in when we draw a spacetime diagram. In this case, Oldham Royal Infirmary, where I was born on 3 March 1968, will be our frame of reference (which we'll assume to be an inertial frame). This means that we set up a grid of Oldham rulers and Oldham stopwatches at rest relative to OldhamRoyal Infirmary. We agree to zero the Oldham stopwatches at the moment of my birth, and because I was born inside Oldham Royal Infirmary, the co-ordinates of my birth event are $x = 0$, $ct = 0$, where x is the distance from Oldham Royal Infirmary and t is the time as measured by the Oldham stopwatch at position $x = 0$. We'll label this event '3 March 1968', and it sits at the origin of the spacetime diagram.

We can now add some more events. In August 1972, I was four kilometres away from Oldham Royal Infirmary in my paddling pool. The time on the Oldham watch at that point reads 4½ years. On 3 March 1989 I was in Florence, Italy, on a tour bus after playing a show with my band Dare while supporting the Swedish rock band, Europe. I know. That's 21 years as measured on the Oldham watch, and I'm around 2000 kilometres from Oldham Royal Infirmary. One more. On 2 September 2009 I was in one of my favourite countries, Ethiopia, filming for *Wonders of the Solar System* at the Erta Ale lava lake with my friendly guard from the Afar tribe.

I could mark every event in my life this way, as measured by the time on the Oldham watches and the distance from Oldham Royal Infirmary. The resulting line on the spacetime diagram is called my worldline. It represents every moment in my life at the locations measured by the Oldham watches and the Oldham rulers. Remember Hermann Weyl's evocative quote: 'Only to the gaze of my consciousness, crawling along the lifeline of my body, does a section of this world come to life as a fleeting image in space which continuously changes in time'. This is what he meant.

Only to the gaze of my consciousness, crawling along the lifeline of my body, does a section of this world come to life as a fleeting image in space which continuously changes in time.

There is another feature of the spacetime diagram that we must mention; the diagonal lines passing through 3 March 1968. These are known as a lightcone, and lightcones play a very important role in relativity. To understand what they are, imagine that someone decides to flash a beam of light out into the Universe from Oldham at the moment of my birth – perhaps in celebration, who knows? After one second, the light would have travelled a distance of 1 light second. We would mark the point in spacetime that the beam of light reached as an event at position 1 second x c on the time axis, and 1 second x c on the space axis. After 2 seconds the light beam would have travelled 2 light seconds, and so on. This light cone, therefore, is the worldline of a light beam that originates at the origin of the diagram – the event of my birth. It extends all the way across the spacetime diagram at an angle of 45 degrees. My worldline wanders around inside the lightcone, as it must because nothing can travel faster than the speed of light. To see this, look at the event marked 'X' on the diagram. It is something that happened far away. Let's imagine that the event is a little alien boy on a planet 50 light years away, paddling in his swimming pool, and that, according to the Oldham watches, this event occurred at the same time as my pool adventure in 1972. We say that these events are simultaneous in the Oldham frame of reference. You'd have to travel much faster than light to get there if you were present at my birth – 50 light years in 4½ years, in fact, and this is not allowed because nothing can travel faster than light. You may have heard this many times, and wondered why. 'It's impossible to travel faster than the speed of light, and certainly not desirable as one's hat keeps blowing off', said Woody Allen. We'll gain insight into why it's not allowed in a moment.

The lightcone in the top half of the diagram is known as the future lightcone of my birth, because it marks out the region in spacetime that I could possibly visit or influence. I could not influence events outside of the lightcone in any way because I would have to travel faster than light to reach them.

There is also a lightcone in the bottom half of the diagram, which represents the time before my birth. This is called the past lightcone of my birth. My parents' worldlines must be contained within the past lightcone, because they obviously influenced it. What's more, every one of my ancestors' worldlines, stretching back to the origin of life on Earth 4 billion years ago, must also be contained within the past lightcone. No events outside the past lightcone could have influenced my birth, because no signal could have made it from them to Oldham on 3 March 1968 without travelling faster than the speed of light.

Let's now ask a question. What does this diagram look like from the point of view of our intrepid French aviator, flying past at a constant speed? We already know that she would see the Oldham watches run slow and the Oldham rulers shrink, so she would place events on my worldline at different places on her spacetime diagram. For simplicity, let's imagine that the aviator agrees to synchronise her watches with the Oldham watches at the moment of my birth, and agrees that my birth in Oldham Royal Infirmary also occurs at position zero on her space axis. In other words, the origins of the two diagrams coincide at $t = 0$.

My life events: Me in my paddling pool on that hot, sunny day in August 1972, and filming in Ethiopia on 2 September 2009.

Right: The Spacetime diagram of my life from Albert perspective, sitting in Oldham Royal Infirmary.

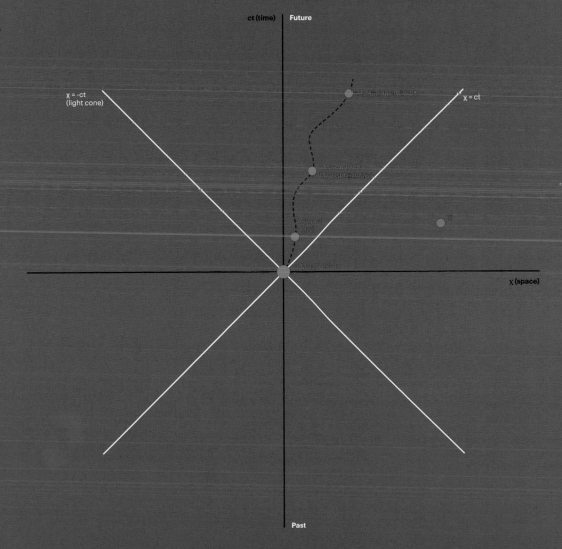

Right: The spacetime diagram from the perspective of the aviator, flying at high velocity in the +x direction relative to me. I've labelled the axis as ct' and x' to emphasise that the time and space co-ordinates of the events are different in the aviator's frame of reference. The event at the origin – my birth – labelled 3 March 1968, remains at the origin because we agreed that both frames of reference have their origins coincident at t = t' = 0.

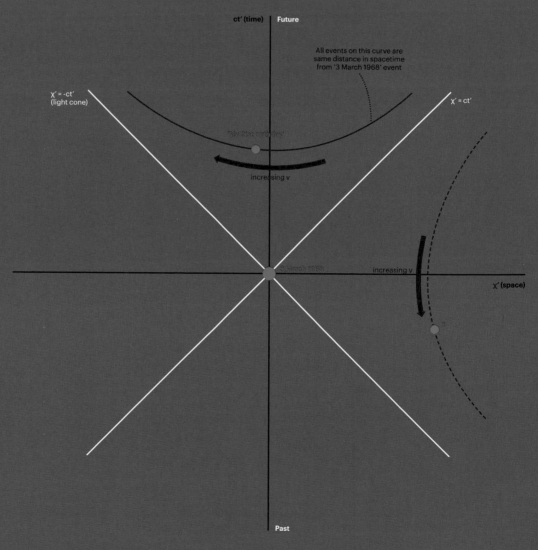

ct' (time)   Future

x' = -ct'
(light cone)

All events on this curve are
same distance in spacetime
from '3 March 1968' event

x' = ct'

'My 21st birthday'

increasing v

'3 March 1968'

increasing v

x' (space)

Past

Although the observer sitting diligently at Oldham Royal Infirmary will not agree with the aviator on the time difference and spatial distance between events on my worldline, they will both agree on the distances in spacetime between the events, given by $\Delta s^2 = c^2\Delta t^2 - \Delta x^2$. This means that Δx and Δt must change in a very specific way, such that Δs always remains the same. The aviator's spacetime diagram is shown in the illustration opposite. Notice that the lightcones do not change, in accord with Einstein's second postulate – both the aviator and the Oldham observer must agree on the speed of light. Now look at the position of the event that represents my twenty-first birthday. We know that the aviator's clocks will tick at a different rate to the Oldham clock, and that the aviator's rulers will be a different length to the Oldham rulers. But we also know that whatever distance and time difference she measures between the '3 March 1968' event and my 'twenty-first birthday' event, they must obey the rule that Δs^2 between the events remains the same. We've drawn all the possible positions of my twenty-first birthday on the aviator's spacetime diagram as a curve. The actual position she marks will depend on how fast she flies by and in what direction. Here, we've assumed that she flies close to the speed of light in the direction of Oldham's positive x direction. Something interesting is immediately obvious. My twenty-first birthday always stays in the future lightcone of my birth. This must be the case, because my birth caused my twenty-first birthday! We'd be in trouble if, from someone else's point of view, my birthday drifted out of the lightcone of my birth and couldn't have influenced it!

So far so good. Look now, however, at the event marked 'X' – the little alien boy in his paddling pool – that lies outside the lightcone of my birth. This event must also maintain its distance in spacetime from 3 March 1968, but to do that it has to move on a different curve. Crucially, it doesn't have to stay in my future. For certain relative velocities between the aviator and Oldham, the event appears, from her perspective, to be in my past! This deserves an exclamation mark. The time-ordering of my birth and event X have been reversed from the perspective of the aviator. Is Einstein's beautiful theory producing nonsense? Can it really be true that the time-ordering of events in spacetime is not agreed upon by all observers? Yes it is true, but this isn't a problem, because event X always stays outside of my future and past lightcones. This means that my birth could not have influenced it, and it could not have influenced my birth. The two events are causally disconnected. This means that it doesn't actually matter what time-ordering we ascribe to such events (which are called 'spacelike separated' events) because they cannot, even in principle, have anything to do with each other. Let's give a specific example to make this clearer.

Imagine that, at the exact moment of my birth in my frame of reference, a huge explosion occurred on the Sun. The Sun is eight light minutes away, which means that the explosion cannot influence anything on Earth for at least eight minutes, which is the time it takes a light beam to travel from the Sun to the Earth. These events are 'spacelike separated', so therefore an astronaut flying past us at high speed might see the explosion happen before, or after, my birth. The time-ordering would be changed. But who cares? What difference does it make? None at all, because the events cannot influence each other.

Notice, however, that after eight minutes the shockwave from the explosion could hit the Earth and destroy Oldham, which would, to use the local vernacular, piss on my chips. Remember, though, that we are talking about events in spacetime. My birth is an event, and the explosion is an event, and my birth is outside the lightcone of the explosion and therefore cannot be stopped by it. My unfortunate death eight minutes later is another event, and that event *is* in the lightcone of the explosion. Nobody will see the time-ordering of these events reversed. Events that are in each other's past or future lightcones are known as 'timelike separated' events, and their ordering cannot be changed.

It is quite remarkable that everything works out, albeit in a rather subtle way. But there is a sting in the tail. Think about my birth event – '3 March 1968' – and event X again. In the Oldham frame of reference, event X lies in my future. In another frame of reference, event X happens simultaneously with my birth, and in the aviator's frame of reference it lies in my past. Events that happen simultaneously in one frame of reference are not simultaneous in another frame of reference. Whilst this doesn't cause problems, as we've seen, it does raise an interesting question. If there is no clear distinction between the future and the past, and indeed if an event lies in someone's future according to one observer and in their past according to another, then what do the concepts of future and past actually mean? When I was born, had event X happened or not? According to me, it hadn't. According to the aviator, it had. This suggests that, in the theory of relativity, events have an existence in spacetime beyond our local concept of past, present and future.

Let's make this more vivid. Recall that event 'X' represents a little alien boy playing in a paddling pool on a planet 50 light years away from Earth. In the Oldham frame of reference, this event happened simultaneously with my summer's day in 1972. Now look at the illustration opposite, which shows how this event appears to the aviator travelling at high speed relative to me. There exist frames of reference in which the alien boy's paddling pool day is in my past, and my entire life, including my paddling pool day, is in his future. My summer's day hasn't happened yet. It's out there in spacetime, in his future, albeit in a region of spacetime inaccessible to him. From my perspective, my 1972 paddling pool day is in my memory. I remember it with fondness. Surely it's gone, hasn't it?

That summer's day hasn't happened yet. It's out there in spacetime, in his future, albeit in a region of spacetime inaccessible to him.

If we take Einstein's theory of relativity at face value, there is no sense in which the past has happened and the future is yet to happen. A spacelike separated event can be in someone's future from one perspective, and in their past from another. This doesn't matter in the sense that such events can have no influence on each other, provided that nothing can travel faster than the speed of light. This is why the speed of light as a universal speed limit is so important in relativity. It protects cause and effect. But this behaviour does raise the question of whether all events that can happen and have happened in the history of the Universe are, in some sense, 'out there'. This idea is known as the Block Universe. Spacetime can be pictured as a four-dimensional blob over which we move, encountering the events on our worldline as we go. We are forced to move over the blob at the speed of light, which from our own personal perspective means that we have to move into the future at a speed of 1 second per second.[2] You have to get old because of the geometry of spacetime.

We should emphasise that, while the Block Universe is a consequence of relativity, it is not necessarily correct. We know that relativity is not fully consistent with quantum theory, and most physicists hope and expect that a quantum theory of spacetime will be developed at some point. Whether this will allow for a more intuitive picture of past and future is unknown. We must always remember that physical theories such as relativity are models of reality that produce predictions that agree with experiment – a test which both the Special and General theories have passed with flying colours for over a century. Is the Block Universe actually real, or just an artefact of Einstein's model? Who knows? But I think its implications are at the very least worth thinking about. On the downside, there is no free will in the Block Universe. All the events in our future 'exist', waiting for us to barrel along our worldline to intersect them. I don't care personally whether I have free will or not. It makes no difference to me. But I find the other side of the coin quite wonderful. In the Block Universe, the past is also out there. My idyllic summer's day in 1972, with my Mum and Dad and sister, doesn't exist only in my memory. It hasn't gone, although I can never revisit it. It is still there; all those people, all those moments, always and forever, somewhere in spacetime. I love that.

[2] You can see this from the definition of distance in spacetime. Set $\Delta x = 0$, because you are in your own rest frame, and note that $\Delta s / \Delta t = c$.

Spacetime calculations

Below: Monet and the aviator.

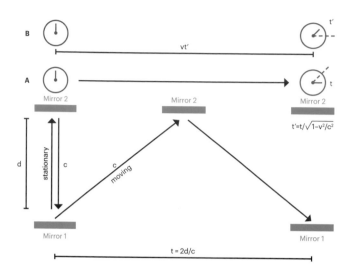

Below: Hyperbola.

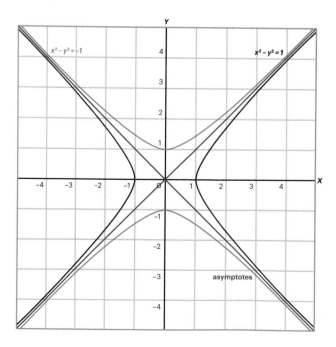

Monet and the aviator

We can use Einstein's two postulates to show why it is that the aviator and Monet measure different intervals of time between any pair of events. This is surely one of the most bizarre ideas ever to come out of a human being's head. It is all the more bizarre for being demonstrably correct. The argument is surprisingly simple. First let us imagine a special type of clock – at the end we will show that the argument must work for any type of clock, but for now we will consider a 'light clock'. A light clock is made up of two parallel mirrors with a beam of light bouncing back and forth between them. Suppose that the two mirrors are a distance d apart. If light travels at a speed c it will take a time $t=2d/c$ for the light to travel from one mirror to the other and back again, as determined by someone who is holding the clock (more formally, we might say 'by someone who is at rest relative to the clock'). Let us refer to the person holding this clock as (and here we will not bother exercising our imagination) 'person A'. Now let's introduce a second person: 'person B'. If person A and person B are both at rest relative to each other then both will clearly agree on how long the light clock takes to tick (let's call one tick of the clock the time it takes for the light to make one round-trip, i.e. $t=2d/c$). Pre-Einstein, and according to common sense, we'd say that the clock takes this time t to tick, regardless of what it is doing or who is doing the measuring. But that is wrong, as we are about to show.

To see how time is not absolute, let's put person A and their clock on a train (Einstein often used trains to explain his theories), and person B on the platform. Now let us consider how the clock is understood by person B. The top illustration shows the path taken by the light as it makes one tick of the clock.

According to person B, the clock moves a distance equal to vt' in one tick, where v is the speed of the train and t' is the duration of the tick. At this stage we will resist the temptation to say that t' (the time of one tick of the light clock according to person B) is equal to t (the time of one tick according to person A). From the figure we can see the path that the light beam traces out as it moves up and down. Obviously, the light travels further according to person B than it does according to person A. Using Pythagoras's Theorem, the distance the light travels according to person B is $2\sqrt{(vt'/2)^2+d^2}$, whilst for person A it is just $2d$ (notice that it would be just $2d$ for person B if $v=0$, i.e. if the train isn't moving). The fact that the light travels further according to person B is not by itself anything to get excited about, because the train is moving. The next step is the shocker.

Einstein's second postulate states that the speed of light in a vacuum is the same in all inertial frames of reference. It follows that person B must agree that the light moves at a speed c. If the light moves at speed c according to both A and B, and if the light travels further according to person B than it does according to person A, then it follows that the light must take longer to make the round trip according to person B than it does according to person A. This is worth re-reading and thinking about, because it is surprising.

We have just proven that, if Einstein's second postulate is correct, it logically follows that the light clock ticks more slowly according to person B (who is on the platform) than it does according to person A (who is on the train). Since we went to the trouble of invoking Pythagoras and a little algebra to write down how far the light travels in one tick according to person B, we can easily write down by how much the moving clock slows down according to person B. The time taken for one tick, according to person B, is the distance the light travels in one tick, divided by the speed of light c, i.e. $t'=2\sqrt{(vt'/2)^2+d^2}/c$. Notice that the time we want to know (t') is on both sides of this equation, which means we have to re-arrange the equation using some low-level algebra. Squaring both sides of the equation gives $t'^2=4(vt'/2)^2/c^2+4d^2/c^2$, which can be re-arranged to read $t'^2(1-v^2/c^2)=4d^2/c^2$. Now we can write down what t' is in terms of v, d and c. It is just $t'=2d/c/\sqrt{1-v^2/c^2}$. And since $t=2d/c$ we can write down that $t'=t/\sqrt{1-v^2/c^2}$. And that is our final answer. So long as v is smaller than c, the square root makes sense and t' is always bigger than t, which means that the person on the platform must

conclude that the person on the train is holding a clock which is taking longer to tick than it would if the clock were not moving. As an aside, the factor $1/\sqrt{1-v^2/c^2}$ appears very often in relativity, and is known as the Lorentz factor or Gamma factor, and given the symbol γ.

Before we start to claim that the world is an amazing place, we ought to convince ourselves that the result we just found is not just some peculiar feature of light clocks. First, let's be clear about why we chose to think about a light clock in the first place. We did that because we could make direct use of Einstein's postulate about the speed of light being the same in all inertial frames. If we had been thinking about pendulum clocks then we couldn't have exploited that postulate so easily. But, with more work, we could have done this calculation using pendulum clocks, or heart beats, or any other type of clock, and the conclusion would have been exactly the same. You can see that this has to be true if Einstein's second postulate is correct:

The laws of physics are the same in all inertial frames of reference,

or, more colloquially, 'it is impossible to tell who is moving and who is standing still'. Suppose that the slowing of the light clock is some peculiarity of light clocks and that it doesn't apply to other clocks. If that were true, person A (on the train) would notice that their light clock was running slow compared to their wristwatch. But that observation would be enough for them to conclude that they are moving, which would be in conflict with Einstein's first postulate. The only way to keep that postulate alive is to say that if person A's light clock takes longer to tick according to person B then so too must person A's wristwatch. It is time to acknowledge that the world is far more remarkable than we had any right to suppose. We have demonstrated that, if Einstein's two postulates are correct, two people in motion with respect to each other age at different rates.

To finish off, we can compute the time interval between the two events we discussed in the text: the time between Monet placing a dab of paint on his canvas and the turn of the lock in his door. According to Monet's timepiece, the interval was eight hours.

But, according to the formula we just derived, the time interval between the same two events as measured by the aviator is 8 hours$/\sqrt{1-\frac{1}{4}}=9.24$ hours.

Hyperbola

The distance between two events in spacetime, $\Delta s^2=c^2\Delta t^2-\Delta x^2$. Physically, for any two events, although the distance in space Δx and the distance in time Δt will change when measured by observers in different frames of reference, they must change such that the distance in spacetime, Δs, remains constant. Mathematically, this is the equation of a curve known as a hyperbola. Let's consider a specific example, equivalent to setting the distance between two events in spacetime to be 1 unit. There are two versions of this 'unit hyperbola', which have the equations $x^2-y^2=1$ and $x^2-y^2=-1$ These are shown in the bottom illustration opposite. If x^2-y^2 is equal to 1, there are two curves; one in the upper half plane and one in the lower half plane. This is the situation for events that are 'timelike separated', i.e. causally connected to each other. For such events, the distance in space between the events, Δx^2, is always less than the distance light could have travelled during the time interval between the events $c^2\Delta t^2$. The spacetime interval Δs^2 will therefore always be positive. If the events are not causally connected, which is to say that the spatial distance between them Δx^2 is always greater than the distance light could have travelled during the time interval between them $c^2\Delta t^2$, then we have the curve $x^2-y^2=-1$. These events are known as "spacelike separated". As we note in the text, the important point is that when we change between inertial frames, the events slide around the spacetime diagram on these four curves, but never hop between them: causally connected events (timelike separated) *always* have their time ordering persevered, but causally disconnected events (spacelike separated) need not.

The Moth and the Flame

How did life begin? I think this is one of the two most interesting questions in science, and the most important question in the history of human thought. Cathedrals have been built, wars have been fought and empires have risen and fallen as innumerable demagogues have sought universal agreement for their guesses.

How did the Universe begin? I think this is the other interesting scientific question, but we know less about it at the moment. There are speculative theories that suggest the Universe could be eternal, and that there was no beginning. If this is the case, then the Universe has always existed and the question is answered: It didn't begin. Whether or not this would be a satisfying answer is up to you. I'd be comfortable with it.

Irrespective of what happened at the beginning of time, we know there was a period 13.8 billion years ago when the part of the Universe that we can see today, containing over 350 billion large galaxies and with a diameter of over 90 billion light years, was compressed into a region of space smaller than a single atom. No life could have existed in such extreme physical conditions, so even if the Universe existed in some form before the Big Bang, it's safe to say that no complex physical structures would have made it through. The observable universe must therefore have been devoid of life at some point in the past, and life must have begun spontaneously somewhere within it, at some point during the last 13.8 billion years. The word 'spontaneously' is worth defining here, because it crops up a lot in discussions about the origin of life. In saying that

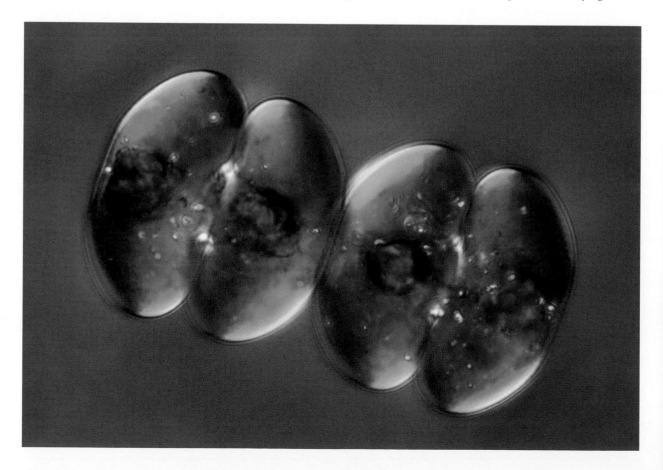

Below: The Blue Marble
– Earth in all its glory,
as seen on 6 July 2015.

'Did I request thee, Maker, from my
clay to mould me man? Did I solicit thee.
From the darkness to promote me?'
— *John Milton*, Paradise Lost

Left: Polarised light
micrograph of two
Cosmarium sp. desmid
daughter cells just after
dividing. Desmids are
a group of feshwater
single-celled algae that
have intricate cell walls.

life appeared spontaneously, we are asserting that life is a
physical process that emerged as a result of the action of the
laws of nature. If we say that the Earth formed spontaneously,
we mean that nobody built it; by saying that living things
appeared spontaneously, we mean the same thing.

The first atomic nuclei formed in the initial minute or so
following the Big Bang, and the first atoms formed in large
numbers when the Universe was 380,000 years old. The
first stars ignited around 100 million years later, and these
assembled the first carbon atoms. It is unlikely that the rich
chemistry of life could have begun spontaneously without
carbon, oxygen and a handful of the heavier elements beyond
the hydrogen and helium atoms that existed before the stars.
Life could have got going anywhere in the Universe after this
time, and may well have done; we don't know.

The Earth formed 4.54 billion years ago out of the
primordial cloud around the young Sun. It is safe to assume
that there was no life on Earth in the early years following
her formation; the conditions were too violent and changeable.
There is good evidence that life had gained a foothold on
Earth around 3.5 billion years ago, and possibly much earlier –
we'll discuss this evidence later. Therefore, we will assume that
Earth was once a lifeless world, and that living things appeared
at some point in the first billion years after its formation.

Nothing that we've said in these opening paragraphs is
controversial from a scientific perspective, but there is one
assumption we'll make which is at least contestable. We will
assume that life began on Earth, rather than arrived here
from space. Since we have discovered no life on planets beyond
Earth, this is reasonable, but it is possible that life began on
Mars, or perhaps even on comets in the outer Solar System,
and was delivered to Earth by impacts from space. This theory
is known as panspermia. Unlikely as it may sound, it is a
testable theory, and that puts it firmly in the realm of science.

It is certainly possible that we could discover life on Mars
over the next few decades, and if the microbial Martians
share our biochemistry and our genetic code, we might be
forced to postulate a common origin on either planet, or
perhaps somewhere else in the Solar System. This would make
the search for the origin of life more difficult, because it is
far easier to explore our own planet's deep history than it is to
explore the history of another world. The only way to find out
is to do the science, and this is one of the reasons why we send
spacecraft to Mars and the potentially life-supporting moons
of Jupiter and Saturn. It goes without saying, however, that we
shouldn't stop searching for the origin of life on Earth whilst
we build spacecraft to search for life beyond it.

Under the assumption that life began on Earth, it must
have been the case that the basic chemistry of life existed on
our planet before living things emerged, and that sometime
and somewhere chemistry became biology. There is no precise
definition of what 'becoming biology' means, but it is worth
emphasising that biology is just a word for (very) complex
chemistry. Living things are constructed from the same set
of chemical elements as inanimate things, and they obey the
same laws of nature. In this sense we can assert that the Earth
is our ancestor and creator, and we would like to know how,
where and when the transition from geochemistry to
biochemistry occurred.

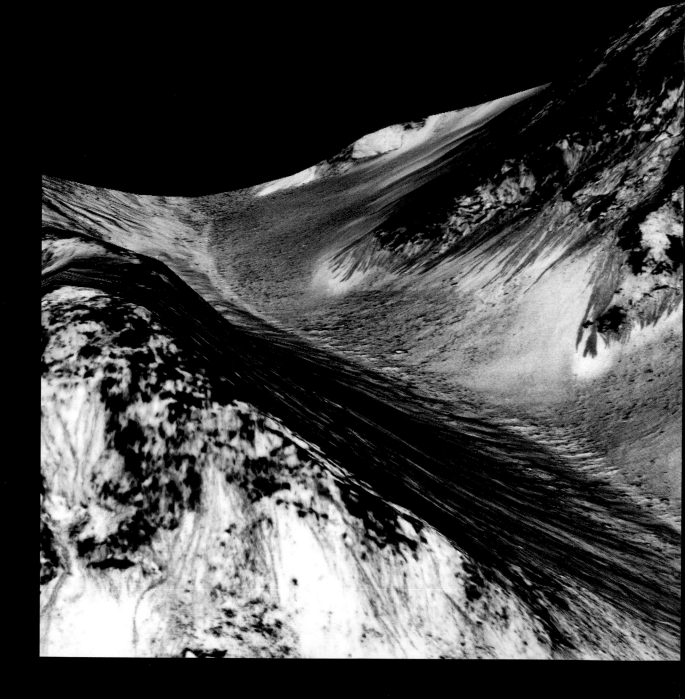

Above: The dark, narrow streaks that mark the slopes of the Hale Crater on Mars in this NASA image from 2015 provide more evidence that liquid may indeed flow on the planet.

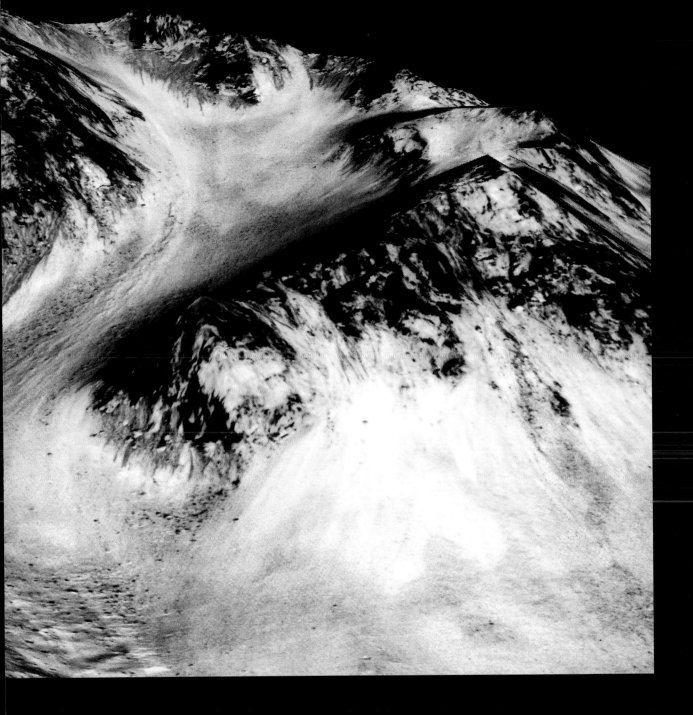

Chemistry is all about the movement of electrons

iving things are made out of simple building blocks with complex interactions. This is obvious in one sense, because everything in the Universe is made out of simple building blocks with complex interactions. We saw in Chapter One that, at the deep sub-atomic level, there are only three building blocks of everyday matter: up quarks, down quarks and electrons. At a higher level, there are protons and neutrons, and higher still are the 92 naturally occurring chemical elements found on Earth. Nobody other than chemistry students or Tom Lehrer remembers all their names, but I am sure virtually every reader of this book will know that they can be laid out in a pattern known as the periodic table, shown on page 158. Each element has a different number of protons in its atomic nucleus, and an equal number of electrons surrounding it; hydrogen has 1 proton and 1 electron, carbon has 6 protons and 6 electrons, and so on. Chemical and biochemical processes are about the sharing and transfer of electrons between elements, allowing molecules to be formed and broken apart.

It's an alien world that is as beautiful as it is toxic, and one of the few places on the planet where we can glimpse one of the pure ingredients that make up the matter of Earth.

Above and below: Indonesian miners carry baskets loaded with sulphur from the crater of the Ijen volcano. More than 300 traditional miners work there under extremely difficult conditions.

Right: Mount Ijen, lit up by its blue flames at dawn.

All the elements beyond element 92, Uranium, were constructed in laboratories, usually by the bombardment of heavy atomic nuclei by neutrons, or by forcing lighter elements to fuse together. The heaviest goes by the name of Ununoctium, and has 118 protons and 176 neutrons in its nucleus. This exotic nucleus is highly unstable and lives for less than a millisecond.

The periodic table is more than just a pictorial arrangement of the elements; it is the key to understanding how and why elements react together to form molecules. The vertical columns, called groups, contain elements with similar chemical properties. The reason for this is that all the elements in a particular group have the same number of electrons in their outer shells, and it is these electrons that are available for sharing or donating to other atoms; they are the particles that make chemistry happen. We explored the structure of oxygen and hydrogen atoms in some detail in Chapter One. Hydrogen has a single electron. Oxygen has 8 electrons, of which 2 sit close into the nucleus and play no part in chemical reactions. The remaining 6 populate its outer shell, and 2 of these are on their own. Oxygen would dearly like 2 more to complete its outer shell, and it will take them from other atoms given half a chance. This is why hydrogen and oxygen

will get together, given a very tiny nudge, to form H_2O. I am aware that this anthropomorphic language is a bit unscientific, but to be honest I don't care. I hope it makes the point, which is that it is the arrangement of electrons inside the atoms of the different chemical elements that leads to chemistry.

Sulphur has 16 electrons, of which 10 fit close into the nucleus, leaving 6 in its outer shell, just like oxygen. This means that sulphur, just like oxygen, will grab 2 electrons from other atoms if it can. In the presence of hydrogen it will form the molecule hydrogen sulphide, H_2S, one of the constituents of the Earth's primordial atmosphere. Carbon has 4 electrons in its outer shell, and it shares them all to form compounds like carbon dioxide, CO_2. Below carbon in the periodic table is silicon, which also has 4 electrons in its outer shell, and it forms similar compounds such as silicon dioxide, SiO_2, and so on. As we discussed in Chapter One, electrons are arranged in this highly structured way around atomic nuclei in accord with quantum theory, which is part of the fundamental set of the laws of nature. The important point is that electrons can be transferred or shared between the atoms of different elements, and this is what drives the formation of molecules. Chemistry is all about the movement of electrons, and the movement of electrons can lead to complexity.

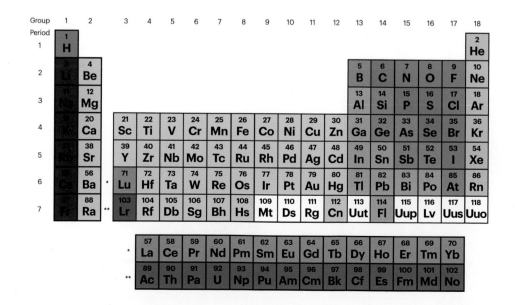

Left: The periodic table, showing the tabular arrangement of the chemical elements.

Right: A firefly squid glowing with rare luminescence. The reaction between oxygen and luciferyl-adenylate results in the release of energy as blue light.

FRANKENSTEIN:

OR,

THE MODERN PROMETHEUS.

BY THE AUTHOR OF
THE LAST MAN, PERKIN WARBECK,
&c. &c.

REVISED, CORRECTED,
AND ILLUSTRATED WITH A NEW INTRODUCTION.
BY THE AUTHOR.

LONDON:
RICHARD BENTLEY, NEW BURLINGTON STREET:
BELL AND BRADFUTE EDINBURGH;
J. CUMMING, DUBLIN.
1839.

Left: The manuscript of Mary Shelley's *Frankenstein* gave few clues as to its authorship; this and the dark nature of the book made it a notorious novel at the time of publication.

Below: The story of Victor Frankenstein and the creation of his monster brought into public consciousness the debate about the ethics of bringing life from dead matter. This cartoon from 1836 depicts a corpse being revived by a primitive galvanic battery.

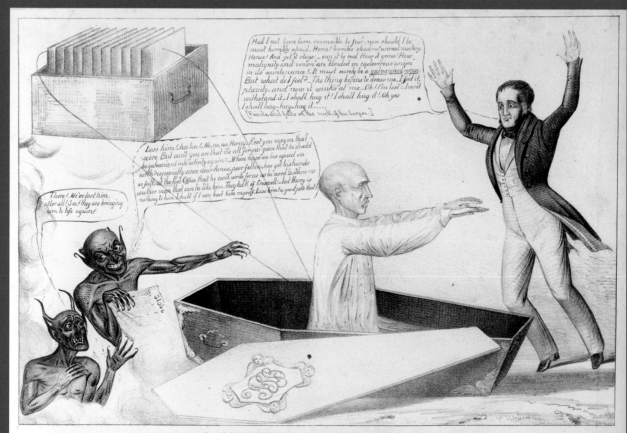

A GALVANIZED CORPSE

Frankenstein's Monsters

It's easy to overlook the philosophical, intellectual and theological storms that the merger between observational astronomy and theoretical physics precipitated.

Any discussions about the historical details of the emergence of the modern scientific worldview are at least partly subjective, and academics spend their careers exploring the subject. If a working physicist is asked to identify the first recognisably modern scientific theory, it is likely they will point to Newton's *Principia* of 1687, not least because Newtonian physics is still in use today and is taught as part of a twenty-first-century degree course. If you want to send a spacecraft to Pluto, you make the navigational calculations using Newton's laws. *Principia* provides a complete and self-consistent model for the geometry and dynamics of the Solar System, with the Sun at the centre and the Earth orbiting around with the rest of the planets. If there was anybody left in 1687 arguing that the Earth occupies a unique physical place, stationary beneath the stars at the centre of creation, they would certainly have had to shut up when presented with a copy of the *Principia*.

The transition from furious debate about an Earth-centred cosmos to the near-universal acceptance of our physical demotion was relatively rapid once Copernicus and others had opened the intellectual floodgates during the sixteenth century. It's easy to overlook the philosophical, intellectual and theological storms that the merger between observational astronomy and theoretical physics precipitated.

Newton was born in 1643, only a year after Galileo died, and Galileo famously encountered quite serious resistance to his support for an orbiting Earth. I've written of my admiration for Kepler's beautiful writing in 'On the Six-cornered Snowflake'; a distinctly modern voice suffused with wit, curiosity and a careful approach to the exploration of nature echoes down the centuries. Galileo was possessed of a similar confidence and amusing turn of phrase. Here he is, writing to Kepler in 1610, taking a magnificently belligerent swipe at the Earth-centred-Universe lobby;

'My dear Kepler, I wish that we might laugh at the remarkable stupidity of the common herd. What do you have to say about the principal philosophers of this academy who are filled with the stubbornness of an asp and do not want to look at either the planets, the moon or the telescope, even though I have freely and deliberately offered them the opportunity a thousand times? Truly, just as the asp stops its ears, so do these philosophers shut their eyes to the light of truth.'

Galileo would have been at home on Twitter.

Our physical demotion from the centre of all things was well established by the end of the seventeenth century and has continued relentlessly ever since. The entirety of our observable universe is an irrelevant pocket of dust in the wider cosmos, which extends way beyond the visible horizon and is conceivably infinite in extent, and I think society has come to terms with this sort of physical irrelevance. It's hard to look at the Hubble Ultra Deep Field Image, containing over ten thousand galaxies in a piece of the night sky you'd cover very comfortably with an outstretched thumb, and feel important. Our spiritual demotion, however, is an entirely different matter. By spiritual demotion, I mean the realisation that our very existence has no more significance than our physical location. This is surely the case if life is the inevitable result of the action of the same set of natural laws that formed the stars and planets. Earth must be one of countless billions of living worlds in the Milky Way galaxy alone. This is absolutely not to suggest that our civilisation is not worth celebrating and fighting to preserve – it is my view that civilisations may be extremely rare, even if life is common.

It is possible to make an argument that there are only a handful of civilisations in the Milky Way galaxy today – perhaps we are the only one? – and this makes planet Earth a rare and valuable natural phenomenon. Value is in the eye of the beholder, and whilst it would be irrational to attach any universal significance to our temporary existence in a possibly infinite cosmos, I do not see any contradictions raised by the use of the word. Intelligence brings meaning to the Universe, albeit locally and temporarily. Our existence obviously means something to you and me, and I do not accept that our physical irrelevance and temporal transience devalues our lives one iota.

This is territory over which philosophy and theology still claim partial dominion, but science inevitably wanders into this intellectual no-man's-land because to discuss the origin of life is to discuss the origin of humanity, with all the intellectual baggage that brings. Is it possible that my feelings, my morality, my hopes, fears and loves will be explained by some future biological *Principia*, as surely as the motions of the planets are explained by Newton? Is my apparent freedom of will an illusion resulting from the action of deterministic

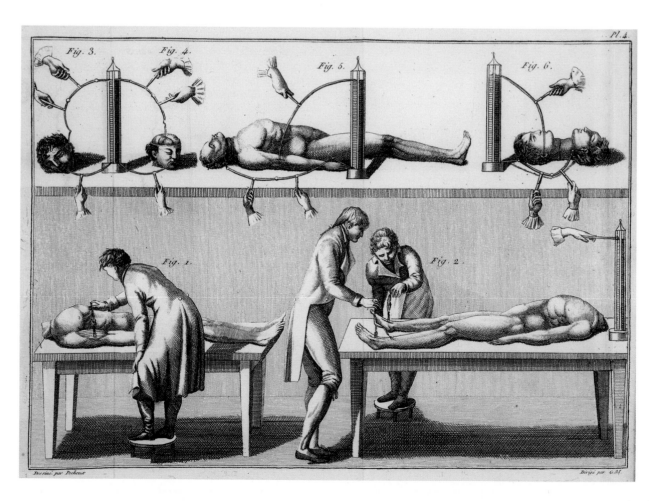

physical laws? Have those shadows on the wall of Plato's cave deceived me into thinking I am special, as the rotating stars on the celestial sphere once conspired to? These are questions of a different emotional magnitude from those about our physical location in the Universe, and it is absolutely clear that they remain unsettled in the minds of many, although this is irrelevant in the sense that the veracity of a scientific theory is not decided by referendum.

I think our modern understanding of biology and the scientific search for the origin of life must form an essential part of any serious philosophical debate about the meaning and value of human life. Having said that, given the overwhelming visceral force of our individual experience of living, it is perhaps not so paradoxical that the place of an individual human being in the Universe is still vigorously debated, whilst the physical position and significance of our planet is not.

The scientific quest to explain the origin of life became fashionable in spectacular style at the turn of the nineteenth century. Advances in surgery, pioneered by anatomists and surgeons such as John Hunter, dovetailed with the discoveries in electricity and magnetism pioneered by Faraday and his contemporaries, and coalesced into the search for a 'vital principle' – the animating force that separates living from inanimate matter. As far back as 1780, Luigi Galvani had been

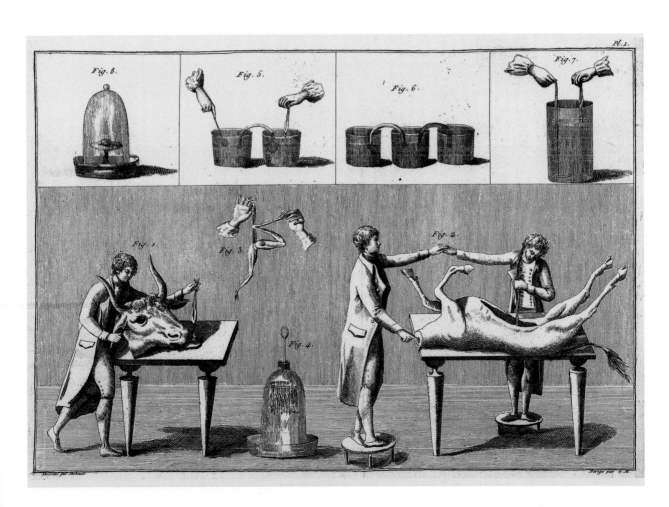

THIS IS THE DEEPEST VIEW OF OUR UNIVERSE EVER TAKEN. IT WAS ASSEMBLED FROM THOUSANDS OF IMAGES TAKEN BY THE HUBBLE SPACE TELESCOPE TO REVEAL A TINY PIECE OF SKY THAT WOULD BE COVERED BY A SMALL COIN HELD 20 METRES AWAY FROM THE OBSERVER. THERE ARE OVER TEN THOUSAND GALAXIES IN THE IMAGE.

I think our modern understanding of biology and the scientific search for the origin of life must form an essential part of any serious philosophical debate about the meaning and value of human life.

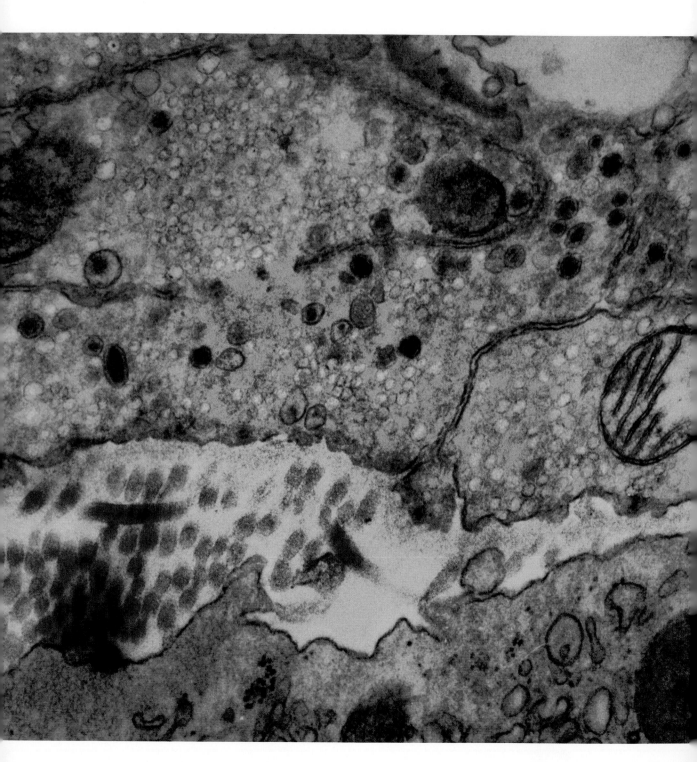

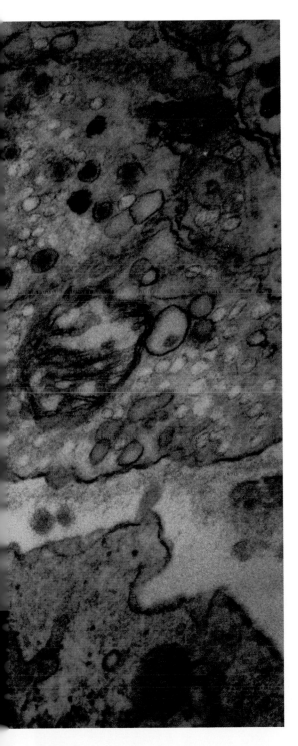

causing dead frogs' legs to twitch 'back into life' by passing electrical currents through them, an approach that reached an infamous zenith in the hands of Giovanni Aldini, Galvani's nephew, on 17 January 1803. Aldini procured the corpse of convicted murderer George Forster, fresh from the gallows at Newgate Prison, and attempted to reanimate it live on stage in front of an astonished audience. The *Newgate Calendar* reported it thus:

> *'On the first application of the arcs to the face, the jaws of the deceased criminal began to quiver, and the adjoining muscles were horribly contorted, and the left eye was actually opened. The arms alternately rose and fell, the fists clenched and beat violently the table on which the body lay, natural respiration was artificially established...A lighted candle placed before the mouth was several times extinguished...Vitality might have been fully restored if many ulterior circumstances had not rendered this inappropriate.'*

The growing fascination and disquiet surrounding the scientific push into such fraught territory was captured most famously in Mary Shelley's novel *Frankenstein; or, The Modern Prometheus*. A writer knows they have done their job when reviews are polarised; it means they are operating in contested intellectual terrain. The poet and novelist Sir Walter Scott reviewed the novel favourably, although contemporary gossip had it that he may have been the author – Shelley had published the work anonymously. A critic writing for the *Quarterly Review* described it as 'a tissue of horrible and disgusting absurdity'. I must remember that and aspire to write something worthy of such a label.

Today, Frankenstein's 'monster' is a creature of B-movie horror films, but in Shelley's novel the animated being is an articulate and moving voice.

'And what was I? Of my creation and my creator I was absolutely ignorant? ... No father had watched my infant days, no mother had blessed me with smiles and caresses ...'

Two centuries later, with the whole of modern medical science, evolutionary biology and genetics to draw upon, we are still unable to reach an accommodation between our desire to discover a reason for our creation and the scientific consensus that no such reason exists beyond the inevitable action of the laws of nature on a young, active planet. The most interesting questions are those that demand a resolution between apparently irreconcilable positions.

Left: The junction between two cells, otherwise known as a synapse, can be seen in this colour-enhanced transmission electron micrograph.

On the Origin of Species

A framework to make sense of life on Earth

Forty years after the publication of *Frankenstein*, in November 1859, Charles Darwin's *On the Origin of Species* provided the necessary conceptual framework for the scientific exploration of the origin of life, much as Einstein's Theory of General Relativity provided the necessary conceptual framework for the study of the origin of the Universe. Darwin recognised that the great diversity of different species on Earth, the endless forms most beautiful, as he memorably called them, are related to one another.

> 'The intimate relation of
> Life with laws of chemical
> combination, & the universality
> of latter render spontaneous
> generation not improbable.'
> — *Charles Darwin*

Above: The title page of *On the Origin of Species* written by Charles Darwin's own hand in 1859. The full text reads: 'An Abstract of an Essay on the Origin of Species and Varieties through Natural Selection, by Charles Darwin, Fellow of the Royal, Geological, and Linnean Soc., London, 1859'.

Left: Charles Darwin, who rocked Victorian society with the publication of his ideas on the origin of life.

We now know this is correct, but for Darwin it was a radical proposal, indeed an act of genius, given the evidence available at the time. He was able to reach this conclusion by proposing a mechanism for new species to emerge from older ones: Evolution by natural selection.

There will be genetic variation in a population, which we now know to be caused by random mutations in the genetic code, the shuffling of genes by sex and a host of other mechanisms. Because organisms pass on genes to their offspring, combinations of genes that make an organism more likely to survive long enough to reproduce will become more common in a population. In this way, populations are shaped very rapidly by their interactions with the environment and with other living things. If populations become separated and have little or no interaction with each other, these processes drive them apart genetically, physically and behaviourally, and this is how new species emerge. Separation can be geographical, as in the case of the unique flora and fauna found on islands such as Madagascar, or it can result from different environmental niches opening up in a given location.

Once it is accepted that species do not appear fully formed, do not remain unchanged, and will inevitably evolve into new species if they are separated in time and space and exposed to different selection pressures, it is at least a possibility that all living things might have shared a common ancestor at some point in the past. As Darwin wrote: 'Therefore I should infer from analogy that probably all organic beings which have ever lived on this earth have descended from some one primordial form, into which life was first breathed'.

Darwin didn't know whether this was correct, but he knew it was possible. In a letter to his friend and colleague Joseph Hooker, he went further, speculating about the origin of life on Earth in some primordial 'warm little pond'. It is said his imagination was fired after reading about an experiment demonstrating that some moulds could survive boiling.

'It is often said that all the conditions for the first production of a living organism are now present, which could ever have been present. But if (and oh! what a big if!) we could conceive in some warm little pond, with all sorts of ammonia and phosphoric salts, light, heat, electricity, &c., present, that a protein compound was chemically formed ready to undergo still more complex changes, at the present day such matter would be instantly devoured, or absorbed, which would not have been the case before living creatures were formed.'

It's hard to overstate how bold and visionary Charles Darwin was. This was 1859, three years before Lord Kelvin declared that the Sun and therefore the Earth could be no more than 30 million years old, based on the known physics of the day. We will discuss the resolution to this problem in Chapter Four. It's very difficult to imagine how some form of primitive single-celled organism could emerge from inanimate building blocks and then be transformed into a human being by the action of natural selection in a few million years. A few billion, on the other hand, is an entirely different matter. Darwin, quite rightly as it turned out, chose to ignore the physicists, and as the years progressed, evidence mounted for his idea of a warm little pond, a geological incubator within which 'the first creature, the progenitor of innumerable extinct and living descendants, was created'.

The oldest life
on Earth

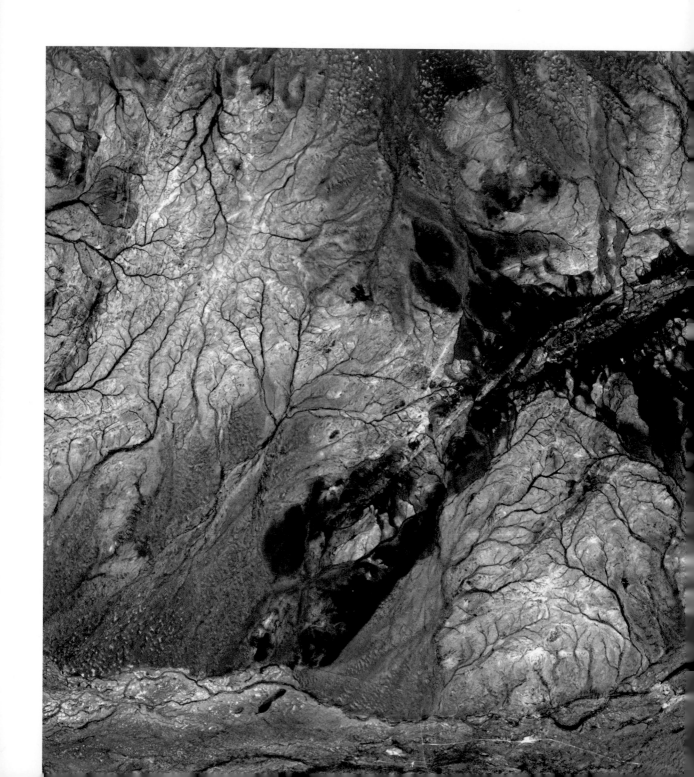

Below: Zircon, the oldest known material on Earth, at 4.4 billion years old, comes from a sedimentary gneiss in the Jack Hills of Australia's Narryer Gneiss Terrane.

If we are to build a scientific picture of Darwin's warm little pond in the broadest sense, as the incubator for the first life on Earth, we need to understand what the conditions on our planet were like when life began. We also need to look for evidence of the earliest life, so we know how far back in time we have to go. This is non-trivial, to use a favourite phrase of physicists, because we can be sure that these events happened a long time ago.

There is strong evidence that life existed 3.4 billion years ago from microfossils laid down in sandstone deposits at Marble Bar in Western Australia. The fossilised objects in the photographs certainly look like the remains of living cells, but visuals can be deceiving. Fortunately, it is possible to carry out a chemical analysis of these ancient structures, and signatures characteristic of a biological origin have been found. The concentrations of different isotopes of carbon in the structures can be used as a biomarker. Carbon has 6 protons in its atomic nucleus, and the most commonly occurring form also has 6 neutrons. This is known as the carbon-12 isotope. There is another naturally occurring form of carbon with 7 neutrons in the nucleus, known as carbon-13. Life prefers to use carbon-12, so therefore carbon deposits formed by biological processes are expected to show an excess of the lighter isotope. This is the case for the Marble Bar structures. There are also high concentrations of nitrogen in the proposed cell walls, again indicative of biological origin. Most biologists accept that these and other samples from different sites constitute strong evidence that single-celled organisms known as prokaryotes were abundant on Earth 3.4 billion years ago.

The oldest known objects on Earth were discovered in a remote region of Western Australia, north of the city of Perth, and remarkably they contain evidence of biology. Zircons are crystals found in igneous (volcanic) rocks. Despite being no bigger than a grain of sand and generally uninspiring to view, they are of immense scientific value because they are near-indestructible time capsules that carry their own internal clocks.

As the zircons form from cooling lava, tiny samples of atmospheric gases are sealed inside. Radioactive uranium atoms are also incorporated into the crystal structure, and using a highly accurate technique known as uranium-lead dating, the time since their formation can be measured to within a few million years. A sample from Erawandoo Hill, in the Jack Hills range, was recently dated at 4,404 +/- 8 million years old, making it the oldest object of terrestrial origin ever to be discovered. The Earth's age is measured to be 4,540 +/- 50 million years old, so these crystals formed as the young Earth was cooling. Analysis of the trapped gases produced surprising results, challenging the commonly held picture of the young Earth as a Hadean hell of seething lava and toxic atmospheric gases. Earth was already a blue planet when some of the more ancient zircons formed, with liquid water on the surface. Atmospheric oxygen levels were low, which is unsurprising because photosynthesis is the primary source of atmospheric oxygen, but other than this, the primordial atmosphere appears to have been similar to that of today, with abundant nitrogen, carbon dioxide and water vapour as well as increased sulphur dioxide levels from the active volcanoes. This new evidence suggests that the very young Earth was a world of moderate temperatures, stable oceans and familiar air.

In November 2015, a team from UCLA and Stanford universities published a paper based on an analysis of over 10,000 zircons from the Jack Hills region, formed over 4.1 billion years ago.[1] The zircons contained carbon deposits, and in common with the Marble Bar fossils, the ratio of carbon-12 to carbon-13 is suggestive of a biological origin. This is a surprising result; as team member Mark Harrison noted, the idea that life existed on Earth a billion years after its formation would have been near heretical only twenty years ago. If the interpretation of the new zircon results is correct, in Harrison's words, 'life may have started almost instantaneously', and a terrestrial biosphere may have been well established 4.1 billion years ago.

The mounting evidence that life began on Earth pretty much as soon as it could lends a sense of inevitability to the emergence

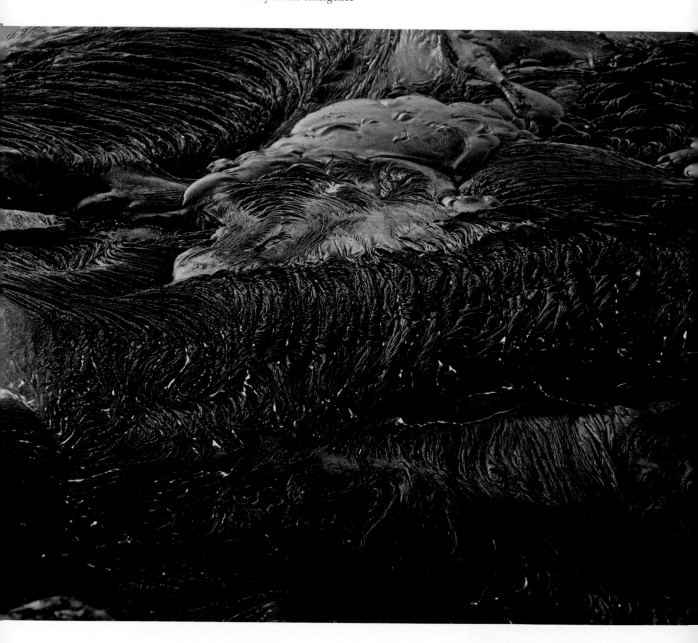

Despite being no bigger than a grain of sand, zircon crystals are of immense scientific value because they are near-indestructible time capsules that carry their own internal clocks.

of biology from chemistry. This is, of course, a subjective judgement, because we have only a single planet as evidence, and firm conclusions are difficult to draw from sample sizes of one. This is another reason why the searches for life on Mars, or the moons of Jupiter or Saturn, or on exoplanets around nearby stars, are so important. We'll have more to say about the study of planets beyond the Solar System in Chapter Four. That said, the observation that life may have emerged 'almost instantaneously' is an interesting one. Christian de Duve, the Belgian Nobel Prize-winning biochemist, argued that chemical reactions tend to proceed very quickly or not at all. Since biology is chemistry, then given the right conditions it follows that biology should happen very quickly or not at all, and the evidence from the zircons of Western Australia seems to point in this direction.

[1] Elizabeth A. Bell, 14518–14521, doi: 10.1073/pnas.1517557112

A warm little pond?

'The link between living and dead matter is somewhere between a cell and an atom.'
— *J B S Haldane, 'The Origin of Life', 1929*

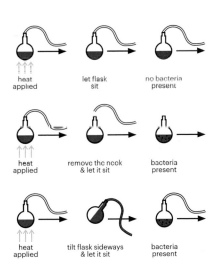

heat applied   let flask sit   no bacteria present

heat applied   remove the neck & let it sit   bacteria present

heat applied   tilt flask sideways & let it sit   bacteria present

Above: Louis Pasteur's pasteurisation experiment illustrates the fact that the spoilage of liquid was caused by particles in the air rather than the air itself. These experiments were important pieces of evidence supporting the Germ Theory of Disease.

Opposite: British biologist Professor J B S Haldane, whose work demonstrated a genetic linkage in mammals and concluded that all life began in the ocean.

The idea that life might simply have 'popped into existence' from a soup of inanimate ingredients may seem either plausible or ridiculous to you. In the mid-nineteenth century, some of the great names in science were firmly on the side of ridiculous. The idea that life could arise from dead matter, known as spontaneous generation, had been discussed since the time of Aristotle. This is not unreasonable, because maggots appear to emerge fully formed from rotting meat. A series of experiments, most famously by Louis Pasteur and, later, John Tyndall, appeared to refute this notion, and led to the so-called law of biogenesis; the idea that living things can be produced only from other living things. As Pasteur wrote of his experiment, rather immodestly, in 1864, 'Never will the doctrine of spontaneous generation recover from the mortal blow struck by this simple experiment' and 'those who think otherwise have been deluded by their poorly conducted experiments, full of errors they neither knew how to perceive, nor how to avoid.'

This is to confuse the spontaneous emergence of an intact, complex organism like a maggot or even a bacterium cell with the spontaneous emergence of life's basic biochemistry – which is perhaps understandable if there is no known mechanism for complex living things to emerge from simpler forms. It is one of the many treasures of Darwin's theory of evolution by natural selection that it describes such a mechanism, and as Darwin himself realised, this makes the spontaneous emergence of life at least a possibility; life can start simple. I don't know why Pasteur didn't notice that *On the Origin of Species*, which was published five years before he made his definitive statement, provides a way out. I leave that judgement to the historians; perhaps he hadn't read it.

Pasteur's powerful dismissal of spontaneous generation may have had an effect, because the search for the origin of life on Earth seemed to become unfashionable for half a century. It may be too strong to claim that two powerful and brilliant essays by well-respected scientists, published within a few years of each other in the 1920s, re-introduced the quest for the origin of life to respectable scientific circles, but they are certainly symbolic of a resurgent interest. Both are entitled 'The Origin of Life'. The first was written in 1922 by the Russian biochemist Alexander Oparin, but wasn't translated into English until 1967. The second was written by the maverick, self-experimenting biologist J B S Haldane and published in the *Rationalist Annual* in 1929. It's always difficult to choose adjectives to describe Haldane; perhaps it's best to say 'brilliant' and leave it at that. My favourite quote of his concerns a perforated ear-drum, which he inflicted upon himself in a decompression chamber whilst trying to investigate the effects of varying oxygen levels on the human body: 'The drum generally heals up; and if a hole remains in it, although one is somewhat deaf, one can blow tobacco smoke out of the ear in question, which is a social accomplishment.'

Neither scientist was aware of the other's work, but they reached similar conclusions in their eloquently argued essays. Both begin by stating the obvious question raised by Pasteur's assertion that life can arise only from life. Oparin writes:

Pasteur's experiments showed beyond doubt that the spontaneous generation of microbes in organic infusion does occur. All living organisms develop from germs, that is to say, they owe their

origins to other living things. But how did the first living things arise? How did life originate on Earth?'

The idea that life could have its origin beyond Earth is raised by both authors, and set aside. It may be correct, as we have already discussed, but it's not a useful working hypothesis because, as Oparin notes, it 'is only the answer to the problem of the origin of earthly life and not in any way to that of the origin of life in general'.

Oparin then turns to the difference between biology and chemistry:

'Do we have any logical right to accept the fundamental difference between the living and the dead? Are there any facts in the world around us which convince us that life has existed for ever and that it has so little in common with dead matter that it could never, under any circumstances, have been formed or derived from it?'

His answer is an unequivocal no.

'The specific peculiarity of living organisms is only that in them there have been collected and integrated an extremely complicated combination of a large number of properties and characteristics which are present in isolation in various dead, inorganic bodies. Life is not characterised by any special properties but by a definite, specific combination of these properties.'

Haldane is more succinct:

'The link between living and dead matter is therefore somewhere between a cell and an atom.'

This is very important. If we are to understand life as a physical phenomenon, we must put aside the extraneous complication introduced by our human experience of living. We are not asking questions about consciousness, or the origin of feelings, or morality, or good or evil, or the other infinite complexities generated *by* life. We should focus only on the difference between an atom and a single cell, and under what circumstances atoms can self-assemble into structures that we would recognise as being alive.

Haldane's and Oparin's essays are lessons in how to think carefully about a difficult problem, and it is remarkable how closely their speculations foreshadow current ideas on the origin of life, especially given the limited understanding of biochemistry available to them. The details of reparation and photosynthesis were sketchy at best, and the discovery of DNA was a scientific lifetime away. Both essays suggest the most probable location for the origin of life as a 'primeval' or 'primitive' ocean where, in Oparin's words, 'individual components of organic substances floating in the water met and combined with one another' until, switching to Haldane, it 'reached the consistency of hot dilute soup'.

The idea of a 'prebiotic soup', Darwin's warm little pond, supporting the gradual development of ever more complex organic chemistry, energised by ultraviolet light and a reactive atmosphere, is perhaps the most common picture of the origin of life in popular culture today. This is in part due to a famous experiment carried out in 1953 by Nobel Prize-winning chemist Harold Urey and his PhD student Stanley Miller at the University of Chicago. It's perhaps not surprising that the Urey–Miller experiment immediately captured the public imagination, comfortably eclipsing Crick and Watson's discovery of the structure of DNA that same year. Haldane closed his essay by creating a vivid and compelling picture

Opposite: Louis Pasteur, the father of pasteurisation, and one of the first to expound the theory of 'all life from life'.

Below: A replica of Pasteur's sealed tube equipment which he used in his experiments to demonstrate that germs are the cause of disease and decay.

of what they were attempting: 'The above conclusions are speculative. They will remain so until living creatures have been synthesized in the biochemical laboratory. We are a long way from that goal.'

Urey and Miller constructed a model primeval ocean inside a 5-litre sterilised glass flask filled with methane, ammonia and hydrogen to simulate the highly reactive reducing atmosphere that was thought to have existed on the young Earth. A pair of electrodes sent continuous sparks into the flask, mimicking the presence of lightning. The resulting 'soup' was then delivered into a cooler flask, the ancient ocean, from which samples could be extracted. The apparatus is shown on page 178.

After a single day, the primeval ocean in the flask turned an intriguing shade of pink. The experiment ran continuously for just over a week, at which point the ocean in the sterilised flask was tested for signs of organic life. Urey and Miller found amino acids, the building blocks of proteins, the basic components of life. The public response to the experiment was one of great

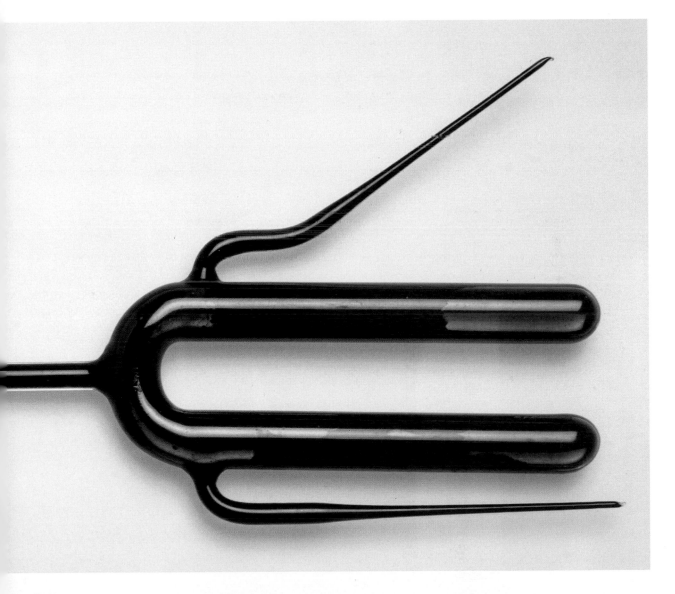

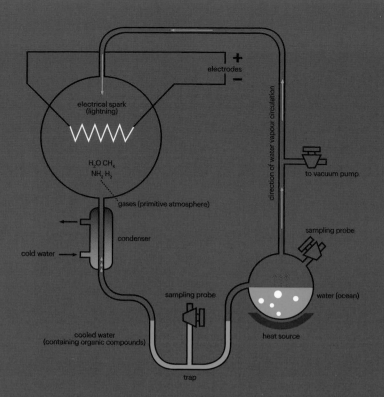

electrodes

+

−

electrical spark
(lightning)

direction of water vapour circulation

to vacuum pump

H₂O CH₄
NH₃ H₂

sampling probe

gases (primitive atmosphere)

condenser

cold water

sampling probe

water (ocean)

cooled water
(containing organic compounds)

heat source

trap

Left: Stanley Miller's apparatus enabled a glass flask containing methane, ammonia and hydrogen to stimulate the reducing atmosphere of Earth and a flask of heated water which created vapour, and a pair of electrodes to mimic the presence of lightning. The 'primordial soup' was then delivered into the closed system where it was cooled and condensed into the trap at the bottom.

Left: Watson and Crick with their model of part of a DNA molecule in 1953, the year they published their conclusions on the structure of DNA.

excitement; Miller appeared on the front of *Time* magazine in 1953, whilst Crick and Watson had to make do with the less glamorous pages of *Nature*. It's easy to see why. The Urey–Miller experiment had all the hallmarks of a microbial *Frankenstein*; the fundamental building blocks of life created from lifeless atoms by a vital spark of electricity. Perhaps if the soup were left for long enough something would crawl out.

Sixty years on, the Urey–Miller experiment still casts a long shadow over the search for the origin of life. The imagery of the shadow is probably appropriate, because the basic premise of the Urey–Miller experiment is probably wrong. The evidence from the zircons informs us that Earth's primordial atmosphere was not a reactive chemical cocktail of ammonia, methane and hydrogen. On top of that, the idea that a mixture of amino acids, gently prodded by ultraviolet light and lightning would, over millions of years, coalesce into something as complex as a living cell is highly unlikely. As Nick Lane puts it in his superb book, *Life Ascending*, if you take a sterilised tin of soup from your shelf and leave it alone for a few million years, perhaps zapping it occasionally with electricity, all that will happen is that the constituent molecules will break apart. It is not very likely that something *more complicated* than the original constituents will appear. The problem is one of physics, or to be more precise, the branch of physics known as thermodynamics.

Life, Thermodynamics and Entropy

Even the simplest living cell is an intricate, highly ordered structure. The smallest living things on Earth are bacteria of the genus *Mycoplasma*. They are only two ten-thousandths of a millimetre across, which still makes them over a billion times the volume of a carbon atom. The simplest known living cells in terms of the number of basic biological building blocks are symbiotic bacteria known as *Carsonella ruddii*, which contain only 182 different proteins. This isn't many, given what they have to do, which is to replicate, amongst other things, but they are still extremely complex objects made up of billions of individual interacting atoms.

The problem with the primordial soup hypothesis is that something as complex as a single cell will not emerge by chance in an isolated, gently stewing pond, no matter how long you wait. The physics behind this assertion is encoded into one of the fundamental laws of nature, known as the second law of thermodynamics. It states that things become more disordered as time passes. A broken egg never reassembles. A dead bird decays. I've lost count of the number of times it's been pointed out to me that a song I was involved in producing many years ago called 'Things Can Only Get Better' runs counter to the second law of thermodynamics. I accept that this is the case. Things Can Only Get Worse, all things considered.

The second law of thermodynamics is often stated in the following form: The entropy of an isolated system never decreases. Roughly speaking, entropy can be thought of as a measure of how many ways the component parts of something can be arranged such that it looks the same, and this is a measure of how ordered the thing is. Higher entropy means more disordered, while lower entropy means more ordered. Living things are very highly ordered. The Austrian physicist Ludwig Boltzmann formulated this definition, and the expression for calculating the entropy of a system in this way is written on his grave in Vienna:

$$S = k_B \, ln \, W$$

S is the entropy, W is the number of ways of arranging the components such that they give rise to the same outcome, k_B is a constant of proportionality known as Boltzmann's constant, and the symbol ln stands for natural logarithm. A higher entropy configuration corresponds to lots of ways of arranging things; a lower entropy configuration corresponds to fewer ways of arranging things.

An example might make this clearer. Think about the molecules of air in a room, all whizzing around and bumping into each other. Each molecule moves around the room at random, and could end up anywhere with equal probability, given enough time. It is very unlikely that all the molecules will end up in one corner by chance, leaving the rest of the room as a perfect vacuum. Why is this so? The answer is one of simple statistics. Allow me to introduce two little pieces of jargon, because it makes everything a lot clearer and easier to write about. This is the only excuse for jargon.

Each unique configuration of molecules in the room is known as a microstate of the system. If we want to describe a particular microstate, we need to know the positions and velocities of every single air molecule. We might decide, quite rightly, that this is not something we're particularly interested in. We're more interested in things we can observe, like the temperature and air pressure distributions in the room. This more coarsely defined, but more practical characterisation of the state of the room is known as a macrostate.

If each particular configuration of air molecules – each microstate – is equally likely to occur,[2] then it follows that the room will be more likely to be in the macrostate that corresponds to the largest number of microstates. Even if we started out with all the molecules in the corner, over time they would end up filling the room. Our system will always head towards the macrostate that consists of the highest number

[2] Strictly speaking we should say that this is true only in equilibrium.

of microstates, which is to say that it will always increase its entropy. The W in Boltzmann's formula is the number of microstates corresponding to a given macrostate.

This is the content of the second law of thermodynamics, and it's hard to argue with it, which is why the physicist Sir Arthur Eddington once said,

'If someone points out to you that your pet theory of the universe is in disagreement with Maxwell's equations – then so much the worse for Maxwell's equations. If it is found to be contradicted by observation – well, these experimentalists do bungle things sometimes. But if your theory is found to be against the second law of thermodynamics I can give you no hope; there is nothing for it but to collapse in deepest humiliation.'

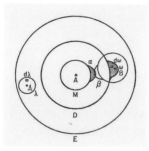

Life appears to run counter to the second law of thermodynamics, because living things are highly ordered. They are macrostates that correspond to a very few microstates, and therefore have a very low entropy. 'Did I request thee, Maker, from my clay to mould me man?' An 80kg lump of clay may have all the ingredients necessary to build a human being (it doesn't, but this is a metaphor), but most random reconfigurations of the ingredients will result in differently configured but indistinguishable lumps of clay. We'd be surprised if we got lucky and arrived by chance in the very particular configuration of ingredients that can sit up and start considering the origin of life. A human seems to be a gross violation of statistical common sense, a physicist doubly so, although I've been called worse. A bacterium is not much better. That's also been said. We've taken a little literary latitude here to make a point, however. As we have already noted, we shouldn't get confused by trying to explain how an organism as complex as a human being emerged from some sort of primordial clay 'in one go', because evolution by natural selection does most of the work. Natural selection is a non-random process and one that can drive increases in the complexity of living things quite astoundingly quickly. Having said that, evolution by natural selection has to get going in the first place, and this certainly requires some form of genetic code that can pass information down the generations, as well as all the associated proteins and machinery needed for the copying and replication of genes. We do seem to have a problem.

One of the first scientists to think carefully about this apparent paradox and to offer a solution was Erwin Schrödinger, who is best known for his foundational work in quantum theory. In 1943, Schrödinger gave a series of lectures at Trinity College, Dublin, in which he posed the question: 'How can the events in space and time, which take place within the spatial boundary of a living organism, be accounted for by physics and chemistry?' The answer, as Schrödinger noted, is that the events within the boundary of an organism cannot be understood in isolation, because organisms are not isolated systems. They can be understood only when viewed as intimately and essentially coupled to their external environment. If I am allowed two literary allusions in a single sentence without performing the statistically unlikely feat of transforming into Morrissey, I might counter Milton with John Donne; a maker is not required to mould a man because no man is an island.

If you take the 7×10^{27} atoms that make up the average human – mainly oxygen, carbon, hydrogen, nitrogen, calcium, phosphorus, potassium, sulphur, sodium, chlorine and magnesium – and throw them into a box, the result will be a high-entropy uniform distribution of atoms, just like the air molecules spread uniformly about a room. It will be very difficult to encourage them all to 'get into the tiny corner' that corresponds to a human being. You might be able to encourage some of the atomic ingredients to form structures by throwing a match into the box, however; there would be a bang as hydrogen and oxygen bind together to form water, but you'd be rightly surprised if a man emerged.

Number	Name	Symbol	ppm (µg/g)	ppb (atoms)
26	iron	Fe	319000	148,000,000
8	oxygen	O	297000	482,000,000
14	silicon	Si	161000	150,000,000
12	magnesium	Mg	154000	164,000,000
28	nickel	Ni	18220	8,010,000
20	calcium	Ca	17100	11,100,000
13	aluminum	Al	15900	15,300,000
16	sulphur	S	6350	5,150,000
24	chromium	Cr	4700	2,300,000
11	sodium	Na	1800	2,000,000

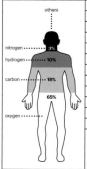

Element	Symbol	% in body
oxygen	O	65.0
carbon	C	18.5
hydrogen	H	9.5
nitrogen	N	3.2
calcium	Ca	1.5
phosphorus	P	1.0
potassium	K	0.4
sulphur	S	0.3
sodium	Na	0.2
chlorine	Cl	0.2
magnesium	Mg	0.1

Less than 0.1: Trace elements include boron (B), chromium (Cr), cobalt (Co), copper (Cu), fluorine (F), iodine (I), iron (Fe), manganese (mn), selenium (Se), silicon (Si), tin (Sn) and zinc (Zn)

And yet a molecule of water is a lower-entropy arrangement of two hydrogen atoms and an oxygen atom than would be the case if they weren't bound together, and that appears to run contrary to the second law of thermodynamics. What has happened here? The answer is very important. Whilst the entropy of the system of atoms has been lowered by the chemical reaction, a large amount of heat was released. In the jargon, an exothermic reaction has taken place. It went bang. This heat is absorbed by the surroundings, increasing the entropy of the environment by more than the entropy decrease associated with the formation of the water molecules. The entropy of the entire system increases, in accord with the second law.

Living things work in the same way from a thermodynamic perspective. They can become more ordered as long as they pay their debt by exporting disorder in the form of heat into the Universe. You are exporting disorder now as you read this book. You are hastening the demise of everything that exists, bringing forward by your very existence the arrival of the time known as the heat death, when all stars have died, all black holes have evaporated away and the entirety of creation is a uniform bath of photons incapable of storing a single bit of information about the glorious adolescence of our wonderful Universe. You are doing this by burning food in oxygen from the air. This is an exothermic reaction, generating plenty of heat for export and more than compensating for the temporary low entropy configuration of your wasteful, highly ordered body. I do seem to be turning into Morrissey: What are the odds?

The Earth's oxygen atmosphere is absolutely necessary for the heat-generating, entropy-exporting reactions that allow us to maintain our complex structure, and this is a crucial insight. We appear to 'defy' the second law of thermodynamics, but we do not because we are not isolated systems. We are part of a larger, out-of-equilibrium system. The oxygen atmosphere is unstable and ready to react with pretty much anything, given a little nudge. We exploit this imbalance to create and maintain our highly ordered structure, and as long as we keep breathing we can do so, at the expense of radiating a large amount of heat. We are like little water wheels, exploiting a waterfall to power our internal factories. If the waterfall dries up, the wheel stops and the factory falls to bits.

The unstable oxygen atmosphere is constantly replenished by photosynthesis, itself a biological marvel that we will investigate in some detail in Chapter Four. Photosynthesis is a remarkable process from a thermodynamic perspective. Plants and algae build complex sugars from carbon dioxide and water, decreasing the local entropy and releasing highly reactive oxygen and heat into the atmosphere in the process. How is this possible? Because of the presence of a waterfall – in this case, the temperature gradient between the surface of the Earth and the Sun. Photosynthesis, which sits at the base of the entire food chain on Earth today, is possible only because there is a great external imbalance; in this case, a glowing source of photons 93 million miles away in space.

In summary, living is possible from a thermodynamic perspective because the natural environment is grossly out of equilibrium. Living things exist in the imbalances, exploiting them to build and maintain their complex structures as a mill

Above: Zircon crystals capture a snapshot of the environment in which they are created, locking away a record of the chemical make-up of our planet at any given time.

Life probably didn't begin in a gently stewing pond, because the thermodynamic gradients are too gentle to drive the emergence of complexity.

uses a waterwheel to extract useful energy from a cascading waterfall, increasing the entropy of the entire system as it does so. In the context of the origin of life, this observation is highly suggestive. Life probably didn't begin in a gently stewing pond, because the thermodynamic gradients are too gentle to drive the emergence of complexity. Living things need to be coupled into a steady, powerful gradient from the external environment in order to build and maintain their complex structures.

The external gradients that most living things exploit today were not available to the first organisms. There was little or no oxygen in the atmosphere because photosynthesis put it there, and photosynthesis, the means by which life exploits the gradient between Sun and Earth, is an incredibly complex biochemical process that surely couldn't have predated life. The search for the origin of life therefore becomes a search for a gradient; a naturally occurring imbalance generated by Earth's geology that may have provided the spark of life; a geological cradle with a steady energy source that could drive geochemistry up the thermodynamic hill towards biochemistry.

We commented earlier in the chapter that Darwin's theory of evolution by natural selection provides the conceptual framework for the scientific exploration of the origin of life. Recall Darwin's famous lines, 'Therefore I should infer from analogy that probably all organic beings which have ever lived on this earth have descended from some one primordial form, into which life was first breathed.' This putative primordial form is a population of living things known as LUCA: the Last Universal Common Ancestor of all life on Earth.

The unbroken chain of life, stretching back 4 billion years, offers an interesting possibility. If LUCA existed, we might hope that the ensuing 4 billion years of evolution by natural selection has not removed all trace of its original biochemistry. There may be commonalities that all extant organisms share, and if so, it's likely that LUCA possessed them, too. Furthermore, if evolution, the eternal tinkerer, has not managed to replace such processes in any of the endless forms most beautiful that it has delivered during the last 4 billion years, then we might feel at liberty to conclude that these processes are fundamental and necessary components of all life. As such they would be a smoking gun, connecting living things today across 4 billion years, a third of the history of the entire Universe, to the warm little pond.

The genetic code, DNA, is one such commonality. All living things share it, from bacteria to people. There is also another, rather more surprising, thing that we all share, and that has to do with the way we manage our energy. Given what we've said about the central importance of thermodynamics to life, this is an exciting and significant observation. There is a common energy management system, and the suggestion is that this is a relic of the conditions present in the cradle of life on Earth. Living things are like books, frozen moments replete with clues about their evolutionary history. In every bacterium cell, in every blade of grass, in every cell in your body, the story of the evolution of life on Earth is documented, incompletely to be sure, but the narrative is not completely erased. Let's follow this thread to see where it leads, and explore the way that living things manage their energy.

The Moth and the Flame

At first glance, the energy-generation mechanisms employed by living things seem quite straightforward. Let us for the moment focus on animals. We burn food in air to release energy, carbon dioxide and water. The basic chemical reaction is shown below. Glucose reacts with oxygen to form carbon dioxide and water, with the release of energy. This is known as an oxidation reaction. As we discussed in Chapter One, oxygen atoms are rather keen on acquiring electrons, and will do so if they are given the opportunity. The 'burning' of sugar can be thought of as sugar molecules transferring electrons to oxygen molecules; the sugar is 'oxidized', and the oxygen is 'reduced'. If you remember anything about school chemistry, you'll probably remember 'redox' reactions, and this is an archetypal example. Redox reactions are all about the transfer of electrons, and so is life.

Right: The basic chemistry of aerobic respiration. Glucose is oxidized to produce carbon dioxide and water, with the release of energy.

Glucose + Oxygen $\longrightarrow$ Carbon dioxide + Water

$$C_6H_{12}O_6 + 6O_2 \longrightarrow 6CO_2 + 6H_2O$$

There are rare occasions when the necessity to find a visual texture for a television programme delivers more than wallpaper. This is one such occasion. The story of the origin of life, perhaps inevitably, has a gothic tinge. I'm not sure whether this comes entirely from *Frankenstein* or whether there is something innately unsettling about the subject that leads inexorably into the shadows. Even Genesis is quite Bauhaus at the beginning: 'And the Earth was without form, and void; and darkness was upon the face of the deep', although it turns a bit Hendrix when the lights come on and everything is told to get fruitful and multiply: 'Behold, I have given you every herb …'.

The title of this chapter comes from a visual metaphor we used during filming that goes to the heart of one of our central questions. What is the difference between living and inanimate matter? What is the difference between a moth and a flame? The basic chemical reaction that powers a moth is the oxidation of glucose. The chemical reaction that powers a candle flame is an oxidation reaction of precisely the same type, as shown below.

$$2C_{18}H_{38} \; (s) + 55 \; O_2 \; (g) \longrightarrow 36 \; CO_2 + 38 \; H_2O$$

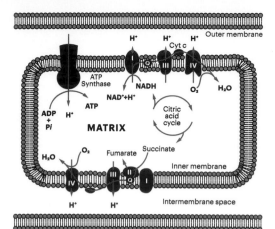

Below: ATP Synthase, an exquisite biological machine, shared, along with DNA, by every living thing on the planet.

Bottom: An ATP molecule. The orange balls are phosphorous atoms, red are oxygen, blue are nitrogen, black are carbon and white are hydrogen. Some of the hydrogen atoms are omitted for clarity.

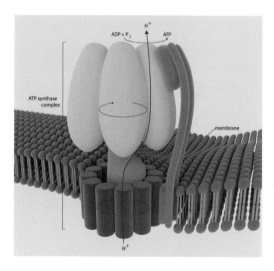

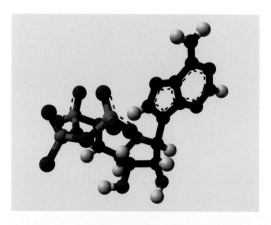

In both cases, electrons are transferred from a long-chain carbon molecule and onto oxygen, but in the case of respiration, some of the energy released in the chemical reaction is syphoned off and used to live. The process by which this happens is intricate, to say the least. In a living thing, the electron doesn't just jump straight onto the oxygen, releasing all the energy at once. That would be a flame. Instead, the electron is passed between a series of atoms – usually iron – embedded in proteins that tune their appetite for electrons. There is nothing uniquely biological about iron atoms transferring their electrons to oxygen; it is known as rusting. The clever thing is the way that biological structures tune the chemistry by embedding the iron atoms in complex molecular structures, enabling them to control the flow of electrons and harness them to do useful things. This chain of embedded iron atoms, which contains around 15 steps in most organisms, is known as the respiratory chain, and it is used not only in respiration in animals, but also in photosynthesis. In one form or another, it is common to all life, and therefore certainly very ancient. All life uses redox chemistry to extract electrons from something and transport them onto something else via respiratory chains.

There is another component to the energy-management system of life that is even more intricate, and also universal. All living things store part of the energy delivered down the respiratory chain by the flow of electrons in molecules known as adenosine triphosphate, or ATP. These molecules are the universal batteries of life, transferring stored energy around your body and releasing it as needed. The way ATP molecules are manufactured is, to say the least, odd, complicated and, to be honest, downright weird. One of the great joys of making television documentaries is that I get to learn about science outside my field. I still recall how I felt when I read for the first time about how cells manufacture ATP; it was like learning that the carbon atoms in my body were manufactured in the cores of long-dead stars. It is such a wonderful story that it seems it can't be true. And, just as the fact that we are all made of starstuff connects us to the great spatial sweep of the Universe, so the story of the manufacture of ATP connects us to the great temporal sweep of the history of life on Earth. It points us back all the way to the warm little pond. Here it is.

As the electrons are passed down the respiratory chain they are used to pump protons across membranes. For every pair of electrons that makes its way through, ten protons are pumped. The proton gradients are huge. In the vicinity of the membranes, which are only 6 billionths of a metre thick, the electric field strength is 30 million volts per metre, which is roughly what you'd experience if you got hit by a bolt of lightning. This great reservoir of proton potential is used to power a machine known as ATP Synthase, a nano-factory that mints new ATP molecules out of two 'empty' molecular battery components known as ADP and P_i. The protons cascade from their reservoirs down great waterfalls, spinning the waterwheel of the ATP Synthase machine at over 100 revolutions per second. The illustration, left, shows a picture of this exquisite biological machine, shared, along with DNA, by every living thing on the planet.

The intricate chemistry and structure of the respiratory chain, and in particular the use of the proton waterfalls

'Life is nothing but an electron looking for a place to rest'
— *Albert Szent-Györgyi*

through ATP Synthase to manufacture ATP, the universal battery of life, is surely telling us something about the deep history of life. Recall that we are searching for clues in the biochemistry of living organisms today that might point to the biochemistry of LUCA, and we have found one; the universal use of proton waterfalls as the energy source for the production of ATP. As we emphasised earlier, thermodynamics is key to understanding how life works, and surely how it began. Living things are the most complex physical structures we know of anywhere in the Universe, and building complexity spontaneously from simple building blocks is a delicate business. Life achieves it, in accord with the unbreakable second law of thermodynamics, by using redox reactions to pump protons around. This must be telling us something about how it got going in the first place? You'd be surprised, after all this, if the answer was no!

LIVING THINGS ARE THE MOST COMPLEX PHYSICAL STRUCTURES WE KNOW OF ANYWHERE IN THE UNIVERSE, AND BUILDING COMPLEXITY SPONTANEOUSLY FROM SIMPLE BUILDING BLOCKS IS A DELICATE BUSINESS.

A Very Different Eden

Past the bioluminescence, beyond the Sun, the lights of the *Alvin* submarine brought a world of rock chimneys and tubeworms into view.

Opposite and above:
Hydrothermal alkaline vents – one of the few places on Earth where you can see how life could have emerged from a restless young planet.

Everything we've discussed in this chapter so far is established science. You will find it all in textbooks. We are now going to bring everything together and present a theory of the origin of life on Earth. This is still science, but science at the cutting edge. Some biologists agree with this theory and some don't, and this is as it should be when new ideas are in the process of forming and being tested. The theory may turn out to be wrong, and if so, its proponents will be delighted because they have learned something about Nature. It didn't happen this way. Real scientists are delighted when they find out they are wrong, and to me that is one of the greatest gifts that a scientific education can bring. There are too many people in this world who want to be right, and too few who just want to know.

Let's revisit the logic of the argument. We assume that life began on Earth, and we have evidence that this happened at some point earlier than 3.5 billion years ago. We know that the thermodynamic barrier to complexity is great, and we know that in order to overcome this, life must operate in an out-of-equilibrium system; it exists in a waterfall. Today, the waterfalls are the oxygen atmosphere and the Sun, via photosynthesis, and neither was available to the earliest life. There are other waterfalls hidden inside living things – the proton waterfalls that power the great ATP synthase nano-factories – and these are *universal*; everything on Earth today, with a very few exceptions, uses protons. This suggests that we are looking at very ancient biochemistry; the biochemistry of LUCA.

Today, living things go to extraordinary lengths to create their internal proton waterfalls, using the complex machinery of the respiratory chains, but what if this is a later addition? What if the original energy source that drove life up the thermodynamic hill from geochemistry to biochemistry was a proton gradient? This leads to *the* question: Was there a place on Earth 3.5 billion years ago where naturally occurring proton gradients could have been harnessed by the first biological machines, allowing for the foundations of life to spontaneously emerge, all the way up to and including DNA, the prerequisite for evolution by natural selection? The answer is yes. What is more, such places still exist on Earth today, and we can visit them.

Hydrothermal vents are cracks in the ocean floor where freshwater heated by geothermal energy to over 300 degrees Celsius meets the cold salt water of the sea. I visited a vent system whilst filming *Wonders of the Solar System* in 2009, 2000 metres down in the Sea of Cortez, just off Mexico's Baja Peninsula. Past the bioluminescence, beyond the Sun, the lights of the *Alvin* submarine brought a world of rock chimneys and tubeworms into view. It is an ecosystem founded upon clever bacteria that can drag electrons off volcanic hydrogen sulphide – redox reactions again – leaving residue mats of yellow sulphur across the vent fields. Vents like these are known as black smokers, after the particles they bellow out into the ocean.

Below: The waters in the vents of the Lost City are around 90 degrees Celsius – the vents are not volcanic in origin.

In December 2000, whilst diving on the submerged mountain range known as the Atlantic Massif between Bermuda and the Canary Islands, *Alvin* discovered a different sort of vent system. There are great towers of calcium carbonate, some 60 metres high, raised by warm waters rich in minerals and reactive gases bubbling up from the deep crust. There is something of the fairytale spires about the place, which is why it was named the 'Lost City'.

The chemistry of the Lost City vents is different to that of those I visited in the Sea of Cortez. The waters in the vents are much cooler, around 90 degrees Celsius, because the vents are not volcanic in origin. Chemical reactions between warm water and the rocks of the sea floor saturate the structures with methane and hydrogen gases, rather than the volcanic hydrogen sulphide of the black smokers. The conditions are rather like those in the Urey–Miller experiment, which led

to a broth of amino acids – the building blocks of life. The chemical origin of the vents makes a big difference to the pH level inside their porous rocky chambers; black smokers are acidic, whilst the Lost City's vents are alkaline. These terms may immediately be suggestive to you; acid means an excess of protons, and alkaline means a deficit of protons.

Four billion years ago, the oceans of our planet were acidic, which means they contained an excess of protons. This acidic seawater would have surrounded the alkaline vent systems like those at the Lost City, delivering a natural gradient of protons though the myriad chambers of the towers. The chambers themselves would have been lined with iron and nickel, present in large quantities in the primordial oceans, which act as catalysts in organic chemical reactions. Conditions were stable, warm, permeated with natural proton gradients and, with the unusual presence of hydrogen gas, highly reactive.

Could it be that this is what LUCA looked like? Not a cell, not a little thing like a bacterium or archaeon, but a warm rocky chamber in a vent system? The argument is compelling, at least to me. Life's proton gradients, which are absolutely central to the production of ATP, are a smoking gun. The presence of highly reactive hydrogen gas in the vents is another. As we'll see in the next chapter, photosynthetic organisms go to extraordinary lengths to stick protons – hydrogen – onto carbon dioxide to make sugars. This is fundamental to life, but it happens spontaneously in the presence of hydrogen. You don't need the machinery of photosynthesis if you have hydrogen around, and you don't need the respiratory chain to pump protons across membranes if you have naturally occurring proton gradients coursing through your chambers. Everything, from the reactive precursors of organic molecules, complete with catalysts, to the proton gradients to drive the climb up the entropic gradient, are present and correct.

If this theory is right, the basic machinery of life, up to and including DNA, was formed inside the rocky chambers of vent systems like those found at the Lost City, and you carry the evidence inside you to this day. Inside your cells, you are recreating the conditions that were present in the primordial oceans of Earth 4 billion years ago. You are making proton waterfalls, because that's what life has always done. When the chemistry inside the vents became sufficiently complex to begin replicating, passing genes down the generations, natural selection could begin to weave its magic. Life found a way to manufacture its own proton gradients, using the out-of-equilibrium conditions beyond the vents, and it put a bag around the whole thing and left. And that is how you came to be.

The basic machinery of life, up to and including DNA, was likely formed inside the rocky chambers of vent systems like those found at the Lost City, and you carry the evidence inside you to this day.

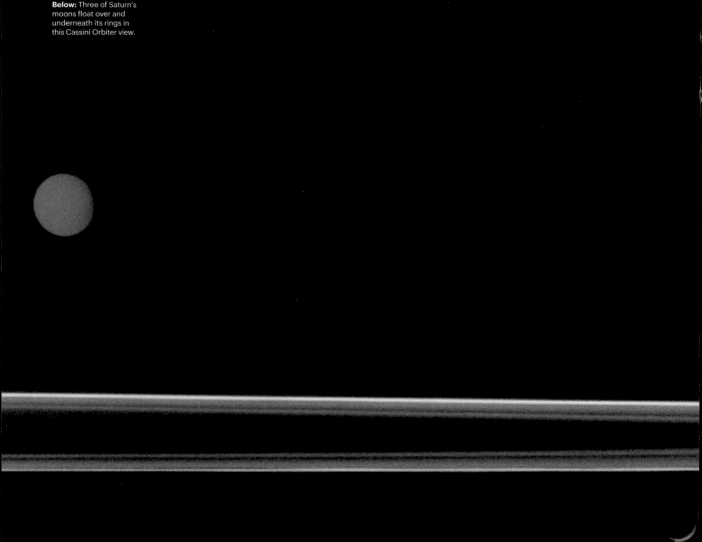

Below: Three of Saturn's moons float over and underneath its rings in this Cassini Orbiter view.

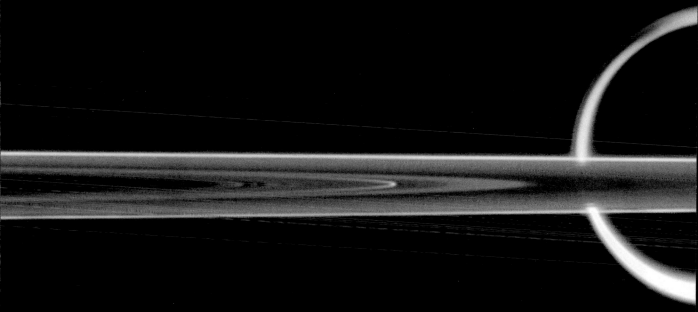

Life beyond Earth

The theory for the origin of life on Earth that we've presented here is certainly plausible, and there are a number of well-respected biologists who support it. As we've emphasised throughout the book, however, an argument from authority is no argument at all. Is there any way the idea that life began in vents could be tested? One way would be to build an artificial vent in the laboratory, in much the same way as Urey and Miller constructed an artificial warm little pond. A group run by Nick Lane at University College London is doing just this, with the aim of observing how complex organic chemistry might emerge in out-of-equilibrium conditions such as those found in the Lost City vents.

There is another possibility, though. If it is true that the spontaneous emergence of life is near-inevitable, given the right conditions, and that vent systems were the cradle of life on Earth, we might expect life to be present on any world that has alkaline vent systems in mildly acidic oceans. It is terrifically exciting that we may well have discovered at least one such world on our own doorstep.

In February 2005, NASA's Cassini spacecraft began to detect something strange about a small icy moon called Enceladus. The moon is only 310 miles across, and the Voyager spacecraft that passed through the Saturnian system in the early 1980s did not return detailed images of its surface. Cassini's precision measurements of Saturn's magnetic field showed that Enceladus appeared to have something like an

Below: Enceladus above the ring plane. The ice fountains at the South Pole are just visible.

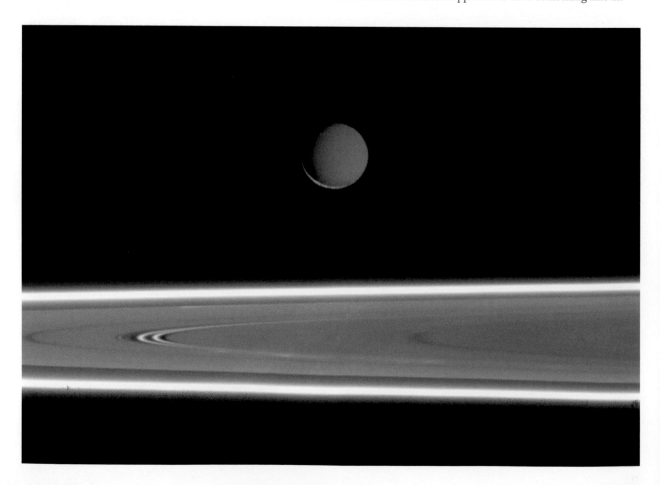

This tiny moon, in the frozen outer reaches of the Solar System, a billion miles away, appears to possess a deep oceanic environment very similar to that on our planet 4 billion years ago.

atmosphere that was distorting the magnetic field of the planet in the vicinity of the moon. Cassini was sent in to have a closer look, and in the words of project scientist Linda Spilker, the discoveries 'changed the direction of planetary science'.

The photographs below were taken by Cassini in October 2015 as it swept low over the surface of Enceladus. The spectacular plumes are made of water, erupting from the surface at 800 miles an hour. They emerge from hot spots on the surface known as the tiger stripes, shown in the photograph on page 205. The ejected material forms the majority of Saturn's outermost ring, known as the E-ring. When Cassini flew through the E-ring, it detected the presence of silica nanograins, which are formed when water interacts with rock at temperatures above 90 degrees Celsius. The plumes themselves are rich in organic molecules, including carbon dioxide, and recent analysis confirms that they are alkaline. Precision measurements of Enceladus's orbit suggest the presence of a subsurface ocean below the South Pole of the moon, perhaps 6 kilometres deep. Bringing all the evidence together, it appears that there is an active hydrothermal vent system on Enceladus, driving plumes of water, rich in organics, out into space. The search is now on for traces of hydrogen in the plumes, which would suggest even more strongly that Enceladus has all the conditions believed to be necessary for the spontaneous emergence of life.

Below: The ice fountains of Enceladus, photographed by Cassini on her final flyby of the Moon in October 2015.

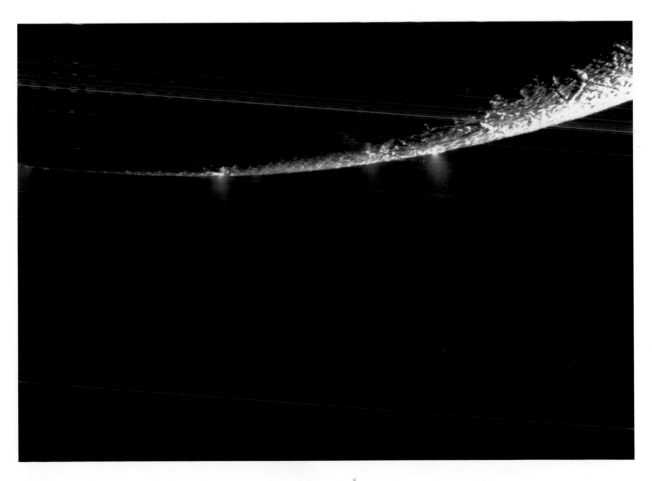

We need a dedicated mission to Saturn to answer these questions, and if it were up to me, I'd start building the spacecraft tomorrow.

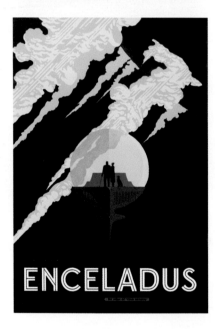

ENCELADUS

Top: The ice fountains of Enceladus, erupting from the South Pole.

Above: A travel poster created by the NASA Jet Propulsion Lab extols the virtues of tourist travel to distant worlds.

Right: The surface of Enceladus, showing the 'tiger stripe' geological features associated with the water plumes.

This tiny moon, in the frozen outer reaches of the Solar System, a billion miles away, appears to possess a deep oceanic environment very similar to that on our planet 4 billion years ago. If this is correct, and if life is close to inevitable in such conditions, then might we expect to find signs of biology in the plumes of Enceladus? We must pose a question, rather than make an assertion, because there are many variables that we don't understand. How long has Enceladus been active? Could the ocean be a temporary phenomenon, driven by the details of her orbit today, which may well have been different in the past? We need a dedicated mission to Saturn to answer these questions, and if it were up to me, I'd start building the spacecraft tomorrow, because the ice plumes of Enceladus provide us with access to the chemistry, or biochemistry, of an alien subterranean ocean. We don't even have to land.

I think this is of overwhelming importance. We may never understand how the Universe began, but we are close to understanding how *we* began. This is surely one of the most profound questions of this or any age, as evidenced by the repeated incursions into the territory by philosophy and theology. But the origin of life is a scientific question, and not a metaphysical one. As Haldane wrote in 'The Origin of Life':

> *'Some people will consider it a sufficient refutation of the above theories to say that they are materialistic, and that materialism can be refuted on philosophical grounds. They are no doubt compatible with materialism, but also with other philosophical tenets. The facts are, after all, fairly plain.*
>
> *'The question at issue is: "How did the first such system on this planet originate?" This is a historical problem to which I have given a very tentative answer on the not unreasonable hypothesis that a thousand million years ago matter obeyed the same laws that it does today.'*

Almost a century on, we know much more about the historical problem than Haldane. We have precise dates for the origin of life on Earth, and a strong candidate for its incubator. We can see how geology might have become biology, and we understand how biological systems, over billions of years, can become sophisticated enough to inquire about their own origins. Can it really be true that the chemical elements, given an ocean, a vent and 4 billion years, can come to understand themselves? I think we are close to an answer.

Then again, since this chapter has a somewhat gothic feel, I think it should end with a hollow laugh, or perhaps the music from Roald Dahl's *Tales of the Unexpected*. Let me leave you with a memory I have of a short story by Arthur C Clark called 'The Nine Billion Names of God'. In it, the monks at a Tibetan monastery commission a giant supercomputer to compile a list of all the possible names of God. This, the monks suggest, is the purpose for which the human race was created. They are to know their creator in every detail. The engineers, with a wry smile, sell the monks the computer, install it, and leave the monastery after dusk to head down the mountain. Should be finished about now, says one of the engineers, but his colleague is silent. 'Overhead, without any fuss, the stars were going out.'

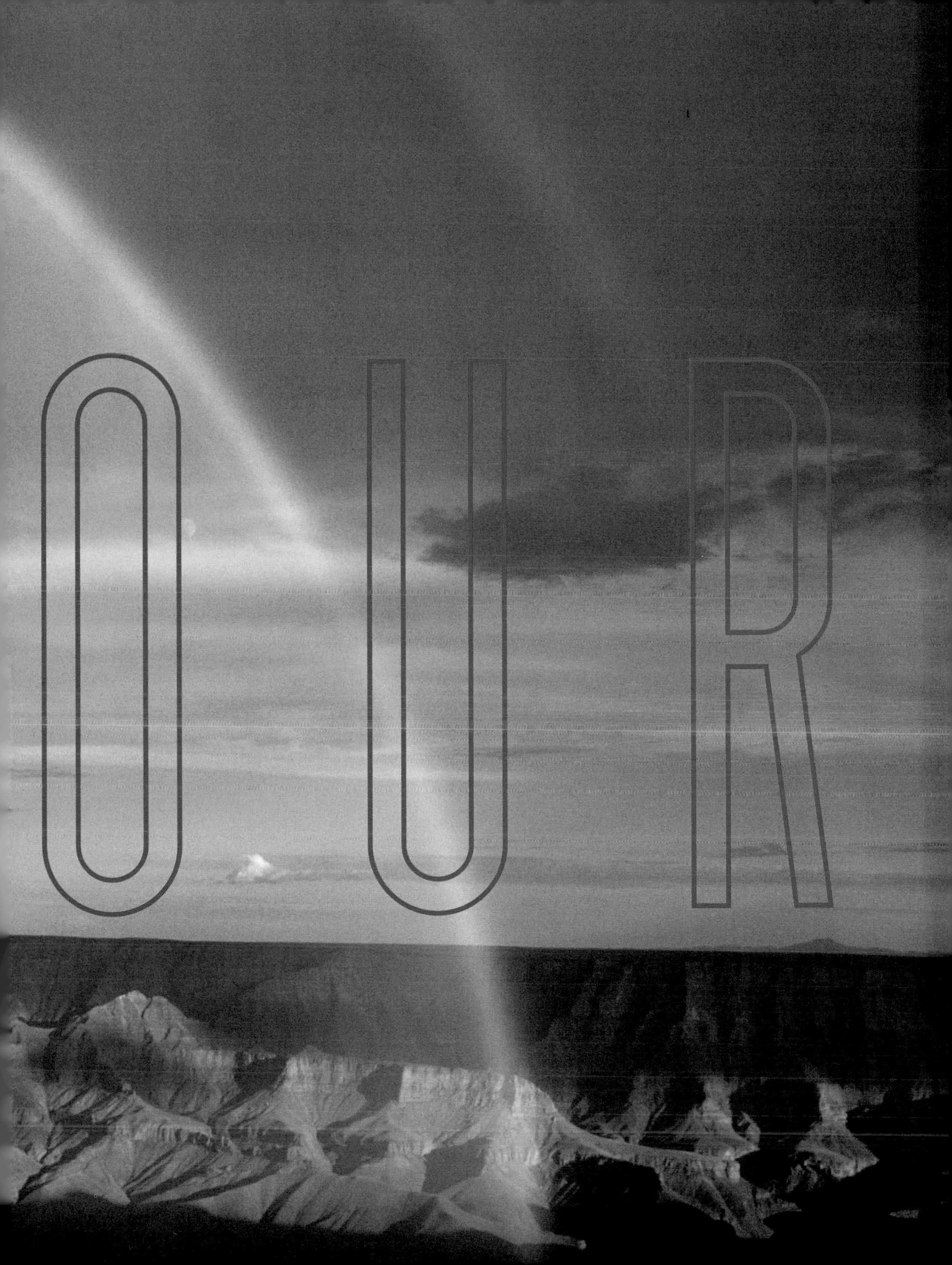
OUR

Pale Blue Dot

'What beauty. I saw clouds and their light shadows on the distant dear Earth... The water looked like darkish, slightly gleaming spots... When I watched the horizon, I saw the abrupt, contrasting transition from the Earth's light-coloured surface to the absolutely black sky. I enjoyed the rich colour spectrum of the Earth. It is surrounded by a light blue aureole that gradually darkens, becoming turquoise, dark blue, violet and finally coal black.'
— *Yuri Gagarin*

Opposite: Two Voyager spacecrafts were launched from Cape Canaveral on 20 August 1977. It was Voyager 1 that took the iconic image of the Earth known as the Pale Blue Dot.

Above: The Pale Blue Dot, taken by the Voyager 1 spacecraft on Valentine's Day, 1990. Twenty-six years later this image stands as a potent symbol of our isolation, our rarity and our value.

There is a picture of us all; a point of light in the dark. This is the Earth, viewed from the Voyager 1 spacecraft on 14 February 1990 from a distance of 6 billion kilometres. The radio waves carrying the image took five and a half hours to make the journey home.

The Voyager missions were launched in 1977 towards the gas giant planets Jupiter and Saturn, with the possibility of a continuation outwards to Uranus and Neptune afforded by a once-in-a-175-year planetary alignment. Voyager 2 reached Neptune in the summer of 1989. The spacecraft's parting glance at the frozen blue planet and her moon, Triton, is one of my favourite photographs. Delicate crescents in the dark at minus 240 degrees Celsius. Cold silence unseen for 4.5 billion years, captured once by a car-sized explorer from Earth. I have no idea when, if ever, this view will be enjoyed again.

Voyager 1 took a different path, flying close above the cloud tops of Titan, Saturn's giant moon, on 12 November 1980. The flyby catapulted the spacecraft upwards out of the plane of the Solar System on a journey into interstellar space. For a decade, Voyager 1 flew away from the Sun at a speed of 17 kilometres per second, until Carl Sagan persuaded NASA to swing the spacecraft's cameras around one last time to take a family portrait; a farewell snapshot of her home solar system as she left for the stars. Thirty-two degrees above the ecliptic plane, Voyager 1 returned a mosaic of sixty frames. Neptune, Uranus, Saturn, Jupiter, Venus and Earth are all there; only Mercury and Mars were unseen. Earth is a crescent, a tenth of a pixel in size, suspended by pure coincidence in an ochre ray from the Sun scattered in the camera's optical system.

Carl Sagan named this photograph 'Pale Blue Dot' and turned it into one of the most valuable images in history, with a powerful piece of writing of the same name.

'Our planet is a lonely speck in the great enveloping cosmic dark. In our obscurity, in all this vastness, there is no hint that help will come from elsewhere to save us from ourselves.
The Earth is the only world known so far to harbor life. There is nowhere else, at least in the near future, to which our species could migrate. Visit, yes. Settle, not yet. Like it or not, for the moment the Earth is where we make our stand.
It has been said that astronomy is a humbling and character-building experience. There is perhaps no better demonstration of the folly of human conceits than this distant image of our tiny world. To me, it underscores our responsibility to deal more kindly with one another, and to preserve and cherish the pale blue dot, the only home we've ever known.'
Carl Sagan
'As we begin to comprehend that the Earth itself is a kind of manned spaceship hurtling through the infinity of space — it will seem increasingly absurd that we have not better organized the life of the human family.'
Hubert H. Humphrey, Vice President of the United States, 26 September 1966
'When you're finally up at the Moon looking back on Earth, all those differences and nationalistic traits are pretty well going to blend, and you're going to get a concept that maybe this really is one world and why the hell can't we learn to live together like decent people.'
Frank Borman, Apollo 8, *Newsweek* magazine, 23 December 1968

If you are the sort of person who likes to overcomplicate things – perhaps the abrasive weathering of accumulated disappointment has exposed your banded cynical formations? – then you may find this naïve. I have had my share of weathering, but I think Sagan's observations are unchallengeable. Our planet is vanishingly small in the vastness, which implies that each of us is also vanishingly small. We must come to terms with being of no cosmic significance, and this means jettisoning our personal and collective egos and valuing what we have. We can no longer assume the platform of gods, or dream of a unique place in their hearts. Science has forced us to look fixedly into an infinite universe, and its volume dilutes special pleading to a vanishingly small and pathetic whimper. And yet what's left is better. No monument to the gods is as magnificent as the story of our planet; of the origin and evolution of life on the

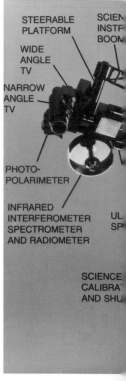

STEERABLE
PLATFORM

SCIEN
INSTR
BOOM

WIDE
ANGLE
TV

NARROW
ANGLE
TV

PHOTO-
POLARIMETER

INFRARED
INTERFEROMETER
SPECTROMETER
AND RADIOMETER

UL
SP

SCIENCE
CALIBRA
AND SHU

Left and above: A test model of the Voyager spacecraft. Through their successful capturing of high-quality images and data they have gifted their creators humility, awe and curiosity.

Opposite: The Family Portrait, captured by Voyager 1, shows a mosaic of planets in our Solar System – Jupiter, Earth, Venus, Saturn, Uranus and Neptune – only Mercury and Mars were not visible from the spacecraft.

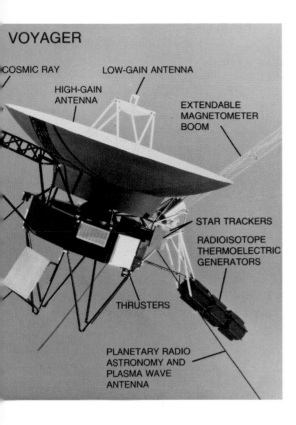

VOYAGER

COSMIC RAY

LOW-GAIN ANTENNA

HIGH-GAIN
ANTENNA

EXTENDABLE
MAGNETOMETER
BOOM

STAR TRACKERS

RADIOISOTOPE
THERMOELECTRIC
GENERATORS

THRUSTERS

PLANETARY RADIO
ASTRONOMY AND
PLASMA WAVE
ANTENNA

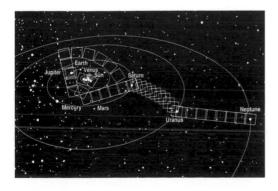

rare Earth and the rise of a fledgling civilisation taking its first steps into the dark. We stand related to every one of Darwin's endless, most beautiful forms, each of us connected at some branch in the unbroken chain of life stretching back four billion years. We share more in common with bacteria than we do with any living things out there amongst the stars, should they exist, and they are more worthy of our attention. Build cathedrals in praise of bacteria; we are on our own, and as the dominant intellect we are responsible for our planet in its magnificent and fragile entirety.

If this sounds hopelessly hippy, ask yourself who else might be considered responsible? Sagan is right, astronomy is humbling, and humility is the first step towards forging a better and a more secure future. Voyager's gift to its creators, delivered in a final glance, is humility, from which responsibility follows. Humility, awe and curiosity in the face of nature are the province of science. We must accept that science has forced us to grow up, and that is a rich and fulfilling position for the human race to find itself in.

The planets are dots in Voyager's mosaic, but they are not featureless. Their shapes and sizes may be beyond the resolution of Voyager's 1970s tube television camera, but there is information in the few photons that made it through the lens. If there are living things out there beyond the two Voyagers, sophisticated and enlightened enough to do science, what could they make of our Pale Blue Dot? They would have only light, but light can carry information across interstellar distances if you know how to decode the messages it contains. The colours of a world are an encrypted database carrying the fingerprints of its constituents and chemistry. Understanding the physical nature of light and the mechanisms by which it is emitted and absorbed allows for the information to be extracted.

In this chapter we'll explore what we know about light and its interaction with matter, and how astronomers are taking the first steps to search for life beyond the Solar System by studying the light reflected and absorbed by the pale dots around distant stars. We'll also follow a parallel path; the study of light, motivated by curiosity alone, has led to discoveries over a thousand years that are both useful in a utilitarian sense and fascinating on a purely intellectual level. The simplest questions about the origin and nature of light and its interaction with matter are still delivering exotic answers today at the edge of our knowledge, and this is precisely where we should be. If, together, we can learn to gaze at the lights of the night sky with excitement and joy and curiosity and with no fear of the infinite unknown, we will have chosen a future free of superstition, driven by the quest for an ever-deeper understanding of nature, freed from the shackles of absolute certainty, save for the recognition of our absolute responsibility for our planet and ourselves.

We stand related to every one of Darwin's endless, most beautiful forms, each of us connected at some branch in the unbroken chain of life stretching back four billion years.

The rainbow connection

Let's chant the glories of Surya, whose beauty rivals that of a flower. I bow down to Him, the radiant son of Saint Kashyapa, the enemy of darkness and destroyer of every sin.
— *A prayer of Chhath Puja*

Where do the colours of the world come from? The Earth has no light of its own, at least, not if we neglect the electric glow of our civilisation. The Pale Blue Dot is a reflector, a mote of dust catching the rays of the Sun. The Sun's light isn't inherently blue; it contains all the colours of the rainbow. Of course it does, it's one of the first things we learn at school. Yet common knowledge is often hard-won. The early development of our scientific understanding of light is intertwined with the question of the origin of rainbows, and this doesn't surprise me.

Rainbows are amongst nature's most intriguing regular forms, a glorious arc on elemental days. They appear above all landscapes on Earth, at any time from dawn until dusk, and yet all share a set of universal properties: the colours always appear in the same order, no matter what the weather. Red points skywards, blue to the ground. They are always centred on the observer, a personal universal phenomenon, and all arc across the sky subtending the same angle between the bright rays of the Sun and the eye of the observer: 42 degrees. A bridge to heaven or a covenant from the gods, such a magnificent symbol demands a divine explanation. And if we allow ourselves for one last time to define the divine as the underlying laws of Nature, then the rainbow is one of the most vivid shadows of the deeper structures that govern the Universe; a visual representation of the behaviour of light. This is why many of the scientific greats have tried to understand them.

As far back as the eleventh century, Ibn al-Haytham searched for a physical explanation for rainbows. He correctly surmised that they are caused by light from the Sun interacting with water in the atmosphere before entering the eye – although he was incorrect in that he thought the rainbow was caused by reflections off clouds, which he believed behaved as giant concaved mirrors. The suggestion that the rainbow is reflected sunlight is not a trivial observation. The theory that vision is active in the sense that the eye generates the light that allows the viewer to perceive objects, rather like a radar system, was widespread in the eleventh century, and had the historical authority of Euclid and Ptolemy to support it. Ibn al-Haytham had little time for the authority of the ancients, however, and placed great emphasis on experimentation and observation rather than pure thought and instinct. This approach, which we now recognise as distinctly modern, is one of the reasons why he is regarded by many historians of science as one of the great early scientific minds. As the historian David C. Lindberg writes, he was 'undoubtedly the most significant figure in the history of optics between antiquity and the seventeenth century.'

Alhazen (the Latinised version of his name) is not as well known as Newton, Galileo, Kepler or Einstein, but I think he deserves a much more prominent place in the history of science because of the self-awareness and humility that is evident in his writings; essential components of the modern scientific enterprise which echo Sagan's thoughts on the Pale Blue Dot. All good research scientists understand that no position is unassailable; there are no absolute truths in science; authority counts for nothing when contradicted by Nature; *nullius in verba*. Here is Alhazen, writing in Basra a thousand years ago:

'Therefore, the seeker after the truth is not one who studies the writings of the ancients and, following his natural disposition, puts his trust in them, but rather the one who suspects his

faith in them and questions what he gathers from them, the one who submits to argument and demonstration, and not to the sayings of a human being whose nature is fraught with all kinds of imperfection and deficiency. Thus the duty of the man who investigates the writings of scientists, if learning the truth is his goal, is to make himself an enemy of all that he reads, and, applying his mind to the core and margins of its content, attack it from every side. He should also suspect himself as he performs his critical examination of it, so that he may avoid falling into either prejudice or leniency.'

Alhazen's greatest surviving work (half his writings have been lost), *The Book of Optics*, was the inspiration for many of the subsequent investigations into the origin of the rainbow and the nature of light. There is no irony here; books are to be read critically. They are not sources of 'truth', but of inspiration; snapshots of knowledge and experience which should be read with a critical eye. It is a measure of the power of the written word that Alhazen's book inspired generations of scientists from cultures widely separated in space and time to seek to improve on his work, as he implored them to do, and to find a rational and experimentally testable explanation for the rainbow.

Kamal al-Din al-Farisi was one of a long line of pioneering scientists who created a vibrant academic culture throughout Persia during the late medieval period. Born in 1265, al-Farisi completed his studies under the tutelage of astronomer Qutb al-Din al-Shirazi at the celebrated Maragheh Observatory near Maragheh, Iran. Al-Farisi became interested in the refraction of light – the bending of light rays when they pass from air into water or glass. Al-Shirazi told Al-Farisi to read *The Book of Optics*, and he became so engrossed in it that Al-Shirazi encouraged him to write an updated review of its contents. The result was a complete revision of the work, and a step towards a correct explanation for the formation of rainbows. Al-Farisi suggested that a rainbow is formed by light entering water droplets from the air, being refracted twice – once on entering and once on leaving the drop – and undergoing at least one reflection from the back surface. Following Alhazen's eloquent entreaties, he conducted a series of experiments to test his theoretical approach; a beautiful early example of the controlled exploration of nature under laboratory conditions. Al-Farisi created a model of a rain-laden atmosphere using large spherical glass vessels filled with water. He placed his glass raindrops into the equivalent of a camera obscura, a dark room with a controlled aperture through which to introduce a beam of sunlight, and flat surface on which to project an image. He observed a rainbow, verifying the broad outline of his theory.

At virtually the same time, but widely separated geographically, the German monk and scholar Theodoric of Freiberg arrived at the same conclusion, documented in *De iride et radialibus impressionibus* – 'On the rainbow and the impressions created by irradiance'. Just like al-Farisi, Freiberg used glass spheres filled with water to model raindrops and explored the interaction between sunlight with water. Despite being thousands of miles apart and with no contact or communication, it is not a coincidence that these two early scientists arrived at the same conclusions almost simultaneously. Both were inspired by and built upon *The Book of Optics*, which was translated from Arabic into Latin in the twelfth century and disseminated around Europe

It is a measure of the power of the written word that Alhazen's book inspired generations of scientists from cultures widely separated in space and time.

Above: Alhazen's *Book of Optics* included the first accurate description of atmospheric refraction and reflection from curved surfaces, leading to him being considered the inspiration for investigations into the origins of rainbows.

Opposite: The anatomy of the eye, as set out by Alhazen in his *Book of Optics*.

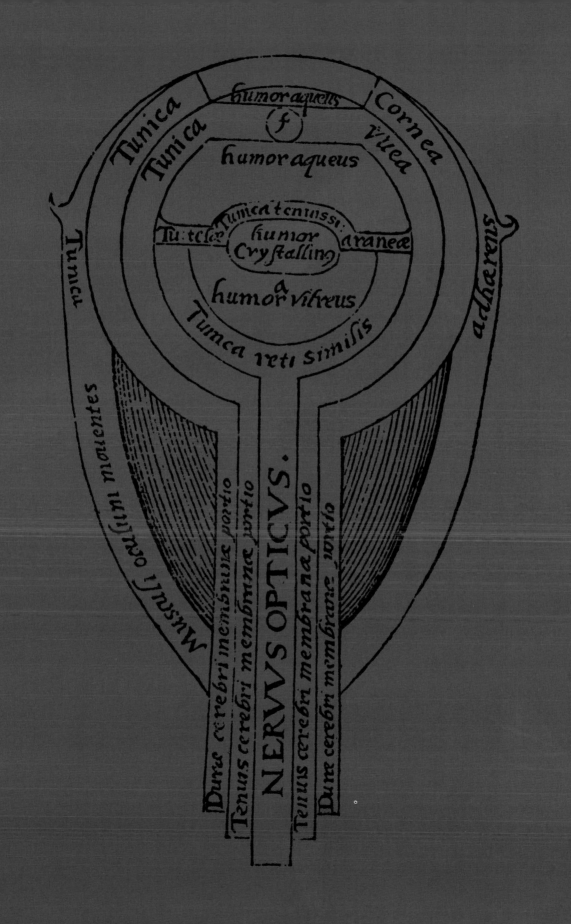

as well as Persia – an early example of an essential principle that we still fight for today; scientific knowledge must be freely available through open publication. There must be no copyright on ideas.

These were great steps forward, but neither scientist discovered the correct explanation for the origin of the rainbow's colours or their most striking geometrical property; the universal angle of the circular arc.

René Descartes was the first to explain the geometry of the rainbow in a 1637 essay entitled *L'arc en ciel*. Perhaps unsurprisingly from the father of Cartesian geometry, his method was geometrical. *L'arc en ciel* contains a well-known and beautiful diagram, shown opposite, which marks out all the angles and lines associated with the formation of a rainbow. Here is how Descartes described the diagram.

'I found that if the sunlight came, for example, from the part of the sky which is marked AFZ and my eye was at the point E, when I put the globe in position BCD, its part D appeared all red, and much more brilliant than the rest of it; and that whether I approached it or receded from it, or put it on my right or my left, or even turned it round about my head, provided that the

Below: Kamal al-Din al-Farisi's beautiful manuscript explaining the mathematical explanation of the formation of a rainbow.

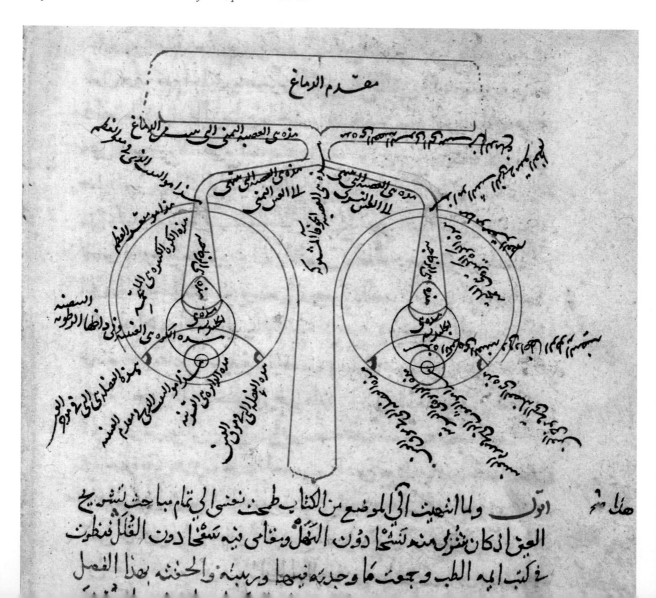

'The Steadfast rainbow in the fast-
moving, fast hurrying hail-mist. What
a congregation of images and feelings,
of fantastic Permanence amidst the rapid
change of a Tempest – quietness the
Daughter of Storm.'
— *Samuel Taylor Coleridge*

*line DE always made an angle of about forty-two degrees with
the line EM, which we are to think of as drawn from the centre
of the sun to the eye, the part D appeared always similarly red;
but that as soon as I made this angle DEM even a little larger,
the red colour disappeared; and if I made the angle a little smaller,
the colour did not disappear all at once, but divided itself first
as if into two parts, less brilliant, and in which I could see yellow,
blue, and other colours ... When I examined more particularly,
in the globe BCD, what it was which made the part D appear
red, I found that it was the rays of the sun which, coming from
A to B, bend on entering the water at the point B, and to pass to
C, where they are reflected to D, and bending there again as they
pass out of the water, proceed to the point.'*

Descartes was able to explain the arc, but not the origin of
the colours, because he did not know that the white light from
the Sun is made up of all the colours of the rainbow. Isaac
Newton made this discovery forty years later. Our purpose
here is to understand the physics of the rainbow, and it is easier
to explain both the geometry and the appearance of the colours
at once rather than letting the story unfold chronologically, so
this is what we'll do.

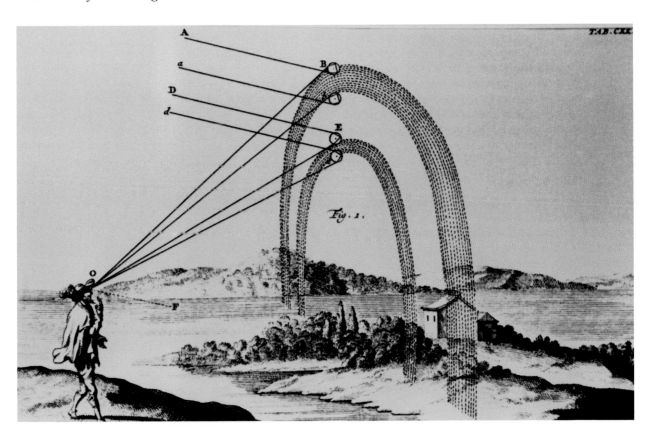

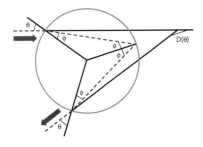

Below: The deflection of a ray of light entering a raindrop from the Sun at angle θ.

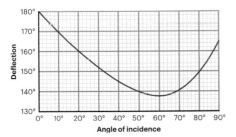

Below: A cluster of parallel rays from the Sun enter the spherical raindrop at different angles relative to the curving surface of the raindrop. On leaving the raindrop, they tend to cluster around the 'caustic' or 'rainbow' ray, shown in red, which emerges at an angle of approximately 138 degrees relative to the incoming rays from the Sun. The precise angle of the rainbow ray is dependent on the colour of the incoming light, and it is this that is responsible for the colours of the rainbow.

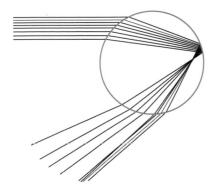

The top illustration (left) shows a ray of light from the Sun entering a raindrop, reflecting off the back surface and entering the eye of the observer of the rainbow. The angle through which the ray is deflected relative to the incoming ray is labelled D(θ). In Descartes' diagram, this is the angle between the lines AB and ED. If you're mathematically inclined, have a look at the calculation in the caption. If you don't fancy that, see the graphical representation of the angle D(θ) in the second illustration (middle, left), because this is the key point. The graph shows how the angle of the light that bounces out of a raindrop changes as the angle of the light from the Sun entering the surface of the raindrop changes.

The important thing is that the angle of the outgoing light ray D(θ) has a minimum value of approximately 138 degrees. Immediately, this should ring a bell; 180 − 138 = 42 degrees, the angle Descartes came up with using geometrical methods and observation, and labelled DEM in his diagram.

To understand why this special minimum angle corresponds to a bright arc in the sky, have a look at the bottom illustration (left). This shows what happens to a whole bundle of rays from the Sun hitting a raindrop across a large section of its curved surface. Visually, you can see that most of the incoming rays come out at the 'special' minimum angle, even though many of them hit the raindrop at different incoming angles relative to the surface. This means that the incoming rays are preferentially focused around the minimum angle of 42 degrees, and this is why the rainbow arc across the sky is brighter than anything else. It's a focusing effect caused by the spherical geometry of raindrops. In slightly more mathematical language, rays that enter the drops over a wide range of angles clustered around 60 degrees will all emerge at a very similar angle, because D(θ) doesn't change very rapidly close to its minimum value. The special outgoing ray, corresponding to minimum deflection and drawn in red on the diagram, is known as the 'caustic' or 'rainbow' ray.

This explains why we see a bright arc, but not the value of the angle – 138 degrees – or the spread of colours. The value of the angle depends on how much a ray of light is refracted when it enters and leaves the raindrop; the relationship between angles θ and φ in the top illustration. This depends on the properties of air and water, and there is a very simple relationship between the two angles known as Snell's law, or occasionally the Snell-Descartes law. The law itself has been known to varying degrees of accuracy since classical times, and almost appears in Alhazen's *Book of Optics*, although it is not clearly stated. The history is convoluted, but the law is simple. We'll state it, and if you don't know any trigonometry then ignore it and skip to the next sentence: sin θ / sin φ = $n_{f,water}$ / $n_{f,air}$, where $n_{f,water}$ and $n_{f,air}$ are the refractive indices of water and air respectively. The refractive index is a number that describes how light travels through a particular substance. To be specific, it describes the ratio of the speed of light in the substance to the speed of light in a vacuum. For water, the refractive index is approximately 1.3, which means light travels around 1.3 times faster in a vacuum than it does in water. For air, the refractive index is very close to 1. This is the number that sets the angle of the rainbow ray, and you can follow the calculation for yourself. In one sentence, the angle of the rainbow is 42 degrees because raindrops are made of water.

On Saturn's moon, Titan, there are raindrops of liquid methane floating delicately downwards like snowflakes in the dense atmosphere. The Sun is weak on this distant world, and the atmosphere often dominated by a thick haze, so rainbows are rare, but they will still be present if viewing conditions are right. The refractive index of liquid methane is 1.29, which leads to rainbows larger than those on Earth with an angle of 49 degrees. That's quite a big difference for a small change in the refractive index, and this is the reason for the colours of the rainbow. Even in the same substance, the refractive index of light is different for different colours. In water, the refractive index of red light is around 1.33. Blue light has a refractive index of around 1.34. When refracted through Earth's water raindrops, the rainbow made by red light is slightly larger than that made by blue light. This is why the outer ring of the rainbow is red and the inner ring is blue, with all the other colours in between. Water droplets split the white light of the Sun into the individual colours that make it up because red light travels at a slightly different speed through water than blue.

With this explanation for the origin of the rainbow, we reach the level of understanding achieved by Isaac Newton in the mid 1680s. It's not the end of the story, though – not by a long shot. There are many subtle features of rainbows

The investigation of the rainbow is a beautiful example of the central theme of this book: simple questions about the origin of everyday things often … lead us down tangled paths through the dense, interconnected undergrowth of physics.

Above and opposite:
On Saturn's moon, Titan, there are raindrops of liquid methane floating delicately downwards like snowflakes in the dense atmosphere. The Sun is weak on this distant world, and the atmosphere often dominated by a thick haze, so rainbows are rare, but they will still be present if the viewing conditions are right.

Top: Thomas Young, who discovered the undulatory (wave) theory of light and explained the presence of the faint arcs above and below a primary rainbow.

that require a more advanced treatment. Double rainbows occur because there can be two reflections inside the raindrops as well as one. There can be faint arcs above and below the primary rainbow called supernumerary arcs, an interference effect first explained by Thomas Young in 1804 by treating light as a wave. The Astronomer Royal of the time, George Biddell Airy, produced a complete theory of the rainbow in 1831, which triggered mathematical research on what is known as the Airy Integral by two of the great mathematicians of the day, Augustus De Morgan and George Gabriel Stokes. This leads to more questions. If light is to be treated as a wave, what's doing the waving? Nobody knew in 1831; the answer was discovered in the early 1860s by the Scottish theoretical physicist James Clerk Maxwell – we'll get to this in more detail later – and as we've already seen in Chapter Two, Albert Einstein was the first to take Maxwell's theory of light at face value, and this lead him to jettison Newtonian physics and construct a new theory of space and time. We could go on, and we will, at least down some of the paths that are opening up.

Let us pause for a moment, though, and reflect that the investigation of the rainbow is a beautiful example of the central theme of this book: simple questions about the origin of everyday things often – more often than not – lead us down tangled paths through the dense, interconnected undergrowth of physics. This shouldn't be a surprise, although it is only human to be constantly surprised at the deep interconnectedness of nature; I would say this is one of the great joys of physics. It shouldn't be a surprise because we've established, or at least asserted with some supporting examples, that the complex world we perceive is a shadow of simpler forms: the underlying laws of nature.

If this is the case, it must follow that there are common explanations for many of the shadows, and investigating one will inexorably lead us to touch on the deep underpinnings of another. This is why the modern trend for directing scientific research into areas deemed *a priori* economically or socially useful is not only misguided but positively harmful to the scientific enterprise, and therefore to the goal of the government advisors who dream up such daft, albeit (to be charitable) well-intentioned policies. Serendipity always was and always will be absolutely central to discovery, *because* the natural world is so intricately interconnected and functions according to a small set of fundamental laws, as far as we know. There are so many ways to discover deep and ultimately useful things that it is futile to imagine that we can predict which investigation of which tiny corner of the natural world will bear undreamt-of fruit. Nature is too complicated. Investigating rainbows might seem whimsical, but it stimulated a great deal of the early research into optics and the nature of light, and ultimately into the nature of space and time.

That said, let us continue down the particular tangled path we've chosen. The investigation of the rainbow has served as an introduction to and raised a series of questions about light that we should now seek to answer. The origin of the light that shines into the water droplets is a good place to start. As we've seen, there was vigorous debate in Alhazen's time about whether vision was an active or passive process, and the study of rainbows played a part in establishing that the light that creates them has its origin in the Sun.

Why does the Sun shine?

Below: NASA's space shuttle Atlantis stands out in sharp relief against the vast backdrop of the Sun during a solar transit on 12 May 2009.

It's very hard to picture the enormity of the Sun; a hundred Earths would line up along its diameter. It would take the average passenger jet six months to fly around it.

Why does the Sun emit light? The answer would seem to be obvious: the Sun is hot, and all hot things shine. But why do hot things shine? This is a deeper question. There is also the question of the energy source that powers the Sun and heats it up in the first place. The energy output of the Sun was well known in the nineteenth century because it is an easy thing to measure if you know the distance to the Sun. One way is to take a known volume of water with a known surface area, place it in direct sunlight and see how long it takes for the water temperature to rise by one degree. This will tell you how much energy has entered the water during the measured time. A more accurate measurement would take account of the loss of solar energy as the light travels through the atmosphere.

Observations at high altitude can help. The first measurement of the solar constant – the power output of the Sun – was made in 1838 by a Frenchman, Claude Pouillet. He estimated that around 1.2 kW of power per square metre falls on the Earth, 93 million miles away from the Sun. The modern measurement for the power delivered by the Sun at the top of the Earth's atmosphere per square metre is 1.41 kW in January, when the Earth is closest to the Sun, and 1.32 kW in July, when the Earth is furthest away; the Earth's orbit is an ellipse with the Sun at one focus. This is a colossal amount of energy. Imagine a sphere 93 million miles in radius, with enough energy to power a bright floodlight, falling on every square metre of the inside of the sphere every second. Sometimes numbers are so large that they are not helpful, but we may as well quote the total solar power output; it is 3.8×10^{23} kW. The total power-generating capacity of our civilisation today is around 16×10^9 kW; twenty million million times smaller. Here we go again, down a tangled path suggested by a simple question. This is a vast amount of energy. What could the source possibly be?

The origin of the Sun's energy was highly controversial during the late nineteenth and early twentieth centuries, because there was no known physical process capable of sustaining such a vast energy output for more than a few thousand years, notwithstanding the enormous size and mass of our star. Again, it's very hard to picture the enormity of the Sun; a hundred Earths would line up along its diameter. It would take the average passenger jet six months to fly around it. It is traditional to say something about the size of Wales at this point; it would take 289 million countries the size of Wales to tile the surface of the Sun. But even with these vast resources of matter, the power output is difficult to explain. In 1862, Lord Kelvin, one of the greatest and most respected scientific voices of the day, declared that the Sun could be no more than 30 million years old, given its colossal power output, in direct contradiction with estimates of the age of the Earth from geological and biological evidence, which pointed to an age in excess of 300 million years.

Kelvin was over-confident and wrong, because he did not admit to the possibility of new physics providing an explanation for the source of solar energy. 'He should also suspect himself as he performs his critical examination of it, so that he may avoid falling into either prejudice or leniency'; Kelvin would have done well in this instance to read Alhazen. The new discovery was nuclear physics. Physicists like to do back-of-the-envelope calculations, and we can use one to see how nuclear physics helps. Kelvin calculated that, if the Sun were made of coal, then this vast burning repository, papered by 289 million countries the size of Wales, would contain enough 'coal' to shine with the measured brightness for 3000 years. This gives some indication of the power stored in a star. Chemical reactions such as coal burning typically proceed at energy scales a million times smaller than nuclear reactions. This is a reflection of the fact that the strong nuclear force, which binds the nucleus of atoms together, is much stronger than the electromagnetic force, which binds atoms together. Chemistry is about rearranging atoms, and nuclear physics is about rearranging nuclei. Ernest Rutherford discovered the atomic nucleus in May 1911 in Manchester, and so Kelvin knew nothing of this hidden, higher-energy layer of physics. Because nuclear reactions typically operate at energies of the order of a million times those of chemical reactions, they will increase the energy available to the Sun by a factor of around a million, give or take. This suggests an age of at least 3 billion years – much closer to the modern estimate of a 10-billion-year solar lifetime. The current best estimates of the age of the Sun from computer modelling are around 4.57 billion years, which agree nicely with the radioactive dating of meteorites in the Solar System.

Below: In solar plants across the world, like this one in Germany, we are harnessing the energy of the Sun to create our own natural energy source.

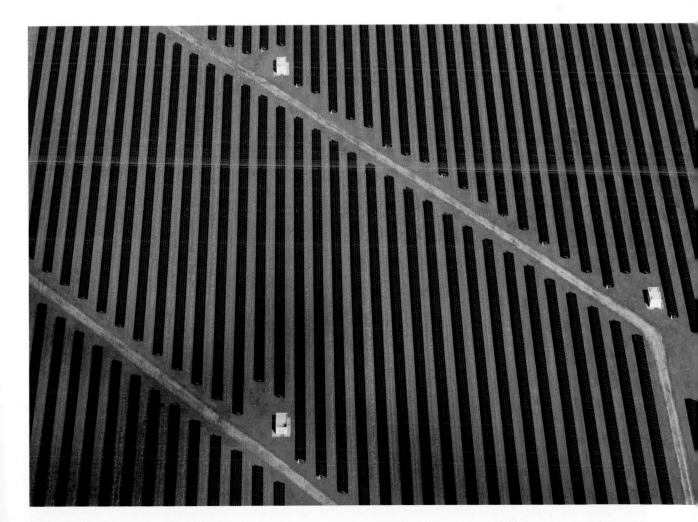

The nuclear physics
of the Sun

All of the four fundamental forces of nature that we met in Chapter One are involved in the energy-releasing nuclear reactions inside the Sun's core. Stars begin their lives as clouds of hydrogen and helium, the atomic nuclei of which were formed in the first three minutes after the Big Bang. Under the action of gravity, the clouds collapse in on themselves, and the collapse heats them up. When the temperature reaches around 100,000 degrees Celsius, the hydrogen and helium nuclei can no longer hold on to their electrons and the cloud becomes a plasma – a hot gas of free electrically charged particles. As the collapse continues, the temperature rises further, and for sufficiently massive clouds the naked hydrogen nuclei approach each other with such speed that, despite their mutual

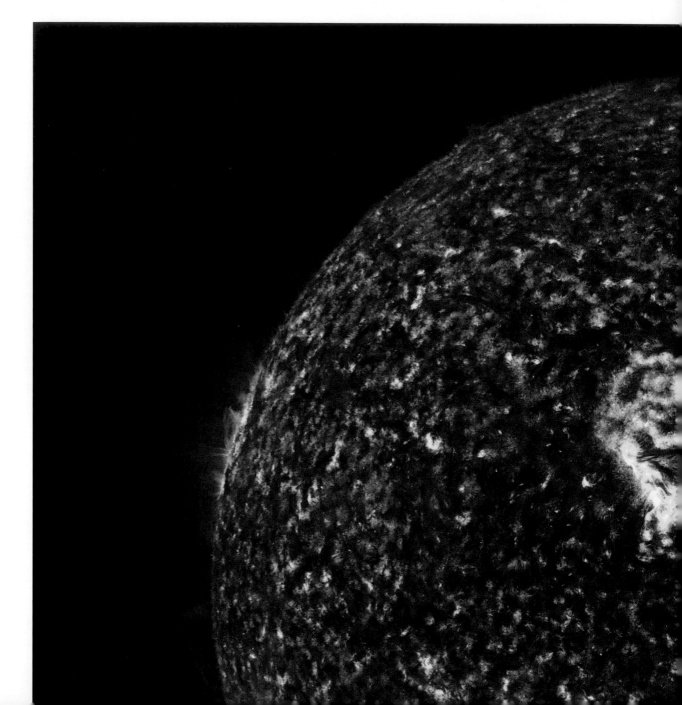

electromagnetic repulsion – recall that a hydrogen nucleus is a single proton, which carries a positive electric charge – they can get very close. When this happens, a transformation takes place under the influence of the weak nuclear force. We met this transformation in passing in Chapter One as I reminisced about my time doing particle physics in Hamburg. There was a point there beyond gentle biography; we explored the constituents of matter using a particle accelerator and by consuming red wine and fine cheeses and attempting to get gout. Physics should be joyous. But I digress... Recall that a proton is made of two up quarks and one down quark and a neutron is made of two down quarks and an up quark. The weak nuclear force can turn an up quark into a down quark,

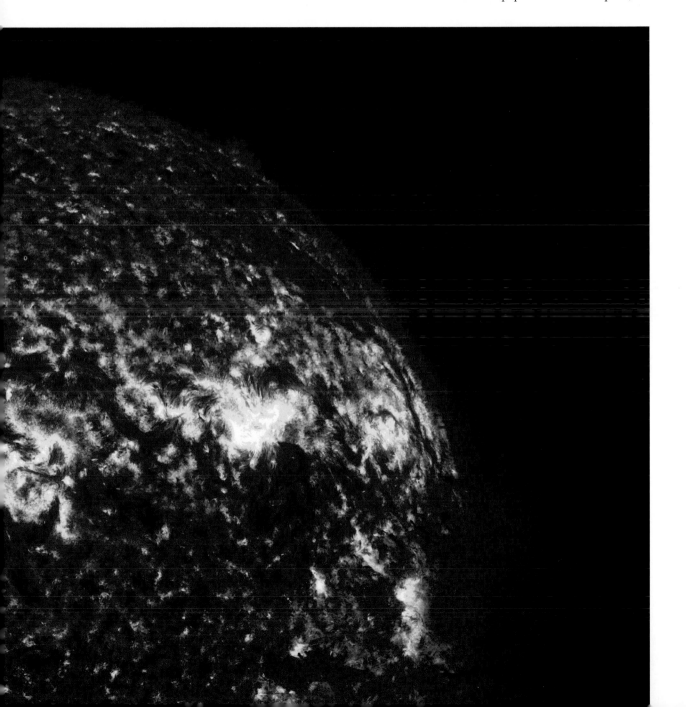

Left: The white dwarf Sirius B shines bright while the Sun gradually radiates its heat away until it is left as a darkening ember, a black dwarf.

Left: Uncovered by NASA's Hubble Space Telescope, these ancient white dwarfs are some of the oldest burnt-out stars in the galaxy, at around 12–13 billion years old.

so a proton can be transformed into a neutron, along with the creation of a positron and a neutrino. Neutrons are electrically neutral, and shorn of their positive electric charge carried off by the positron, they are free to approach the proton closely enough for the strong nuclear force to take over and bind them together tightly. The resulting atomic nucleus, made up of one proton and one neutron, is called a deuteron.

The formation of a deuteron from two protons is known as nuclear fusion. It releases a vast amount of energy because the deuteron is less massive than two free protons. Einstein discovered that mass can be transformed into energy according to the equation $E=mc^2$ (by taking Maxwell's equations describing the nature of light seriously – the tangled path), and it is the energy of fusion which is the power source of all the twinkling stars in the night sky.

The numbers involved are absolutely huge; if we could take a cubic centimetre of the Sun's interior and convert all the protons into deuterons, we could power an average-sized town for a year. Inside the Sun the fusion process doesn't stop with the creation of deuterons. Another proton quickly fuses with the deuteron to form a helium-3 nucleus, and two helium-3 nuclei then fuse together to form a helium-4 nucleus, with the release of two protons. At each stage, mass is transformed into energy, which heats up the star. This energy also halts the gravitational collapse, because the super-heated plasma exerts

an outward pressure that balances the inward pull of gravity. This is why stars are long-lived structures – they exist in a delicate yet stable equilibrium, as long as they have nuclear fuel to burn in their cores. Our Sun burns six hundred million tonnes of hydrogen fuel every second into helium, with the loss of four million tonnes of mass, which is released as energy. To get a sense of how many individual fusion reactions this corresponds to, consider that there are sixty billion neutrinos per square centimetre per second passing through your head from the Sun as you read this book, and only one is released every time a proton turns into a neutron. We'll have more to say about these neutrinos later on, because they are very interesting. At this rate, the Sun has enough nuclear fuel to last another five billion years, at which point it will begin to fuse helium into carbon and oxygen before running out of options to release more fusion energy and collapsing into a fading ember known as a white dwarf.

White dwarfs are dense, exotic objects held up against the crushing force of gravity by a quantum mechanical effect known as the Pauli exclusion principle. They are planetary-sized spheres of stellar mass; a sugar-cubed piece would weigh a tonne. The Sun's exposed carbon-oxygen core will gradually radiate its heat away, leaving a darkening ember known as a black dwarf; it will last, if not for eternity, then for a very long time. In a thousand billion years the stellar remnant will fade from view as its temperature continues to fall. Its eventual fate is dependent on physics that we have yet to understand. It is thought that matter itself is unstable over very long timescales, and if this is the case then black dwarfs will evaporate, given enough time – of which there is likely to be an infinite amount. Lower limits on the lifetime of black dwarves suggest they should be around for at least 10^{32} years, which is ten thousand billion billion times the current age of the Universe.

Nuclear fusion is the origin of the Sun's energy, and ultimately the source of its light. The physical processes that produce the light that arrives at the Earth are different, however. It is the glowing surface of the Sun that we see in the sky, not its hidden nuclear-fired core. The surface of the Sun has a temperature of only 5500 degrees Celsius, and the light it emits is characteristic of this temperature, and not the 15 billion degrees at which the fusion reactions take place.

The idea that objects emit light according to their temperature is a familiar one. We speak of things as being 'white hot', and are familiar with the cooling red embers of a dying fire. The temperature of something is related to the colour of light it emits, and this is a clue to the origin of that light. Simple questions lead to deep answers, and the question of how hot things emit light is *the* classic example. The first thing to say is that it's an old question; Isaac Newton considered it in his treatise on light, *Opticks*, published in 1704, and his suggested answer is correct in broad outline. '*Do not all fix'd Bodies, when heated beyond a certain degree, emit Light and shine; and is not this Emission perform'd by the vibrating motion of its parts?*' It is the motion of the building blocks of matter that produces light, but it was not until the mid-nineteenth century that we began to understand the mechanism for this emission, and the quest for answers ultimately led to quantum theory and the construction of the technological foundations upon which our modern society rests.

If we could take a cubic centimetre of the Sun's interior and convert all the protons into deuterons, we could power an average-sized town for a year.

Why do hot things shine?

**Part 1: James Clerk Maxwell and the
Golden Age of Wireless**

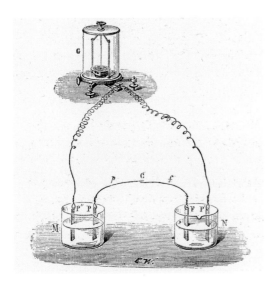

Maxwell discovered a unified description of the experimental and theoretical work of a generation of physicists, including some of the great names commemorated today in the units we use to describe electricity: Volt, Ampère, Faraday, Gauss.

$$\nabla^2 E - \frac{1}{c^2}\frac{\partial^2 E}{\partial t^2} = 0,$$

$$\nabla^2 B - \frac{1}{c^2}\frac{\partial^2 B}{\partial t^2} = 0.$$

Left: Maxwell's wave equations for the electric and magnetic fields.

Matter is constructed of electrically charged particles, and when charged particles are shaken around, they emit light. More precisely, they emit electromagnetic radiation. The discovery that light is an electromagnetic phenomenon was made by the Scottish physicist James Clerk Maxwell in a series of papers published between 1861 and 1862.

We've already met Maxwell's equations in Chapter Two, as the inspiration for Einstein's Theory of Special Relativity. To recap, Maxwell discovered a unified description of the experimental and theoretical work of a generation of physicists, including some of the great names commemorated today in the units we use to describe electricity: Volt, Ampère, Faraday, Gauss. If Maxwell's only achievement were simplification, however, Einstein wouldn't have described his work as 'the most profound and the most fruitful that physics has experienced since the time of Newton'.

Maxwell's 'profound' achievement was not merely to unify, but to discover something quite new. He discovered that light is intimately connected to electricity and magnetism in a piece of work representing one of the most vivid examples of what physicist Eugene Wigner termed the *unreasonable* effectiveness of mathematics in the physical sciences; the notion that mathematical beauty, occasionally alone, can lead to a deeper understanding of the physical world.

By the mid-1800s Faraday and others had discovered that electricity and magnetism are related. If an electric current is pulsed through a wire, a compass needle close to the wire is deflected in time with the pulse. If a magnet is moved in and out of a coil of wire, an electrical current flows through the wire whilst the magnet is moving. This is the basis of the electric motor and generator. Faraday thought deeply about the connection between the wires and the magnets. He reasoned that there must be some sort of physical link between the electrical current in a wire and the compass needle in order to deflect the needle; things don't just move of their own accord. He pictured this physical link as a 'field', which might be visualised as the pattern formed when iron filings are scattered onto a piece of paper above a magnet.

Faraday's rather mechanical idea of electric and magnetic fields was not widely accepted at the time, primarily because it didn't appear to be necessary. The mathematical equations that described electric and magnetic phenomena were written in terms of things that can be directly measured – volts and amps and forces that cause compass needle deflections. The deeper level of abstraction represented by the fields appeared to add unnecessary complication.

Maxwell discovered that this was emphatically not the case. He embraced the deeper description and rewrote all the equations describing electrical and magnetic phenomena in terms of electric and magnetic fields, rather than currents, voltages and forces. In doing so, he was forced to add an extra term into one of the equations for reasons of mathematical consistency. That term, which is called Maxwell's displacement current, had a remarkable consequence. Once present, Maxwell saw that he could rewrite his equations in a different form, known as wave equations. In this form, the equations are able to describe a self-propelling disturbance in the electric and magnetic fields.

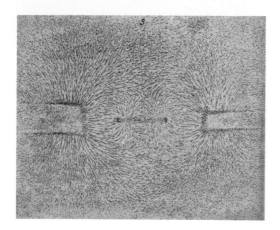

Maxwell's wave equations can be pictured as describing energy sloshing backwards and forwards between the electric and magnetic fields, radiating outwards from an electromagnetic disturbance in the way ripples radiate outwards on a pond in response to a splashing stone. The difference is that there is no water or any other medium needed to support the disturbance – the fields themselves are sufficient to carry the energy away, one rising as the other falls. This is a fascinating observation in itself, but there was a great and most marvellous denouement. I cannot imagine how Maxwell reacted; he must have felt he was allowed a brief glimpse beyond the shadows at one of Nature's clean foundations. This self-propelling disturbance has a speed, according to Maxwell's wave equations – in the equation on page 231 it is represented by the symbol c. Perhaps unsurprisingly, the speed has to do with the strengths of the electric and magnetic forces – the amount by which a change in one field induces a change in the other. The speed is predicted to be the ratio of the strengths of the two forces, and Maxwell knew these quantities because Faraday and others had measured them in experiments in their laboratories. If you're familiar with a bit of electromagnetism from school, you may recognise their names and symbols; the permittivity of free space, ε_0, and the permeability of free space, μ_0. When Maxwell put the numbers in, he discovered that the speed of the

Above and opposite:
Faraday pictured the physical link between the electrical current in a wire and the compass needle as a 'field', one that could be visualised as the pattern formed when iron filings are scattered on a piece of paper above a magnet.

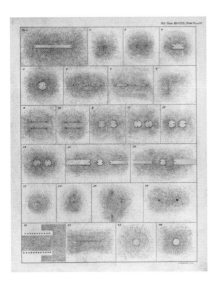

disturbance came out as the speed of light! Immediately, he would have known that he had found a deeper description of the nature of light itself: light is a travelling disturbance in the electromagnetic field that drives itself along at precisely 299,792,458 metres per second.

Einstein wrote about how he imagined Maxwell must have felt in an essay entitled 'The Fundaments of Theoretical Physics': 'Imagine his feelings when the differential equations he had formulated proved to him that electromagnetic fields spread in the form of polarised waves and with the speed of light! To few men in the world has such an experience been vouchsafed. At that thrilling moment he surely never guessed that the riddling nature of light, apparently so completely solved, would continue to baffle succeeding generations. Meantime, it took physicists some decades to grasp the full significance of Maxwell's discovery, so bold was the leap that his genius forced upon the conceptions of his fellow workers.'

These words afford an insight not only into the magnitude of Maxwell's discovery, but also into the mind of a true explorer of nature. It is amongst *the* most wonderful feelings available to a human being to understand something about the physical world for the first time. Few experience the privilege of genuine discovery, but the overwhelming excitement of understanding is available to all and is what drives a child to become a scientist.

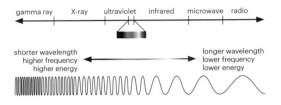

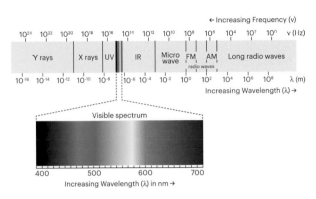

Below: Light as an
electromagnetic wave.
The wavelength is the
distance between two
crests.

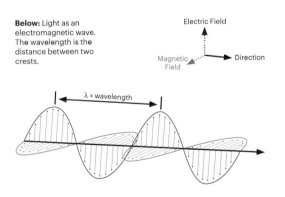

Left: Jodrell Bank radio
telescope. It can send
messages to Venus
and catch the echo
in four minutes. It will
record radio signals of
disturbances in space
which happened 1000
million light years ago.

Light as an Electromagnetic Wave

Light is a wave, according to Maxwell, and it therefore has a wavelength. The wavelength is defined as the distance between two wave-crests, see illustration opposite. Visible light waves are a tiny fraction of the electromagnetic waves travelling through the Universe. They span wavelengths from around 400 nanometres (400 thousand millionths of a metre) in the blue to 700 nanometres in the red. Beyond the red, the electromagnetic spectrum extends to wavelengths too long for our eyes to detect. They are still light – still the sloshing back and forth of electric and magnetic fields driving through the void – it's just that our eyes didn't evolve to see them. Instead we feel them in the residual heat of a fire or the ground at the end of a hot summer's day. Beyond the infra-red, we arrive at microwaves, with wavelengths unsurprisingly about the size of a microwave oven. The spectrum then seamlessly slides into the radio region, with wavelengths the size of mountains. For most of our history we have been blind to these more unfamiliar forms of light, but until recently everyone had a detector capable of intercepting them and turning them into sound. When tuning an old-fashioned radio, you're simply tuning an electronic circuit so that it is sensitive to a particular wavelength of light, broadcast from a transmitter. Music can be encoded in the wave by varying the amplitude of the waves (am radio, standing for amplitude modulation) or the wavelength itself (fm radio, standing for frequency modulation). Today you may be more likely to get your music over the internet, but if you're using wifi, electromagnetic waves are delivering the data, with wavelengths of the order of 10 centimetres.

Just as there is plenty of visible light in the Universe that isn't manmade, so there are also naturally occurring microwaves and radio waves. And, just as for visible light from the most distant galaxies, the microwave and radio light carries information about these distant places across the Universe and into artificial eyes. The sky is ablaze at a wavelength of 21 centimetres, which is the wavelength of light emitted by hydrogen atoms when their solitary electron flips its spin from parallel with the proton to anti-parallel. Telescopes such as the 76-metre Lovell at the University of Manchester's Jodrell Bank Observatory scan the skies at or around these wavelengths.

At shorter wavelengths, beyond the visible, there is ultraviolet light. The Sun glows brightly in the UV, which we cannot see but we feel its effect on our skin as sunburn. At shorter wavelengths there are X-rays, which can penetrate skin just as visible light penetrates glass, but are absorbed by bone, making them useful for medical imaging. Finally, at ultra-short wavelengths, are gamma rays, produced by high-energy astrophysical events such as supernova explosions and in nuclear radioactive decay processes. Gamma ray bursts are some of the highest-energy phenomena in the known Universe; bright flashes of electromagnetic radiation thought to be caused by the deaths of super-massive stars or collisions between binary neutron stars. The brightest gamma ray bursts release energy equivalent to converting a hundred planet Earths into pure radiation.

It is amongst *the* most wonderful feelings available to a human being to understand something about the physical world for the first time.

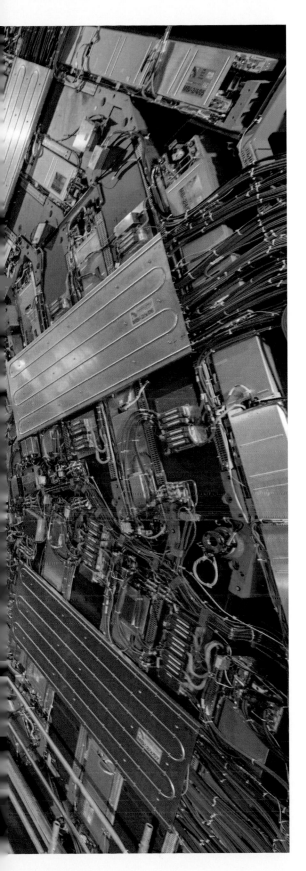

It is interesting, and perhaps revealing of Einstein's character, that he didn't mention that Maxwell's insight turned out to be extremely useful. Heinrich Hertz confirmed the existence of Maxwell's electromagnetic waves in a series of experiments conducted between 1886 and 1889, in which he inadvertently invented the radio transmitter. I say inadvertently, because when asked by one of his students the perennial question of which scientists often tire, 'What use is all this?' Hertz replied, 'It's of no use whatsoever. This is just an experiment that proves Maestro Maxwell was right. We just have these mysterious electromagnetic waves that we cannot see with the naked eye. But they are there.'

On reading Hertz's 1888 journal article, a young Italian named Guglielmo Marconi noticed that Hertz's work could be used for signalling, and by 1901 (arguably), and certainly by 1902, he had transmitted messages using radio waves across the Atlantic, just over a decade after Hertz's assertion that his research was of little practical use. Marconi received the Nobel Prize for his pioneering work on radio transmission in 1909. This is often the way in fundamental physics research; anyone who works at CERN, or NASA, or the European Space Agency, or the European Southern Observatory, or in any field that doesn't produce clearly identifiable widgets, will have been asked to justify the expenditure on curiosity-driven acquisition of knowledge at some stage in their careers. Pointing to the fact that the questioner would probably be dead if a Scottish biologist named Alexander Fleming hadn't isolated penicillin in 1928 because he was curious, rarely does the trick. As Fleming later said, 'When I woke up just after dawn on 28 September 1928, I certainly didn't plan to revolutionise all medicine by discovering the world's first antibiotic, or bacteria killer, but I suppose that was exactly what I did.' How anyone can fail to recognise that understanding the natural world, in which we live and of which we are a part, is unlikely to be useless. Perhaps Fleming could have specified in his will that those who cannot grasp this should be denied the use of his serendipitous discovery? A Darwinian solution to stupidity, admittedly, but evolution by natural selection is also a fact of life. Reason red in tooth and claw.

Einstein also points the way towards the rich insights yet to come as a result of Maxwell's discovery; 'he surely never guessed that the riddling nature of light, apparently so completely solved, would continue to baffle succeeding generations.' As we have already seen in Chapter Two, Einstein felt so strongly about the value of Maxwell's discovery because the universal speed of light was the clue that led him to replace Newton's laws of motion with the Einstein's Theory of Special Relativity. On its own, this is a most beautiful demonstration of the interconnected character of fundamental physics. Studying electrical currents in wires ultimately mandates a reformulation of our understanding of space and time. But there's much more! F. Scott Fitzgerald said that inserting an exclamation mark is like laughing at your own joke, but I will now attempt to justify its use.

Why do hot things shine?

Part 2: Max Planck and the quantum revolution

We now understand in broad outline that matter emits light because it is made up of moving electrically charged particles. In the language of fields, when electrical charges jiggle they create a changing magnetic field, which creates a changing electrical field, which creates a changing magnetic field, and so on, and the resulting moving disturbance *is* light. Maxwell's equations describe this process mathematically.

This should immediately suggest a link between the temperature of something and the light it emits. The temperature of something is a measure of how fast its constituents are 'jiggling around'; the higher the temperature, the more jiggling, and therefore the 'more light'. We've been deliberately vague here, but the details matter. The correct answer, discovered by the German physicist Max Planck in 1900, saw the introduction of the fundamental physical constant that lies at the heart of quantum theory – Planck's Constant.

Here's why we are allowed an exclamation mark, Fitzgerald be damned. In order to answer the question of how hot things emit light, we've already been led to the door of Einstein's Theory of Special Relativity via Maxwell's equations. We now find that we stand at another door and the other great pillar of twenty-first-century physics, quantum theory, lies beyond. Yet again, we face the interconnectedness of physics. Without an understanding of quantum theory, we wouldn't understand the structure of atoms, possess accurate theories describing the action of three of the four fundamental forces of nature, or be able to read the stories of distant planets from their reflected light alone. At a more prosaic level, there would be no transistors, and therefore no electronics, and the modern world would be a very different place. Imagine a valve-powered iPhone; it would have a shit battery life.

Planck's foundational insight came to him on the evening of 7 October 1900. We know this because he spent the afternoon at his house in Berlin with a colleague, Heinrich Rubens, discussing theoretical models for the emission of light from hot objects. The experimental results, which were well known and of high precision, are shown schematically in the illustration, left.

The problem with the theoretical models of the day was that they all overestimated the amount of short-wavelength light emitted at a given temperature. Use of the term 'overestimated' might be to understate the problem; the preferred pre-Planckian model, known as the Rayleigh-Jeans law, predicted that an infinite amount of energy should be radiated away at shorter wavelengths by a hot object. This is obviously not right. The problem lay with the use of one of the foundational theorems of classical physics known as the equipartition theorem. If a lump of matter is considered as a series of little oscillating electric charges that radiate light, in accord with Maxwell's equations, then the equipartition theorem states that all oscillations available to the electrical charges will happen, and they will all share the available energy equally. Faster vibrations correspond to shorter wavelengths of light, and according to classical theory there are more fast vibrations available to the charged particles than slow vibrations. If there is no reason why faster oscillations can't happen, they should dominate and more light should be radiated away at the short-wavelength ultraviolet end of the spectrum, simply because there are more vibrations available. This was known

Below: The wavelengths of light radiated by a hot object depend on its temperature. Hotter objects radiate more light at shorter wavelengths.

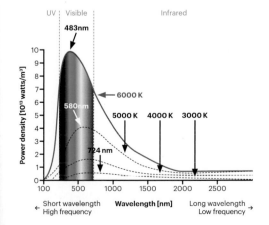

as the Ultraviolet catastrophe, because it is not how hot things
behave. Indeed, as can be seen in the illustration on page 181,
cooler objects don't emit much UV light at all.

When Rubens left the house after a long lunch, Planck
was no nearer to a solution, but by the evening he'd sent his
friend a formula, scribbled on the back of a postcard. Planck
described it as an act of desperation, having tried everything
else he could think of. In his scientific biography of Albert
Einstein, Abraham Pais writes that Planck's reasoning was
'mad, but his madness has that divine quality that only the
greatest transitional figures can bring to science'.

For reasons unknown, not even fully to himself, Planck
decided that light can only be emitted in packets, or quanta,
whose energy is related to their wavelength through the
formula $E = h c / \lambda$, where c is the speed of light, λ is the
wavelength of the light and h is a completely new constant of
nature which is now known as Planck's Constant. With that
assumption he was able to derive the correct description for the
spectrum of light emitted by an object of a given temperature.
To see how this works, notice that Planck's formula says that

Until Einstein, everyone assumed that Planck's insight related to the structure of matter itself, and not to Maxwell's electromagnetic field.

shorter wavelengths of light carry more energy, and since there is only a limited amount of energy available, shorter wavelengths will be harder and harder to radiate. The extreme scenario would be for a wavelength that would require more energy than is present in the object: Planck's assumption provides a natural cut-off at the short-wavelength end of the spectrum, and solves the Ultraviolet catastrophe.

Planck thought this was a neat mathematical trick, and didn't appreciate its fundamental physical significance for many years. The reason we quote from a biography of Einstein is that it fell to Einstein, yet again, to take Planck's prediction seriously as a fundamental discovery about nature. In 1905 he proposed that light is not only emitted and absorbed in little packets, but is actually composed of little packets, called photons. This is not a trivial distinction. Until Einstein, everyone assumed that Planck's insight related to the structure of matter itself, and not to Maxwell's electromagnetic field, which must surely be able to oscillate freely in accord with his beautiful equations. Einstein suggested something much more radical – that the electromagnetic field itself is made up of

little particles of light. Just as he replaced Newton's laws with Special Relativity, Einstein proposed that Maxwell's equations are an approximation to something deeper. As late as 1913, Planck was having none of it. In a proposal written in support of Einstein's admission to the Prussian Academy in that year, Planck wrote: 'In sum, one can say that there is hardly one among the great problems in which modern physics is so rich to which Einstein has not made a remarkable contribution. That he may sometimes have missed the target in his speculations, as, for example, in his hypothesis of light quanta, cannot be held too much against him, for it is not possible to introduce really new ideas even in the most exact sciences without sometimes taking a risk.'

Einstein's instincts, as usual, turned out to be correct. There is a deeper theory than Maxwell's called quantum electrodynamics, which was formulated by Richard Feynman and others during the 1940s and 50s. It was for this theory that Feynman, Julian Schwinger and Sin-Itiro Tomonaga shared the 1965 Nobel Prize in Physics. Einstein himself received the 1921 Nobel Prize for his explanation of something called the photoelectric effect, which was motivated by Planck's insight. Light shining on a metallic surface causes electrons to be released from that surface, but if the light is all above a certain wavelength, no electrons will be released no matter how bright the light. The explanation is that photons of light of too long a wavelength have too little energy to release the electrons, and it doesn't matter whether a million or a billion or a trillion photons hit the metal, no electrons will be emitted because they will never encounter a photon with enough energy to release them. Einstein's explanation is regarded, along with Planck's explanation for the observed spectrum of light emitted by hot objects, as the birth of quantum theory.

We now have everything we need to understand how glowing objects emit light, and why cooler objects emit redder light. Temperature is a measure of how fast things move around, which is a measure of how much energy is available. Electrically charged particles emit light when they are accelerated, in accord with Maxwell's equations. Thinking in this way doesn't explain the colour of the light emitted by hot objects. For that, we need quantum theory. Light can be treated as a stream of particles, whose energy is inversely proportional to the wavelength of the light in accord with Einstein's extension of Planck's hypothesis. Richard Feynman introduced a beautiful way of picturing the process known as a Feynman diagram (see left).

Electrons can emit and absorb photons. The photon will carry away energy and momentum from the electron and deliver it to another one. In this case, we can image one electron being inside a lump of glowing lava. If it's got a lot of energy, it is more likely to emit a photon of high energy, which can be radiated out and absorbed by another electron, which could be inside your retina. This is how you see the world. Since high-energy photons have shorter wavelengths, hotter objects will have a higher probability of emitting short-wavelength photons, simply because the charged particles inside them have more energy on average with which to emit them. Hot things are more likely to emit short-wavelength blue photons, which is why hot things glow blue and cooler things glow red.

We can now round everything off and answer our initial question about why the Sun shines. It shines because its outer layers are jiggling around, heated by the nuclear fusion reactions in its core. The temperature at the surface is approximately 5500 degrees Celsius, and this is a measure of how much energy is available for the charged particles in its surface to emit photons. The solar spectrum is shown in the illustration, left. Because the surface is 5500 degrees Celsius, the peak power is radiated in the visible part of the spectrum. All visible wavelengths are present, which is why the Sun appears 'white hot' in the sky. The surface is hot enough to radiate into the ultraviolet, down to wavelengths of around 250 nm, and there is a long tail of emission into the infrared. Planck's theoretical curve, for a perfect emitter (known as a black body) of temperature 5500 degrees Celsius, is also shown.

Below: A Feynman diagram of an electron emitting a photon, which is absorbed by another electron.

Bottom: The solar spectrum. Super-imposed is the calculation from Planck's formula showing the spectrum from a 'blackbody' at a temperature of 6000 degrees Celsius.

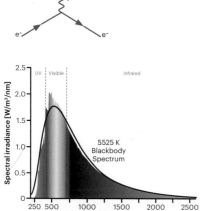

A serendipitous aside; the solar neutrino problem

The question of the nature of light and how hot objects emit it is a deep one. It requires a good selection of the tools available to an early twentieth-century physicist, in the guise of Maxwell's equations and quantum theory, to answer satisfactorily. If we are also asked to explain how the Sun shines, then we require mid-twentieth-century nuclear physics. The nuclear fusion process we've described was first outlined in detail in a classic theoretical paper, 'Energy Production in Stars', by Hans Bethe in 1939, but experimental confirmation that there are nuclear reactions in the Sun's core came, I find quite astonishingly, in my lifetime.

In 1964 John Bahcall and Raymond Davis Jr. proposed an experiment using 100,000 gallons of cleaning fluid to detect the neutrinos produced in the nuclear fusion of hydrogen

The question of the nature of light and how hot objects emit it is a deep one. It requires a good selection of the tools available to an early twentieth-century physicist.

Opposite and above:
The interest in neutrinos and neutrino oscillations fuels ongoing research at laboratories across the world.

[1] http://www.nobelprize.org/nobel_prizes/themes/physics/fusion

into helium in the Sun. In an essay written in 2000, Bahcall recalled that the sole motivation of their experiment was to 'see into the interior of a star and thus verify directly the hypothesis of nuclear energy generation in stars.' [1] The first results were published in 1968, and whilst neutrinos were seen, there were fewer than predicted. The number of neutrinos detected was a factor of two or three lower than most refined theoretical models of the Sun suggested. This discrepancy between the observed neutrino flux at the Earth's surface and the predictions from nuclear physics became known as 'the solar neutrino problem'. A series of experiments around the world followed, many throughout my professional career. I remember lecturing an advanced course on neutrino physics in the 1990s in which I presented the solar neutrino problem as one of the unsolved problems in modern physics. Experiments observed neutrinos from the Sun, from cosmic ray collisions high in the Earth's upper atmosphere, and from nuclear reactors. Beams of neutrinos were produced in particle accelerators and angled through the Earth to detectors beneath mountains. The experimental searches were backed up by a great deal of theoretical effort.

The answer to the solar neutrino problem is now known. It came as quite a surprise and has led to one of the most active and exciting areas of research in modern particle physics.

The upshot is that the nuclear physics and the solar models are both correct, but the neutrinos themselves behave in a strange way during their voyage through the Sun and across 93 million miles of space to the Earth. If you look back at the illustration on page 40, you'll see that there are three kinds of neutrino; the electron neutrino, the muon neutrino and the tau neutrino. These are known in the jargon as 'flavours'. Only electron neutrinos are produced in the nuclear reactions in the Sun, and it is the number of electron neutrinos that theoretical physicists calculated and the experimentalists expected to see in their detectors on Earth.

It turns out, however, that nature is slightly 'misaligned'. Neutrinos don't travel as electron, muon or tau neutrinos, but as a mixture of them. The precise fractions of each that will be detected on Earth depends on the distance they have travelled since they were created, and on what they have travelled through. The early detectors on Earth were only set up to detect electron neutrinos, and they saw fewer than the nuclear physics models predicted – not because there were fewer neutrinos arriving at the Earth from the Sun, but because some of them were arriving as muon or tau neutrinos which escaped detection. This peculiar behaviour is known as neutrino oscillations, and explaining precisely how and why it happens is an unsolved problem. The 2015 Nobel Prize in Physics was awarded to Takaaki Kajita and Arthur B. McDonald for their experimental proof that muon neutrinos created in cosmic ray collisions in the Earth's atmosphere and electron neutrinos created in the Sun's core can transform into the other flavours as they travel from their point of origin to detection.

The interest in the strange behaviour of neutrinos extends way beyond the nuclear physics of the Sun and the behaviour of cosmic rays striking the Earth. In yet another example of the serendipitous twists and turns of science, the discovery of neutrino oscillations has opened up a wonderful can of worms – and cans of worms are a physicist's delight. In order to oscillate in the observed way, at least two of the neutrino types should have very tiny but non-zero masses; around a millionth of the mass of the lightest Standard Model matter particle other than the neutrinos: the electron. We now have good evidence that the Higgs particle is responsible for the masses of the other Standard Model particles, but the enormous difference in mass between the neutrinos and everything else suggests that some other mechanism may be responsible for the neutrino's tiny mass. One such mechanism, known as the see-saw mechanism, requires a new super-heavy neutrino with a mass of the order of 10^{15} GeV; the mass of the proton is approximately 1 GeV. This would be a window into super-high energy physics close to the energies at which it is thought the three non-gravitational forces combine, known as the GUT or Grand Unification scale. Apologies for the units of mass, pronounced G E V or 'Giga electron-volts'. They are more sensible for particle physicists to use than grams. The proton's mass is approximately 1.673×10^{-24} grams, which is an unwieldy quantity. If physicists can use numbers close to 1, they are much happier.

Below: The space-age Super-Kamiokande Neutrino Detector is housed under Mount Ikeno in Japan, and here, 1000 metres underground, scientists study solar and atmospheric neutrinos.

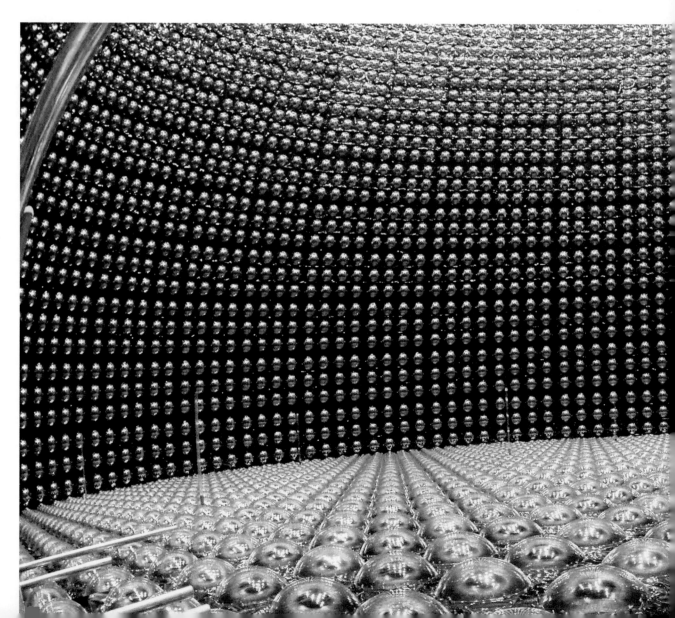

Without a difference in behaviour between matter and anti-matter, known as CP violation, we would not exist.

The neutrinos may also have been intimately involved in producing the observed discrepancy between matter and anti-matter in the Universe today – another of the great unsolved mysteries in the physics of the early Universe. Without a difference in behaviour between matter and anti-matter, known as CP-violation, we would not exist. To quote the 2015 Nobel Prize committee, 'the discovery of neutrino oscillations has opened a door towards a more comprehensive understanding of the Universe we live in.'

John Bahcall finishes his lovely essay on the mystery of the neutrinos with this magnificent paragraph:

'At the beginning of the twenty-first century, we have learned that solar neutrinos tell us not only about the interior of the Sun, but also something about the nature of neutrinos. No one knows what surprises will be revealed by the new solar neutrino experiments that are currently underway or are planned. The richness and the humour with which Nature has written her mystery, in an international language that can be read by curious people of all nations, is beautiful, awesome, and humbling.'

FOUR COLOURS DOMINATE: THE BLUE OF THE OCEANS, THE GREEN OF THE TEMPERATE NORTHERN LANDMASS, THE OCHRE OF THE DEEP CONTINENTAL DESERTS AND WHITE OF THE CLOUDS AND POLAR SNOWS.

Above: The 'White Marble' – an Arctic view of Earth from the Blue Marble 2012, taken by NASA's Suomi-NPP Satellite.

Pale blue green planet

Part 1: The Oceans

'Far out in the uncharted backwaters of the unfashionable end of the western spiral arm of the Galaxy lies a small unregarded yellow sun. Orbiting this at a distance of roughly ninety-two million miles is an utterly insignificant little blue-green planet whose ape-descended life forms are so amazingly primitive that they still think digital watches are a pretty neat idea.'
— *Douglas Adams*, The Hitchhiker's Guide to the Galaxy

Opposite and above: At Thingvellir the continental drift between the tectonic plates of North America and Eurasia can be seen with the naked eye. Many of the rifts are filled with glacial meltwater, which makes them some of the world's most famous – and coldest – sites for diving.

The white light of the Sun shines onto the Earth and is reflected back out into space. Our planet is an infinitely colourful world close up; cities, jungles, grasslands and savannah have been painted by life – there are few monochrome places. From high altitude, a simpler picture presents itself. The White Marble image (see page 249) shows an unusual polar view of Earth, centred on Eastern Europe and Russia and extending from the North Pole to the Persian Gulf and India. Four colours dominate in this photo: the blue of the oceans, the green of the temperate northern landmass, the ochre of the deep continental deserts and the white of the clouds and polar snows. What is the origin of these colours, and what can they tell us about the physical and biological processes taking place on the Earth's surface?

In the southwest of Iceland there is a valley called Thingvellir. The first Viking settlers located their parliament in this valley over a thousand years ago, and although parliament was moved in 1798, the site still plays an important role in Icelandic culture. It is a place that symbolises the coming together of a people; a place where information can be exchanged and disputes settled; a place for trade and meeting old friends; a place to work together – a necessary, if not sufficient, requirement for survival on an isolated rock. The valley is narrow and steep in places, which gives the visitor the opportunity to spread out their arms and, almost, touch two of Earth's great continental landmasses. To the east lies North America; to the west, Eurasia. Thingvellir is the only place on land where the mid-Atlantic ridge is visible – a fleeting glimpse of the geological seam that runs the length of the Atlantic Ocean. The ridge is currently spreading at a rate of 2 centimetres per year in the North Atlantic, driving the continents apart. If you've ever wondered why South America looks like it would fit perfectly with Africa, this is the reason. The two continents were one, 130,000 years ago, and the volcanic activity along the mid-Atlantic ridge has carried them quickly apart, the new land of the ocean floor created along a fault line that passes straight through Thingvellir. The Icelandic parliament used to sit at the *Logberg*, or Law Rock, a rocky outcrop that vanished long ago as the landscape shifted. In this part of the world, geology outpaces politics.

There is a place in the great valley that is flooded by crystal glacial meltwater from the central Langiokull glacier, filtered on its journey coastward from the interior through hundreds of kilometres of volcanic rock. The water, transparent and cold, creates one of the world's most famous dive sites.

This is a book inspired by a television programme. Television is a visual medium, and very often the demonstration of some physical principle or other is good for the screen but not for print. However, in our film about the colours of the world, the production team dreamt up a magnificent way of demonstrating why the oceans are blue which works for both media. The sequence involved me diving into the fissure at Silfra (as the site is known) wearing a red dry suit. I imagine the experience is as close as you can get to a spacewalk without actually visiting the International Space Station, because you cannot see the substance of the water; when the sediments settle, it is as if you are unsupported in a silent walled rift. The view from inside the mask was of a blue, enclosed world, but the clue to the origin of the blue light was the red of the suit. On

Left and below:
Thingvellir, in Iceland, is beloved by divers for its almost crystal-clear waters running through dramatic fissures and channels.

the surface, it was very red. As we descended through 15 metres into the rift, the illumination through the clear waters was still bright, but the suit became black.

The colour of an object is determined by the way light interacts with it. A carrot is orange, for example, because *b-carotene* molecules selectively absorb blue photons. Orange is what's left of the visible spectrum when blue light is removed and, since we see a carrot by its reflected light, it appears orange. Similarly, the dyes in my dry suit absorbed all the colours of the spectrum other than red. The colour from the suit gradually bled away as I descended deeper into the fissure because water molecules absorb red light very strongly. By the time I reached a depth of around 15 metres, there were very few red photons left from the sunlight that entered the water at the surface to reflect off my suit and into the camera lens. The suit continued to absorb all the other colours, which pass through the water relatively unimpeded, which is why the suit turned black, even though illumination levels were still high.

The way water absorbs visible light is quite unique. We saw in Chapter One that water molecules are made up of two hydrogen atoms, bonded to a single oxygen atom. The

Since the energy of a photon is directly related to its colour, a particular molecule will only absorb certain colours of light, determined by the different possible arrangements of electrons inside it.

structure is maintained by the distribution of electrons around and between the atomic nuclei. Electrons can only arrange themselves in very specific ways inside molecules, determined by the laws of quantum theory. Rearrangements can happen without breaking up the molecule, but each different arrangement will, in general, have a different energy. If the arrangement of electrons inside a molecule is to be changed, a photon with just the right energy to make the change must be absorbed. Since the energy of a photon is directly related to its colour, a particular molecule will only absorb certain colours of light, determined by the different possible arrangements of electrons inside it.

This is the process by which virtually everything we see acquires its visible colour; but water is different. The arrangement of the electrons inside water molecules does change as a result of the absorption of electromagnetic radiation, but the energies required are too high for photons in the visible part of the spectrum to be involved. Instead, it is vibrations between the hydrogen and oxygen nuclei inside the water molecules themselves that are driven by the absorption of lower-energy infrared and visible (red) photons.

Left and below: The further I descended into the fissure, and the more depleted the red photons from the sunlight above became, the darker my bright red suit grew.

There are three basic modes of vibration of a water molecule, shown in the top right illustration, but a tremendous array of combinations is possible, leading to water's extremely complex absorption spectrum – which is shown in the graph below. Many of these vibrations are excited by long-wavelength infrared photons, and this is the mechanism exploited in a microwave oven. There are also vibrations that can be excited by visible red light, removing it from the spectrum. Water is virtually opaque to ultraviolet light, and to infrared light, which is where the intra-nuclear vibrations kick in. But there is a valley, mainly in the blue and green, where water does not absorb light strongly. This is why water looks 'almost' transparent. The steep rise in absorption towards the red part of the visible spectrum is the reason why my red dry suit lost its colour. At a depth of 15 metres, the intra-nuclear vibrations of the water molecules have absorbed most of the red photons from the Sun that entered the surface, and there are few left to be reflected by the dry suit. In deeper water, all that is left is blue light, which is scattered around rather than absorbed.

This is what gives large bodies of liquid water their planet-defining blue hue. We are a 'Pale Blue Dot' because of the delicate interaction between electromagnetic radiation and the rotating, wobbling, vibrating molecules formed by the first and third most common elements in the Universe: hydrogen and oxygen.

As an aside, it's interesting to note the sensitivity of the absorption spectra of molecules to slight changes in their constituents. Heavy water is chemically identical to H_2O, but it contains deuterium rather than hydrogen. It has the chemical formula D_2O. Deuterium is an isotope of hydrogen, and its nucleus contains a single neutron alongside the proton. This has no effect on the chemistry, which is driven purely by the number of electrons that surround the nucleus and therefore the number of protons inside it. The physical presence of the neutron does have a very noticeable effect on the absorption spectrum, however. Instead of absorbing light in the red part of the visible spectrum, the vibrational modes are shifted to higher energies, and therefore excited by shorter wavelength photons beyond the visible. This is in accord with intuition; it takes more energy to make a more massive nucleus vibrate back and forth. As a result, since virtually none of the visible spectrum is removed, heavy water is colourless even in large quantities. If the Earth were covered in oceans of D_2O, it would not be a blue planet.

Opposite: The relative absence of red light at depth is the reason why underwater photographers often use blue/green filters on the front of their cameras. The picture is effectively over-exposed, but the filter selectively reduces the amount of blue/green light falling on the sensor, allowing the dimmer reds to be visible.

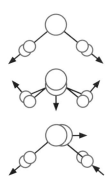

Below: The three basic modes of vibration of a water molecule.

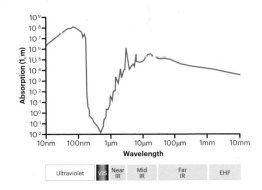

Below: The absorption spectrum of liquid water.

Bottom: Comparison of absorption of H_2O and D_2O

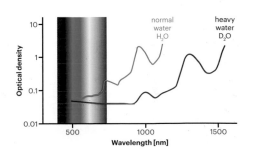

Pale blue green planet

Part 2: The Sky

During a lunar eclipse, the shadow of our world is visible, and it is lonely and dark against the Moon.

The Earth's blue skies are not the result of the selective absorption of sunlight, but of selective scattering. Here again, the demonstration cooked up by the television production team is rather instructive. On the crisp Monday morning of 28 September 2015, a total lunar eclipse was visible from the UK. Every two and a half years or so, the Sun, Moon and Earth align such that the Earth, positioned briefly between our star and satellite, casts a shadow across the face of the Moon. It is a beautiful and relatively common sight, and one that delivers a powerful component of the feeling I experienced when I watched a total solar eclipse from Varanasi, in India, in 2009. Both are a display of moving shadows, cast across the Solar System by orbiting balls of rock, and once you have that in your mind, the effect of an eclipse is all the more powerful. During a lunar eclipse, the shadow of our world is visible, and it is lonely and dark against the Moon. In Varanasi, by the banks of the Ganges on a dripping tropical July morning, heavy with sweet incense and sweat, a million voices fell silent as the shadow of the Moon darkened the magical old Ghats. In England, thousands of miles, seven long years and a great spiritual rift away, as I prepared to recount my feelings on a quiet English moor, two 'witches' decided to mark the occasion by singing the theme from Walt Disney's *Frozen*.

The Earth's shadow completely covers the Moon during a total lunar eclipse, but the Moon doesn't fall into absolute

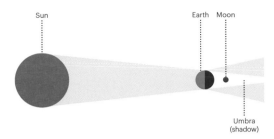

Sun   Earth Moon

Umbra
(shadow)

darkness. Instead, it glows a dim, deep red. The red illumination of the lunar surface is the result of sunlight being deflected onto the Moon by Earth's atmosphere. The Moon is normally viewed in direct sunlight; it reflects 12 per cent of the visible spectrum – a little less from the dark basalt seas laid down by ancient volcanic eruptions, and a little more from the brighter anorthosite highlands. Asked to describe moonlight in a single word, you'd probably say white; not too different from sunlight. This is because Moon rocks reflect light reasonably democratically at all wavelengths; bright rainbow in – dimmer rainbow out. There are certainly no reds, greens and blues visible to the naked eye. During an eclipse, the illumination is very different. The Earth's atmosphere acts as a filter, removing most of the solar spectrum other than the red light, which remains to illuminate the maria and highlands. This is why the Moon turns red during a lunar eclipse.

The same physical process turns the sky red at sunset. As the Sun falls, or should we say as the Earth rotates beneath the Sun, the sunlight has to travel through an increasing amount of atmosphere on the way to our eyes. The image of the Sun reddens, and as the Sun approaches the horizon, the sky itself turns from blue to red. To understand what is happening, we need to know how photons of different wavelengths, and therefore energies, interact with the molecules, dust and water vapour in the Earth's atmosphere.

Below: The Super Moon during the lunar eclipse of 2015, gradually turning a beautiful, dramatic deep red.

Above: The red illumination of the lunar surface occurs when sunlight is deflected onto the Moon by Earth's atmosphere.

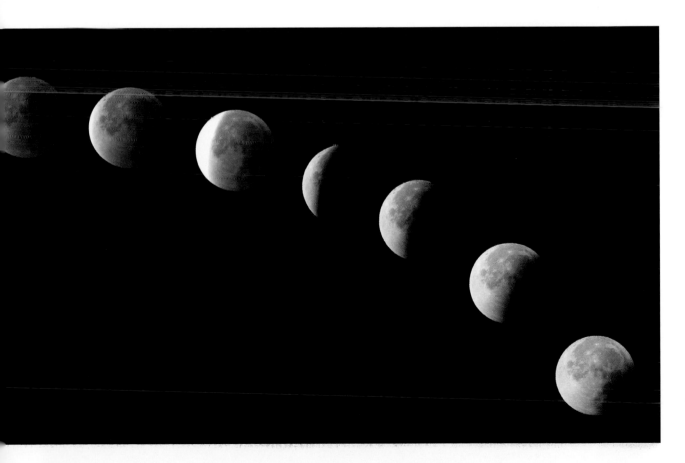

The changing colours of Earth's skies, and the deep red of the lunar surface during an eclipse, are caused by a process known as Rayleigh scattering, named after the British physicist Lord Rayleigh (John William Strutt). The process can be described as the elastic scattering of photons off the oxygen and nitrogen molecules that make up our atmosphere. Picture billiard balls bouncing off each other; this is a good image if the wavelength of the incoming light is significantly larger than the size of the molecules, which is the case for visible light making its way through the air. The wavelengths of visible photons are between 400 and 650nm, and oxygen and nitrogen molecules are over a thousand times smaller.

In modern language, Rayleigh's formula shows that the probability for a photon to scatter is inversely proportional to the fourth power of its wavelength. This means that blue photons (450nm) are over three times more likely to scatter off gas molecules on their way through the atmosphere than longer wavelength red photons (650nm). The illustration opposite shows the percentage of sunlight that is scattered on its way through the atmosphere when the Sun is directly overhead. Around one in five blue photons scatter, whereas only one in twenty red photons will be deviated from a straight-line path from the Sun into your eye. This is why the sky appears blue and the Sun takes on a yellow tinge. As the Sun drops towards the horizon and the photons have to journey through more

From Earth's orbit our atmosphere is rarely visible... The dominant atmospheric features that are visible from space are the bright white clouds.

Opposite: Sunset spreads an orangey-red hue across the sky as the yellow and red photons bounce around in the air.

Below: The percentage of sunlight scattered by the Earth's atmosphere when the Sun is directly overhead, as a function of wavelength.

Bottom: The thin blue line that separates our planet from the vacuum of space, as seen from the ISS.

air, the chance of any photon scattering will increase, and in particular more of the blue light is scattered away. This is why the skies become increasingly orange and even red in the evening, leaving a fading, deepening disc of red as the Sun falls below the horizon.

Thanks to the Apollo astronauts, we can see what the Sun looks like in a sky with little or no atmosphere. The photographs overleaf were taken on 19 November 1969 by the team of astronauts on board Apollo 12. The Sun is bright white over the 'Ocean of Storms' because none of the colours of the rainbow have been scattered away and the sky is deep black.

From Earth's orbit our atmosphere is rarely visible, although photographs of the limb of the Earth from the International Space Station provide a dramatic view of the thin blue line that separates us from the vacuum of space. The dominant atmospheric features that are visible from space are the bright white clouds. Clouds are white because they are composed of water droplets, which are typically of comparable size to the wavelength of visible light. Rayleigh's calculation does not apply here, and the dominant scattering process is known as Mie scattering, after the German physicist Gustav Mie. Larger particles, such as water droplets, scatter light with a probability that is almost independent of wavelength, and this democratic deflection is the reason why clouds on Earth are bright white.

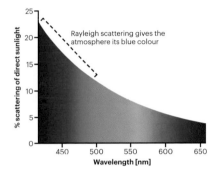

Rayleigh scattering gives the atmosphere its blue colour

Thanks to the Apollo astronauts, we can
see what the Sun looks like in a sky with
little or no atmosphere.

Above and opposite:
The bright white light of Sun in the lunar sky illuminates astronaut Alan Bean and the craters he encounters on his moonwalk.

Pale blue green planet

Part 3: The Land

Beneath the white clouds, lined by the blue oceans, is the land. The polar regions are white, the equatorial belts a dusty Mars-red, but the temperate north on the White Marble image is green. As I write, looking at that photograph (see page 249), I'm taken aback by just how green Europe and northern Asia are. There is no sign of concrete or highways or cities. The surfaces of Britain, France, Germany, the lowlands of Norway and Finland and out across the eastern planes of Russia, halfway around the globe to the North Pacific coast, are uniformly verdant. The ring of green is completed by North America, just visible through the clouds off the upper limb. These are the places where we know there will be abundant food, shelter and rain, because we recognise green as the colour of life. But why are plants green?

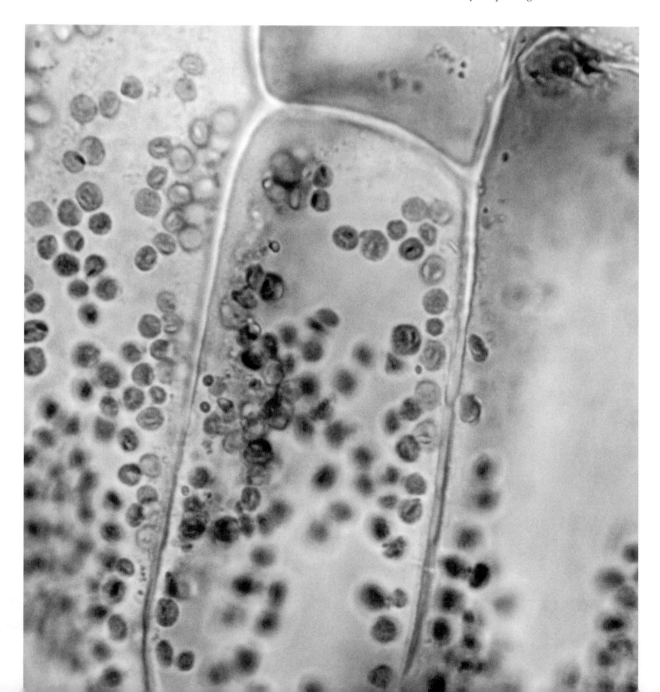

'A teardrop of green.'
— *Ron McNair, physicist and NASA astronaut, on viewing the Earth from the Space Shuttle*, Newsweek *magazine, 10 February 1986*

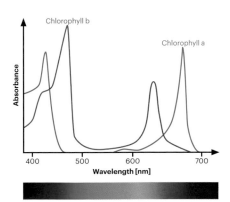

As with many of the simply phrased questions we've asked in this book, there are multiple answers to this of increasing depth, and at the end of the thread lies that most wonderful answer for a scientist: we don't quite know yet. With that exciting and tantalising admission of ignorance, a most magnificent and humble thing, let's start with what we do know.

A very simple answer is that green is the colour that life throws away. Just as the oceans are blue because water molecules do not readily absorb blue photons, so plants are green because chlorophyll, the pigment contained within all green plants, absorbs blue and red photons and the green photons are reflected back out into our eyes. The diagram, left, shows the absorption spectra for the two most common forms of chlorophyll, labelled *a* and *b*. They absorb wavelengths at both ends of the visible spectrum, but leave the green centre well alone. To make more progress in understanding why this might be the case, we need to know a little about the complex biological magic of photosynthesis.

The biochemist Albert Szent-Gyorgi once observed, 'Life is nothing but an electron looking for a place to rest.' Photosynthesis is the process by which plants use energy from the Sun to move electrons around, and today it lies at the heart of the entire food chain. You'll probably remember this basic equation from school:

$$6CO_2 + 6H_2O \rightarrow C_6H_{12}O_6 + 6O_2$$

Strictly speaking, we should refer to this as oxygenic photosynthesis, because the source of the electrons in this case is water, which falls apart, releasing oxygen into the atmosphere as a waste product. Ripping electrons off water is extremely difficult to do. There is perhaps another corner of your mind where, amongst the windmills, you've filed away a school science experiment; the electrolysis of water. Water can be split into hydrogen and oxygen by passing electricity through it, but it's not easy because water is a very stable and tightly bound molecule. If there was an energy-efficient way of splitting water using our current technology, the world economy would be based on hydrogen rather than oil.

Photosynthesis has been around for a very long time, and probably dates back at least 3.5 billion years to some of the oldest organisms, known as cyanobacteria. These early forms of life would not have possessed the advanced biochemical machinery necessary to split water, and would have grabbed their electrons off less-stable molecules such as hydrogen sulphide, readily available in the oceans of the young Earth. Just as in plants today, they would have forced those electrons onto carbon dioxide to make sugars, the building blocks of living things. They also had the ability to use the electrons liberated by sunlight to manufacture ATP, life's universal battery. At some point earlier than 2.5 billion years ago, an evolutionary innovation known as the oxygen evolving complex allowed organisms to replace hydrogen sulphide with the more readily available water, and the whole lot was linked together to form the Z-scheme, which is present in all green plants today.

The Z-scheme is one of the wonders of evolutionary biology. The sugar-manufacturing piece alone, known as photosystem 1, consists of 46,630 atoms. The ATP piece is known as photosystem 2. The oxygen-evolving complex has such an intricate structure that it was not fully understood until 2006.

The power source for all this machinery is the plentiful stream of photons from the Sun, and chlorophyll is the primary collector of photons. There are several types of chlorophyll, which perform different functions that depend on their molecular structure and their surrounding proteins. At the reactive heart of photosystem 2, chlorophyll absorbs light most strongly at a wavelength of 680nm, which is in the red part of the spectrum. The energy absorbed reconfigures the distribution of electrons in the molecular structure, resulting in one being made available to the first electron transport chain of the Z-scheme, which whisks it away to manufacture ATP. This leaves the chlorophyll with a voracious appetite to regain its lost electron, which it grabs from water with the help of the oxygen evolving complex. The structure that contains the chlorophyll molecules is known as the P680 reaction centre, and when it has absorbed a photon it is the strongest-known biological oxidising agent. This is why it has the power to split water, delivering the oxygen we breathe into the Earth's atmosphere in the process.

After progressing through photosystem 2, the electron is ready to enter photosystem 1, the business end of which contains another set of chlorophyll molecules inside a different structure called the P700 reaction centre. It absorbs light most strongly at the slightly higher wavelength of 700nm, deeper into the red. In this guise, chlorophyll absorbs light just as before, but with a different result. It now becomes the most powerful known biological reducing agent, which means that its appetite is focused on getting rid of its energised electron onto anything it can – in this case, via a few more pieces of molecular machinery, onto carbon dioxide. The result, with the addition of a few protons, is to turn CO_2 into sugars. The missing electron is replaced by the spare one that popped out of photosystem 2.

This may seem unnecessarily complicated, but it probably isn't. If you gave a chemical engineer the job of pulling electrons off water and putting them onto carbon dioxide, she'd probably laugh in your face. Water doesn't want to give up electrons, and carbon dioxide doesn't want to receive them. The job of pulling electrons off a stable thing is very different to the job of putting electrons onto a stable thing, and this is why there are two separate reaction centres allowing the chlorophyll pigments to perform these different tasks.

The Z-scheme is an awesome thing, which is probably why every organism on the planet that carries out oxygenic photosynthesis does it in precisely the same way. It almost certainly only evolved once, probably in a cyanobacterium somewhere in a primordial ocean. These clever cyanobacteria somehow found their way into the cells of other organisms and became the chloroplasts – the seat of photosynthesis in all the green plants on the planet today. This may give you pause for thought, because without the Z-scheme there would be very little oxygen in our atmosphere and complex life on Earth wouldn't exist.

Below: Z-scheme

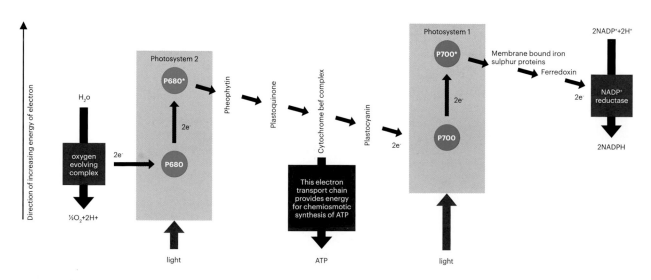

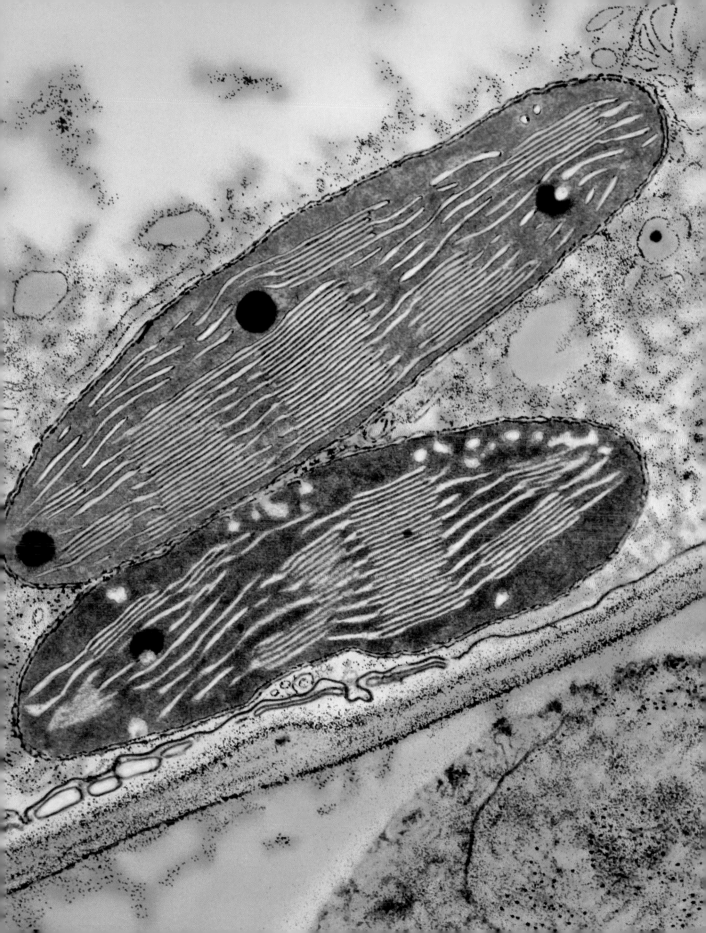

If the two reaction centres absorb light most strongly in the red, then why are all plants green? The answer is that the P700 and P680 reaction centres don't absorb sunlight directly. This is done by a complex array of different chlorophyll pigments, and other pigments called accessory pigments, which channel the light into the reaction centres in a cascade that gradually increases the wavelength towards the red part of the spectrum, allowing the chemical business to begin. The accessory pigments are revealed in the autumn, when the chlorophyll decays away, as the reds, oranges and golden yellows of autumn leaves. The two most common chlorophyll pigments outside of the reaction centres absorb light in both the red and blue parts of the spectrum. Together with the accessory pigments, they harvest over 90 per cent of the Sun's light, leaving only a very small band of green to be reflected away.

Photosynthesis is complicated and wonderful. It uses almost all of the sunlight falling on the surface of the Earth to power the plants that lie at the base of our planet's food chain, and oxygenates the atmosphere in the process. Why don't plants use 100 per cent of the visible spectrum and have black leaves, rather than reflecting 10 per cent of the light away? Nobody knows. The answer is probably an important lesson in evolutionary biology. Evolution by natural selection doesn't find optimal engineering solutions to problems. If an engineer designed a plant, it would have black leaves. Rather, organisms are a bit of a bodge job, the result of 4 billion years of mutations, selection pressures and genetic and physical mergers. The greens that dominate the temperate regions of planet Earth could well be a frozen evolutionary accident.

Previous page:
This coloured electron micrograph shows two chloroplasts in the leaf of a pea plant (*Pisum sativum*). Chloroplasts convert light and carbon dioxide into carbohydrates.

Right: The molecular structure of chlorophyll A, which has the molecular formula $C_{55}H_{72}O_5N_4Mg$.

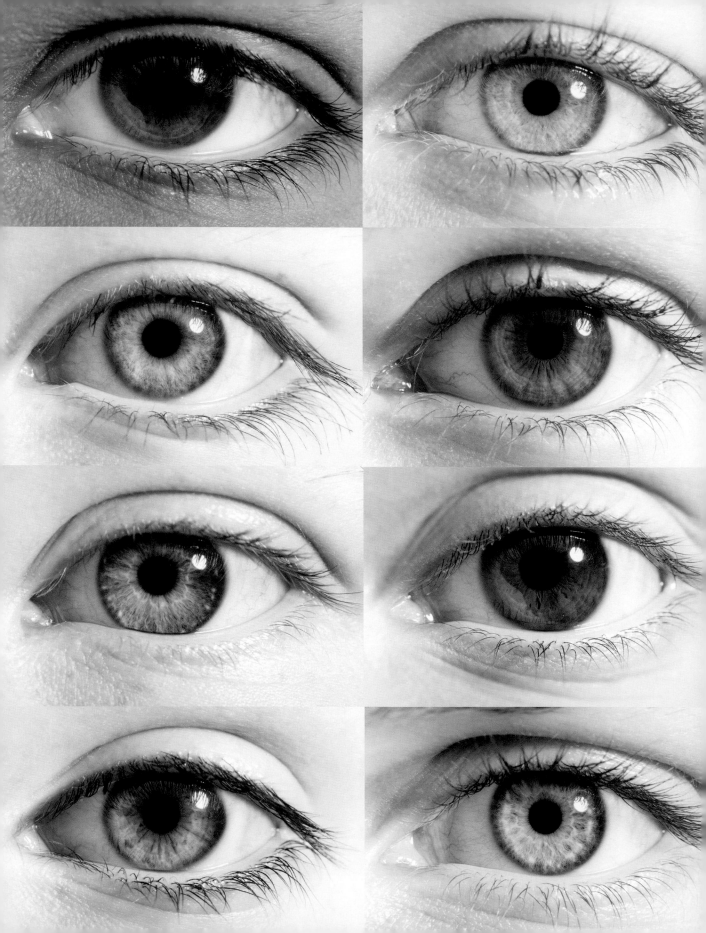

Pale coloured dots

Having taken a wander through the origin of Earth's defining colours, we can now return to the beginning and cast our minds out towards the stars. Is there any way we can use what we know about the reflection and absorption of sunlight on Earth to explore other worlds, and to search for the signatures of life beyond our Solar System? The answer is yes, and astronomers are doing just that.

The first planet to be discovered outside the Solar System is known as PSR B1257+12 B. The discovery was announced in January 1992. PSR stands for pulsar – a rapidly rotating neutron star around 1.5 times the mass of the Sun but with the radius of a city. Pulsars rotate extremely fast – the parent star of the first planet spins around once every 0.006219 seconds. The timing accuracy is important, because it is by measuring wobbles in the spin rate that the existence of planets can be inferred.

There are three known planets in the PSR B1257 system, which have been named Draugr, Poltergeist and Phobetor. Poltergeist was the first to be discovered. I know; I was curious about their names as well. Poltergeist means pounding ghost, the Draugr are the undead in Norse legend who live in their graves, and Phobetor is the personification of nightmares and the son of Nyx, Greek goddess of the night. Astronomers are such Goths. Mind you, the PSR B1257 system wouldn't be a very nice place to live – the planets are bathed in radiation from their violent host. Draugr is the closest in, orbiting once every 25.262 Earth days. It is the lowest-mass planet yet to be discovered, at only twice the mass of our moon.

The Kepler Space Telescope was launched on 7 March 2009 and has revolutionised the search for extra-solar planets. Kepler looks for periodic dips in the light of stars as planets pass across their face as seen from Earth. By studying the details of the light drop, and with additional data from supporting observations by ground-based telescopes, a great deal of information about the planets can be deduced. I write on 11 May 2016, a day after the discovery of 1284 new planets was announced by the Kepler team. In this new sample alone, there are 550 rocky Earth-like planetary candidates, and nine of these orbit in the so-called habitable zone around their parent stars, which allows them to have surface conditions compatible with the existence of lakes and oceans. The 21 rocky planets less than twice the size of Earth discovered by Kepler are shown in the illustration, left.

The Kepler and ground-based data allow for the size, mass and orbital parameters of the planets to be measured, which can be used to estimate their density and temperature and gives a guide to their composition. To go further, starlight that has interacted with the planetary atmosphere itself must be analysed directly, and this can be done.

The first atmospheric analysis of a large rocky planet was reported in February 2016 by a team from University College London, using data from the Hubble Space Telescope.[2] The planet, called 55 Cancri e, is one of five known worlds that orbit around the yellow dwarf star 55 Cancri A, only 40 light years from Earth. The star also has a smaller red dwarf companion, 55 Cancri B. The planet is around 8 times the mass of the Earth, and has an atmosphere of hydrogen and helium. No water vapour was detected, but there were hints of hydrogen cyanide, which astronomers believe indicates a carbon-rich atmosphere. This world is an exotic, violent

Below: Potentially Earth-like planets in the habitable zone around stars discovered by the Kepler Space Telescope (as of May 2016).

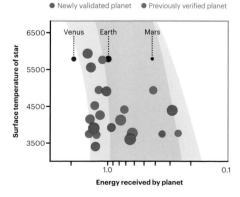

2 http://arxiv.org/abs/1511.08901

place, with a year that lasts 18 hours and surface temperatures in excess of 2000 degrees Celsius. It is clearly not a world where we would expect to find life. The significance of the measurement is in the successful retrieval of the vanishingly faint spectrum of a small, rocky planet from the bright, overwhelming light of its parent star.

The direct observation of the light from exoplanets is still in its infancy, but the James Webb Space Telescope, due for launch in October 2018, will allow planetary atmospheres to be probed in unprecedented detail. Kepler's successor, the Transiting Exoplanet Survey Satellite, will be launched in 2017 and will add huge numbers of Earth-like worlds for the JWST to observe, including Earth-sized planets around red dwarf stars. The discovery of water vapour on such a world would be exciting. The discovery of high oxygen levels would be a smoking gun for the presence of photosynthetic organisms. We may be very close indeed to discovering that we are not alone in the Universe.

Would that matter? These planets are beyond physical reach, at least for the foreseeable future, and it is extremely unlikely, in my view, that these planets will be populated by intelligent beings. If life is present, I would guess that it would be microbial. But I could be wrong. In any case, of course it matters. The lights in the night sky are powerful, majestic, but impersonal. The detailed knowledge of a thousand worlds of ice

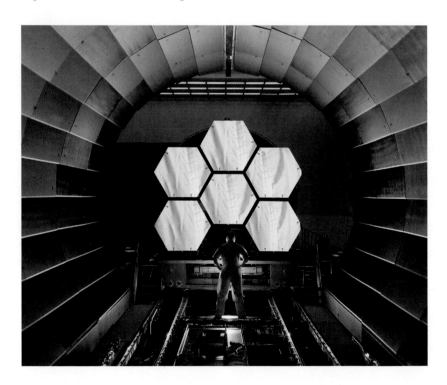

If we discover that life is common across the Universe, will it still be possible to glance up at those bright old stars and not feel as one nation beneath them?

and snow and fire won't, I regret, help us to live better lives – the folly of human conceits is too deeply engrained for that. I believe we will need a collective shock if we are to 'deal more kindly with one another, and to preserve and cherish the pale blue dot'. The shock could be something negative. Perhaps we'll have to come together to fix the climate we're mangling, or deflect a doomsday asteroid. Or, it might be something positive. Astronomy turns data into dreams; if we discover that life is common across the Universe, will it still be possible to glance up at those bright old stars and not feel as one nation beneath them? Why study rainbows? Then we'd know the answer.

'Why are there so many songs about rainbows
And what's on the other side
Rainbows are visions
But only illusions
And rainbows have nothing to hide
So we've been told
And some choose to believe it
I know they're wrong, wait and see
Some day we'll find it
The rainbow connection
The lovers, the dreamers, and me.'
Kermit the Frog, The Muppet Movie

Index

Picture Credits

Acknowledgements

Forces of Nature has been a long time in the making. Since January 2014 a world-class team led by Danielle Peck and Giselle Corbett have shown huge intellectual and creative ambition and a large dose of stoicism to deliver the television series that accompanies this book. We'd like to thank everyone involved in the production for the endless commitment they have given to the project.

We'd particularly like to thank Matthew Dyas and Stephen Cooter for sticking with it and producing such beautifully crafted and thoughtful films. They were supported by a hugely talented team who have grappled week after week with the demands of production on this scale. So a very big thank you to Alex Ranken, Alice Jones, Suzy Boyles, Duncan Singh, Helene Ganichaud, Mags Lightbody, Francesca Bassett, Emma Chapman, Louisa Reid, Robert Hanger, Wendy Clarke, Laura Stevens, Rebecca Hickie, Nik Sopwith, Simon de Glanville, Julius Brighton, Tim Cragg, Paul O'Callaghan, Graeme Dawson, Adam Finch, Lee Sutton, Damien Sung, Andy Paddon, Paul Thompson, Benji Merrison, Vicky Edgar and Marie O'Donnell.

We'd also like to add a particular thanks to Darren Jonusus who has once again set new standards of craft and creativity in the edit.

Also a huge thank you to Laura Davey the Production Executive of BBC Science who has seen this production through many difficult days in her usual calm and supportive manner.

We'd also like to thank Professor Jeff Forshaw and Professor Matt Cobb for the generous time and thought they have given to the project.

The team at HarperCollins have once again shown their patience and brilliance in equal measure. Holding their nerve in the face of daunting deadlines and a book without words, they have delivered these beautiful pages seemingly overnight. We'd like to thank Zoë Bather, Julia Koppitz, Helena Caldon, Madeleine Penny and of course the very brilliant Myles Archibald (who must spend less time in the dentist's waiting room).

Andrew would like to thank Anna…again…for her love, support and patience through the many late nights.

I would like to thank The University of Manchester and The Royal Society for allowing me the time to make *Forces of Nature*. I would also like to thank Sue Rider, my endlessly wise and supportive agent and friend.

Brian Cox and Andrew Cohen
May 2016

For my dad, David.
— *Brian Cox*

For Benjamin, Martha, Theo, Dan, Jake,
Lyla, Ellie, Toby, Phoebe, Max, Zak, Josh,
Isaac and Tabitha because curious young
minds always ask the smartest of questions.
— *Andrew Cohen*

William Collins
An imprint of HarperCollins*Publishers*
1 London Bridge Street
London SE1 9GF

WilliamCollinsBooks.com

This combined edition first published by William Collins
in 2017

This combined edition originally published in two separate
volumes:

Human Universe first published by William Collins, an
imprint of HarperCollins Publishers, in 2014.

Forces of Nature first published by William Collins, an
imprint of HarperCollins Publishers, in 2016.

Text © Brian Cox and Andrew Cohen 2014, 2016, 2017

Photographs © individual copyright holders

Diagrams, design and layout © HarperCollins Publishers
2014, 2016, 2017

By arrangement with the BBC.

The BBC logo is a trademark of the British Broadcasting
Corporation and is used under licence.

BBC logo © BBC 2014

22 21 20 19 18 17
10 9 8 7 6 5 4 3 2 1

A catalogue record for this book is available from the British
Library.

ISBN 978-0-00-826191-7

All reasonable efforts have been made by the author and
publishers to trace the copyright owners of the material
quoted in this book and of any images reproduced in this
book. In the event that the author or publishers are notified
of any mistakes or omissions by copyright owners after
publication, the author and publishers will endeavour to
rectify the position accordingly for any subsequent printing.

Colour reproduction by FMG
Printed and bound in China